STO

Man's Dependence on the Earthly Atmosphere

PROCEEDINGS OF THE

FIRST INTERNATIONAL

SYMPOSIUM ON SUBMARINE

AND SPACE MEDICINE

United States Submarine Base,

New London, Connecticut

September 8–12, 1958

The Symposium on Submarine and Space Medicine was sponsored by the Advanced Research Projects Agency in cooperation with the American Institute of Biological Sciences under ONR Contract Nonr 2673(oo).

Man's Dependence on the Earthly Atmosphere

edited by

KARL E. SCHAEFER

United States Naval Medical Research Laboratory

New London, Connecticut

THE MACMILLAN COMPANY   NEW YORK

First Printing

Library of Congress catalog card number: 61–9079

The Macmillan Company, New York
Brett-Macmillan Ltd., Galt, Ontario

Printed in the United States of America

Foreword

This symposium found us on the threshold of great events in both sea and sky—events which may shake the world and all the people in it; events in which physiologists, psychologists, and other biologists will surely play their part. Our responsibility in this new age is that of keeping men alive, alert, responsive, and purposeful even when they are necessarily confined in lonely and remote sealed cabins for prolonged periods. From this point of view the symposium might have been called "Death in Closed Vessels," the grim but dramatic title of one of the chapters in Paul Bert's classical monograph. Much of the symposium was concerned, directly or indirectly, with tolerances of men for abnormalities in the physical and chemical environment of sealed cabins.

The subjects presented at the symposium were chiefly from physiology, although psychology and engineering were also represented. It must be admitted that the chief responsibility for survival, either in a submarine under the polar ice or in a satellite in the vast recesses of space, lies with the engineer. If he can install and maintain a normal environment with gadgets that really work, a man should have no serious difficulty in surviving. Much that was learned during World War II about the physiology of anoxia, acapnia, and hypercapnia is no longer of any practical value in commercial aviation because the engineer has been so successful with the pressure cabin. Engineering results were equally good on the epoch-making voyage of the *Nautilus* under the Arctic icecap, and when Project Mercury put a man into space. But physiology remains a second line of defense for the time when the arrangements of the engineer become overtaxed or exhausted. Psychology, of course, has its applications

v

throughout the whole project, but becomes of special importance when the failures of the engineer make the situation particularly stressful and the physiological tolerances become strained. Unfamiliar situations may breed panic which can wreck normal physiological regulations. We cannot afford, therefore, to neglect any aspect of physiology or psychology which might become involved in emergency situations. Most of the subjects presented at this symposium were certainly in this category. If they did not contribute directly to the practical job of putting a man into a sealed cabin, they did at least contribute substantially to better medicine and a more complete understanding of the nature of life—certainly, a noble, worthy object for a member of *homo sapiens.*

This symposium was initiated by Dr. Karl E. Schaefer, Head of the Physiology Branch, and Captain Joseph Vogel, the Officer-in-Charge, of the Naval Medical Research Laboratory at New London. Captain P. W. Garnett, Commanding Officer of the New London Submarine Base, and Captain Joseph Vogel were our official hosts. The local arrangements and the entertainment were both excellent and much appreciated. The writer, then president of the American Institute of Biological Sciences, was privileged to serve as one of two honorary chairmen, with Dr. Howard T. Karsner, Medical Research Adviser to the Surgeon General of the Navy. The entire meeting required a great expenditure of time, money, and effort on the part of many people, to whom we express our gratitude. The attendance was large, both civilian and military, and included eleven speakers from seven foreign countries. The opportunity to attend this distinguished gathering of experts was certainly appreciated by the audience. Undoubtedly, however, the major part of the total effort was that expended by the 61 speakers in the preparation of their papers. A tremendous amount of first-class experimental work was presented during the five days of the meeting. From all of this it is fair to conclude that the space age is enlisting the best efforts of scientists from all countries and all disciplines. As usually happens, the practical needs of the hour provide a most effective stimulus for important advances in both applied and theoretical science. The symposium was without doubt a memorable event in the lives of those in attendance, and this volume will extend its benefits to the many interested people who were unable to be present.

WALLACE O. FENN,
Honorary Chairman

May 29, 1959
School of Medicine and Dentistry
The University of Rochester
Rochester, New York

Preface

The first International Symposium on Submarine and Space Medicine was arranged to meet the obvious need for integrating the existing knowledge of these two closely related fields of research. Utilization of both the true submersible and the sealed space cabin will present formidable problems related to environmental medicine.

The development of closed ecological systems is required if man is to be involved in the space and submarine operations of the future. For this reason the design engineer must be supplied with a quantitative description of man's needs and his tolerances to environmental changes. The complexity of this problem, particularly the need for knowledge concerning tolerance limits to environmental changes under conditions of prolonged exposure, were described by most of the speakers at this symposium. Most available data are based on short-term experiments; this is also true of material on toxicological susceptibilities. Tolerance levels, or threshold-limit values, obtained under such circumstances have to be reduced significantly to be applicable to conditions of chronic exposure.

This symposium provided a comprehensive review of the latest pertinent developments in the field of environmental physiology and cited the problem areas in which research is urgently needed. For example, it is not known to what extent man is dependent upon the natural composition of the earth's atmosphere. Two papers dealt with the physiological role of nitrogen and might stimulate study in this neglected field.

Furthermore, the proceedings of this symposium pointed out a serious lack in conceptualization. Recent progress in the study of physiological cycles, presented in three papers, demonstrates how antiquated the conventional meaning of concepts like homeostasis, steady states, and adaptation has become. The proceedings presented evidence that the ranges of adaptation to conditions of prolonged confinement are different for individual systems. Physiological and toxicological stresses may result in pathophysiological changes or diseased states without impairing performance. A summary of data and experiences obtained in altitude adaptation during various Himalaya expeditions showed that adaptation can be reached at altitudes above 18,000 feet but is lost after several months; thus, the ceiling height for permanent living was fixed at about 18,000 feet. All these findings, and other data on CO_2 toxicity, suggest the need for further study and the introduction of several tolerance limits based on different levels of activity. This lack of adequate concepts in environmental physiology at a time when new dimensions are opening up in this field could produce grave consequences.

To meet the requirements of space flight, bold proposals are being made to alter man's bodily functions in order to create self-regulating man-machine systems which eliminate conscious control. A close analysis of such proposals often reveals oversimplification and a lack of integrated knowledge of the field. This symposium was conceived with the objective of achieving an integration of knowledge. The effects of various environmental changes upon the main physiological systems, such as the metabolic, circulatory, respiratory, and central nervous systems, were therefore discussed in individual sessions. These initial discussions developed into presentations on environmental effects on consciousness. The program concluded with papers relating to the more general problems of human ecology in confinement.

The contributions of the individual speakers were of the highest order. Besides presenting his own experimental work, nearly every person spent considerable effort to arrive at a thorough, synthetic evaluation of the status of his field. The distinguished investigators participating in the symposium entered immediately into the spirit of the undertaking and made it their own. At the end of the first day's session on metabolism, an atmosphere of confidence, intellectual stimulation, and satisfaction had already been established, and acted like a force of crystallization. During the following days, excellent presentations of basic research in circulation, respiration, and central nervous system activity kept things moving. On the last day of the symposium, toxicological problems and human ecology in confined spaces, including the role of environmental cycles, were discussed. Thus, problems of applied physiology received the benefit of the progress gained on the preceding days in the exchange of basic environmental research.

Both the audience and those responsible for the arrangements of this meeting deeply appreciated the joint efforts of chairmen and speakers of the individual sessions who contributed so magnificently to the success of this conference.

The session on consciousness, under the brilliant chairmanship of Hallowell

Davis, President of the American Physiological Society, was a highlight of the symposum. A rather extended exchange of ideas on the problems of specific effects of environmental changes on consciousness took place during this session. It was, perhaps, symptomatic of the present situation that an area formerly shunned by physiologists aroused so much interest.

Not without significance was the fact that many of the contributors to this particular meeting had experienced extraordinary environmental conditions. Among the participants were members of the successful Mt. Everest expedition, as well as members of the bathyscaph crew who had descended to depths greater than 10,000 feet. There were those who had reached altitudes above 100,000 feet in balloons and others who had just crossed the North Pole under the ice with the nuclear-powered submarine. There were also those who had started their investigations of the gravity-free state, and of oxygen, nitrogen, and CO_2 toxicity with self-experiments. One can draw a simple conclusion: It appears easier for persons who have participated in these experiments to talk about physiological states and consciousness. Unfortunately, few efforts have been made in physiology to develop this approach to a level which could compare with that reached in modern physics.

Since the session, "Environmental Effects on Consciousness," with the subsequent panel discussion developed as an organic unit within the symposium, we decided to publish this part as a separate volume. The other part of the symposium appears under the title, "Man's Dependence on the Earthly Atmosphere."

At the end of the symposium, Captain Albert R. Behnke, MC, USN, the senior scientist in submarine medicine, summarized the historical development in this field and emphasized that this conference indicated the arrival of a new era in environmental physiology research. This forces upon us a thorough evaluation of our knowledge about man himself. In so doing, we must recognize the existence of an inner frontier, on which progress has to be achieved if we are to meet the challenge of space.

KARL E. SCHAEFER

September 1960
New London, Connecticut

Acknowledgments

This symposium could not have taken place without the extraordinary efforts of Dr. Orr Reynolds, U.S. Department of Defense, who arranged for the necessary financial assistance. The support of the U.S. Navy was signified by the presence of Admiral B. Hogan, Chief of the Navy's Bureau of Medicine and Surgery. Appreciation must also be expressed to both the American Institute of Biological Sciences and the Office of Naval Research for their handling of the organizational problems of the symposium. Thanks are also due Captain J. Vogel, MC, USN, Officer in Charge of the U.S. Naval Medical Research Laboratory, for his strong encouragement of the idea of holding this symposium and Captain P. W. Garnett, USN, Commanding Officer, U.S. Naval Submarine Base, New London, Connecticut, for making available the facilities of the Submarine Base.

The editorial task of reviewing the manuscripts was carried out jointly by the sectional chairmen. Their splendid efforts during the conference made the discussions a most valuable source of information on present-day thinking about many topics of environmental physiology. Many individuals and groups, such as the steering committee, participated in the organization and conducting of the conference. In this connection I would like to thank, in particular, Dr. W. Miles, Scientific Director of U.S. Naval Medical Research Laboratory. It is also a great pleasure to acknowledge the personal interest and assistance of Mrs. Ileen Stewart of the American Institute of Biological Sciences, as well as Mrs. Jessie Kohl and Miss Betty Ebert of the U.S. Naval Medical Research Laboratory in New London, Connecticut.

Finally, I want to express my warm personal thanks to Dr. Robert C. Stroud for his help and advice throughout the entire project.

Welcoming Address

Captain J. VOGEL, MC, USN,
Officer in Charge of the U.S. Naval Medical Research Laboratory

---

In 1957, Dr. Karl Schaefer and I traveled through Europe and the United Kingdom. Our purpose was to visit scientists engaged in physiological research which pertained to our primary interest, submarine medicine. Although we were very cordially received at the various laboratories and established excellent liaison, we found there the same difficulty existing among workers in our own country. It was apparent that there existed a similar lack of cohesiveness and, consequently, loss of effective results from individual investigations because of weak communications. This symposium represents our efforts to achieve the interchange of ideas and information so necessary to the attainment of our common goal.

Discussing the problem of human ecology in confinement and logically considering the effects of confinement on the organism as an entity will undoubtedly give us a more accurate assessment of the state of the art. Once we have accomplished this, the areas requiring further investigative effort to fill the gaps in our knowledge will be clear.

Soon after our return to New London, the first satellite was launched. This event proved to be the spark needed to touch off tremendous interest in and research activity directed toward manned flight into space. We were quick to realize that the basic problems of confinement faced by those engaged in space medicine would be similar to those we in submarine medicine had been working to solve for quite some time. These problems had multiplied and become acute—or should I say, chronic—with the advent of the nuclear-powered submarine, a true submersible. In preparation for the sea-going operation of this completely new powerplant, the first large-scale experiment in human confinement, "Operation Hideout," was undertaken. In this experiment, 23 men were confined aboard a submerged submarine for a period of 60 days and subjected to atmospheric variations. As a result of this test, the tolerance limits for carbon dioxide were determined and a great deal of other valuable data were assembled.

Our attendance at various scientific meetings, such as the Astronautical Society's, has made even more pointed the similarity of the problems of confinement in space vehicles and in the true submersible. We therefore welcome our lusty younger brother, space medicine, through whose strength and vigorous research efforts our joint endeavors will attain the goal more swiftly, surely, and safely.

It is most fortunate that our Medical Research Laboratory is located at the Submarine Base, for this is a place which gives birth, nurtures, and develops submarine personnel as well as submarines. Considerable effort in the Laboratory is directed toward an assessment of the picture of the physiological problems encountered incident to the operation of our submarines. We have been able, by virtue of the fine cooperation received from the personnel of the Submarine Base, the Submarine School, and the Submarine Forces Afloat, to increase our knowledge through participation in the submarine activities in which they are engaged. We have been able to place scientifically trained observers aboard submarines during new phases of operations such as the 31-day complete submergence of the USS Skate, the transpolar expedition of the USS Nautilus, and other less spectacular but important pioneering cruises.

We hope that this meeting will open new and better lines of communication and serve as a foundation for future assemblages such as this, with the opportunity for free exchange of ideas and presentation of the accomplishments of research in this field.

Contents

xiii

PART TWO

Effects of Acute and Chronic Environmental Changes on Metabolic Functions

PART THREE

Effects of Various Acute and Chronic Environmental Changes on Circulation

PART FOUR

Effects of Acute and Chronic Atmospheric Changes on Respiratory Mechanisms

PART FIVE

The Effect of Specific Environmental Conditions on Respiratory Functions

PART SIX

Toxicological Problems in Confined Spaces

PART SEVEN

Human Ecology in Confined Spaces

Contents

Introduction

Basic Physiological Problems in Space Medicine

ROBERT T. CLARK

*Department of Physiology-Biophysics, School of Aviation Medicine, USAF,
Randolph Air Force Base, Texas*

The physiological information required to allow man's eventual exploration of space means that investigators must gather as much basic data as possible from both animal and human experimentation. The School of Aviation Medicine has organized part of its efforts in this area as follows:

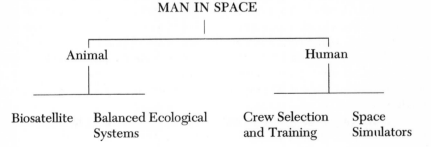

MAN IN SPACE

Animal — Human

Biosatellite — Balanced Ecological Systems — Crew Selection and Training — Space Simulators

BIOSATELLITE

Completely sealed, self-containing capsules for small animals have been developed, which may serve as experimental models for future cabins designed to carry humans in space vehicles for extended lengths of time. Information obtained from such capsules not only will be of considerable aid from a physiological standpoint, but will help in the design, development, and improvement of environmental engineering equipment.

A self-contained capsule occupying less than 0.5 cubic feet and weighing less than 15 pounds has been developed to maintain four mice for at least 5 days (Fig. 1). This capsule, including instrumentation, can withstand high acceleration and will function under gravity-free conditions. A breakdown of the capsule is shown in Fig. 2. This figure shows the oxygen-sensing device, oxygen regulator, fan, cages with feeders for four mice, and nylon cloth for the carbon dioxide and water vapor absorbent.

Dr. Hans G. Clamann, the investigator in charge of this phase of the work, has endeavored to provide the data and equipment necessary to insure survival of the mice specifically with respect to (1) automatic oxygen supply; (2) carbon dioxide and water vapor absorbers; (3) circulation of capsule air; (4) combination of adequate food and water devices; (5) positioning and suspension of the mice to withstand high G's in any direction; and (6) monitoring of oxygen tension as well as capsule pressure, temperature, and acceleration.

An automatic regulator has been constructed by our shops which is combined with a small, high-pressure cylinder containing sufficient oxygen for four mice over five days. The regulator is of the demand type and will not only provide oxygen in accordance with the oxygen consumption of the mice, but will also maintain the proper pressure in the capsule.

A cylindrical container constructed of mesh wire, divided into four compartments, constitutes the animal cage proper (Fig. 2). Attached loops of small coil-springs hold the feeders. These consist of lengthwise open cylindrical plastic tubes, closed at the ends by notched pieces of plastic for the coil-springs. This is then wrapped with the proper absorbents before being placed in the capsule. Each food container holds up to 20 grams. Taking constancy of body weight of mice over a two-month experimental period as a criterion, a food consisting of a mixture of oatmeal, ground roasted peanuts, and a small amount of gelatine mixed with water fulfilled the nutritional requirements satisfactorily. Furthermore, the paste-like, gluey consistency of this food eliminates scattering, the necessity of a separate water supply, and the drifting of food and water under gravity-free conditions.

To absorb carbon dioxide and water vapor, Dr. Clamann placed the absorbing material in a flat, nylon bag arranged to prevent smaller particles down to dust size from escaping. After filling, the bag was wrapped around the animal cage and feeders and hooked together. In this way the absorbent was secured against drifting and at the same time offered maximum surface for absorption. After experimenting with several carbon dioxide absorbents, lithium hydroxide was used because of its dual capacity to absorb water and carbon dioxide. In a test with one mouse for five days in a closed container, Dr. Clamann found that 60.4 grams of LiOH absorbed 26.4 grams of CO_2 and 20.1 grams of water.

Several layers of gauze padding wrapped under the bag of absorber were used to catch the feces and urine. The gauze was impregnated with activated charcoal powder and a mild disinfectant to prevent the growth of mold and fungi, and to minimize the odor from waste material. Since waste material, both solid and liquid, would drift around during the gravity-free state, the gauze

FIGURE 1 (*left*).
Experimental sealed capsule for mice.

FIGURE 2 (*below*).
Breakdown of experimental sealed capsule for mice.

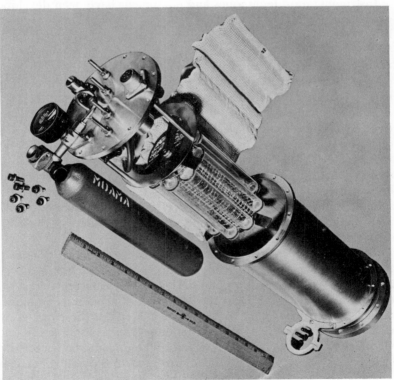

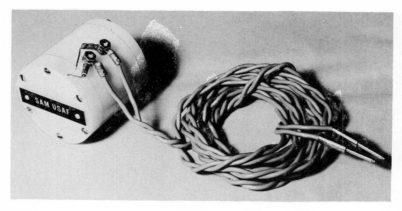

FIGURE 3.
Electrochemical oxygen-sensor.

securely placed around the mouse cage would act as a trap as well as a chemical neutralizer.

Instrumentation techniques and equipment have been developed by our electronics engineer, Mr. Robert Adams, and our Flight Surgeon, Captain Ray Ware, to determine the viability of the mice throughout a missile flight without restraining the animals in any way. This was accomplished by a tiny radio transmitter small enough to be mounted on each animal that would transmit the electrocardiogram (and pulse) and respiration. This could be picked up by a receiver and fed into a recorder or telemetering transmitter.

To meet further needs for miniature equipment in the animal capsule, Dr. Ryan Neville developed an electrochemical oxygen-sensing device less than one quarter of a cubic inch in volume and about one hundredth of a pound in weight (Fig. 3). Performance criteria realized with the device are: insensitivity to spatial orientation, vibration, acceleration, or other type of motion; a linear current output related directly and specifically to oxygen partial pressure; a rapid response characteristic; continuous operation over extended periods; insignificant power consumption; and insensitivity of the instrument to stray electric or magnetic fields.

Parallel with the studies on the sealed capsule for mice, Doctors H. L. Bitter, Lynn Brown, Richard Bancroft, and Hans Clamann have been conducting similar work on small primates. These studies are providing the information and data, along with the development of the equipment and instrumentation, that are necessary to insure the survival of the completely isolated monkey, and at the same time to monitor from a distance the physical environment and physiological condition of the primate. So far the experiments have been conducted on Rhesus monkeys (4 to 6 pounds) enclosed in self-contained capsules ranging from 6 cubic feet to less than 2 cubic feet in size

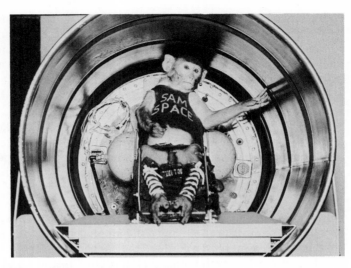

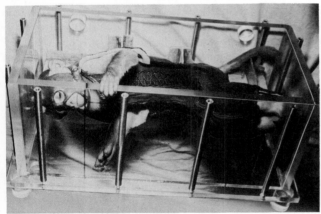

FIGURE 4 (*top*).
Experimental capsule for small primates, seat in recumbent position.

FIGURE 5 (*above*).
Experimental capsule for small primates, seat in supine position.

(Figs. 4 and 5). For some of the metabolic studies the monkeys were held in a semireclining position (Fig. 4), but for missile launching, orbiting, and re-entry into the atmosphere the animals will have to be in the supine, transverse position as shown in Fig. 5.

According to preliminary data collected by the above investigators, oxygen consumption of about 75 liters per day for a Rhesus monkey of about 6 pounds can be assumed. However, changes in oxygen consumption due to varying activity may be expected, even though the primate is trained and also strapped down in a special chair where only free movements of the arms are possible.

The training periods were conducted daily, with the monkeys restrained in chairs designed for simulated space flights. After several weeks of this type of training the animals were ready for further psychological and physiological studies. For the psychomotor test the animals were trained to depress a lever mounted on a panel directly in front of them in the capsule. The electronic system was designed to produce a shock stimulus to the monkey if the lever was held down or remained up longer than 3 to 4 seconds. After a period of time the animals became proficient. They were then tested for performance during the gravity-free state and also under high G-stress. In both cases the animals performed well (approximately 40 seconds in the gravity-free state and over 12 G).

Supplying the dietary needs of a small primate is an important problem in a space flight of any duration. Since the monkey has a tendency to over-eat, the feeding mechanism must offer food only at certain times. It was found that the monkey can thrive on the same diet of roasted peanuts and gelatine designed for mice, thereby eliminating the difficulties associated with the gravity-free state. Dr. Clamann has designed an automatic feeding device that will work in the weightless state and also prevent the monkey from over-eating.

Even though the Rhesus monkey has a high water output, LiOH has been found adequate for both the absorption of water and carbon dioxide. However, a more efficient method has been devised for the collection of water and feces whereby the waste material is trapped in a plastic bag fitted around the pelvic region of the animal.

A BALANCED ECOLOGICAL SYSTEM

The possibility of using the process of photosynthesis as a method for regenerative gas exchange in space vehicles is under investigation by Lt. Col. John Fulton and Dr. William A. Kratz at the School of Aviation Medicine. Current results indicate that algal cultures may be maintained on a continuous basis indefinitely in closed systems with animals. If these cultures are maintained in the log phase of growth by either periodic or continuous harvest of algal cells and replenishment of growth medium, they are capable of providing reasonably balanced gas exchange with a thermodynamic efficiency of 18 to 19%. The present model of the photosynthetic gas exchanger provides sufficient O_2 output and CO_2 uptake to support the respiratory requirements of four 25–30 gram mice. Under the same setup, but using a 6 pound monkey as the animal phase, approximately 25% of the respiratory requirements are met. By increasing the illumination and/or the concentration of the algal cells, the efficiency of the system can be made to support all the respiratory requirements of a small primate. In any photosynthesis gas-exchange system, a CO oxidizer must be included in the equipment circuit. Dr. Syrrel Wilks has definitely demonstrated that various green plants, including algal cells, give off CO in amounts that could become toxic over a period of time. In the gas-exchange system described for mice, this could occur within three days.

CREW SELECTION AND TRAINING

The final selection of personnel for extraterrestrial flight will probably require the highest physiological, psychological, and mental capacities to which crews can be trained. With this in mind, Dr. Bruno Balke two years ago began to train a group of subjects picked at random from the staff at the School of Aviation Medicine.

The subjects ranged in age from 19 to 51 years. The training consisted of exercise by running cross country twenty minutes to an hour five days a week. Only 2 of the 15 subjects had previous athletic training. Each subject was required to cover as much distance as he could in the allotted time. Before training, and at regular intervals during training, each subject was given a performance capacity test. This consisted of walking on a treadmill 3.5 miles per hour with a 1% increase in grade each minute until a pulse rate of 180 was reached (Fig. 6). Cardiovascular, respiratory, and chemical data were collected during the test. In order to give a better indication of metabolic reserves, another type of performance test was given before and during training in which the subject walked 3.5 miles per hour for two hours on a treadmill at a grade-level set to produce a pulse rate between 150 and 160. The results indicated that all subjects, regardless of their previous physical condition, were able to improve considerably their cardiovascular, respiratory, and metabolic reserves. However, since it is known that natives who live permanently at high altitudes (Andes Mountains) have exceptionally high performance capacities, the group was taken to a laboratory site above 14,000 feet at Mt. Evans, Colorado for further training. After only a few weeks at high altitude, the performance capacities of the subjects were about equal to those of a permanent resident at high altitude. Furthermore, their times of useful consciousness at an extreme simulated altitude of 30,000 feet increased from less than 3 minutes to over thirty minutes, and their susceptibility to bends after exercise at a simulated altitude of 38,000 feet was negligible. This group of physically trained subjects, then, would seem ideal as the first crew to undergo the stresses of a space simulator.

A SPACE SIMULATOR

Before attempting to simulate many of the physiological stresses that might be encountered during space flight, a study was initiated by Lt. Col. George Steinkamp, Captain Julian Ward, and Dr. George Hauty, to determine the psychological factors involved in sealing a subject within a one-man space simu-

FIGURE 6.
Treadmill for performance capacity measurements. The picture shows a subject being tested immediately after a 10-day sealed environmental flight.

lator for a 7-day period. Criteria used in choosing the subject were a high level of intelligence, motivation, and good health. The partial pressure of O_2 was automatically maintained at 150 mm Hg pressure and the total cabin pressure at 380 mm Hg pressure. The cabin temperature and humidity were held within normal, comfortable limits. The EKG, CO_2 pressure, O_2 pressure, and cabin temperatures were continuously monitored and recorded.

Each day the subject spent 12 hours monitoring radar tracking and operator systems, six hours and twenty minutes for sleep, two hours and ten minutes of general recreation (reading, writing), one hour and thirty minutes for eating and changing CO_2 absorbent, and one hour for mathematical computations.

From a psychological standpoint, the subject tolerated the close quarters and day-by-day routine remarkably well. He denied any hostility toward the observers on the outside, although his diary did indicate an increased hostility as the experiment progressed. The physiological responses during the flight indicated some degree of dehydration and moderate weakness in the lower extremities. Within one hour after the flight he was asymptomatic.

This experiment showed that a properly motivated subject could stay within a closed environment for long periods of time. The next logical step was to repeat the experiment with the addition of physiological stresses that might be expected under flight conditions. Two exceptions were acceleration and the gravity-free state. These were to be conducted with proper equipment outside the simulator. This experiment was conducted by Dr. Balke in a two-man sealed environment. The two subjects were selected from the group that had undergone the rigid physical training program at Randolph Field and Mt. Evans, Colorado. They were placed in the sealed environment immediately upon their return from the mountains for a 10-day experimental period.

The subjects were kept continuously at simulated altitudes between 14,000 and 20,000 feet under ambient O_2 pressures. The operation of the chamber was controlled throughout the experiment by the subjects themselves. Experimental procedures varied from day to day. Cardiovascular and respiratory data were collected during both rest and work (bicycle ergometer). Psychological and psychomotor tests were carried out at regular intervals each day. Some of the physiological variations that could exist within the cabin of a high performance vehicle were simulated each day. For example, the humidity was allowed to vary from 70% to 98%, and the cabin temperature from 75° F to 98° F. Carbon dioxide was allowed to build up over several hours to concentrations above 7% in order to study the possible change in sensitivity of the respiratory center to CO_2 as a result of hyperventilation. Emergency procedures were carried out in which the subjects were exposed to simulated altitudes up to 50,000 feet. They were expected to get into their pressure suits as the chamber ascended and then to perform routine duties for as long as an hour after the chamber reached 50,000 feet. On the last day of the experiment, the subjects were exposed to combinations of high temperature, humidity, and altitude.

Immediately following the 10-day flight, both subjects were given a performance capacity test on the treadmill (Fig. 6) in order to determine the decrement in physiological reserves that might have occurred as a result of the gruelling experiences within the sealed environment.

The results of the experiment indicate that subjects who have high physiological reserves can withstand severe stresses possibly encountered during space flight. The performance capacity of both subjects remained high, probably due to the altitudes plus work routine maintained during the experiment.

Since the ages of the subjects were 34 years and 51 years, the experiment further demonstrates that potential crewmen can build up considerable body reserves independent of age. Older pilots seem to be more stable mentally. It would seem, therefore, that the ideal pilot of the future might well be an individual in the middle age bracket who maintains high physical capacities. In order to test this deduction, experiments are now underway to extend the above studies to include subjects under varied degrees of physical training.

Basic Physiological Problems in Submarine Medicine

KARL E. SCHAEFER

Head, Physiology Branch, Medical Research Laboratory, U. S. Submarine Base,
New London, Connecticut

INTRODUCTION

If the problems we face in the "space age" are to be solved, scientists of many different disciplines must join efforts. The recent symposium on the use of satellites for biological research was a step in this direction and brought biologists and engineers together. In spite of the high quality of the presented papers, the discussion revealed that the thinking of the various disciplines was miles apart in the beginning. It was, therefore, very gratifying to see how the various approaches started to merge on the last day of the four-day conference. One was left, however, with a lot of questions and with some bewilderment.

The question, "What is man and what is nature?" represents, of course, a summary of the burning problems of biological and psychological research which R. M. Hutchins, with his gift for timely generalization, emphasized in his Frankfurt lecture in 1948. Recently I was reminded that these problems are not hopelessly theoretical or too general. When the group in charge of the Subic Program visited here, one member, Comdr. Hoover, USN, said, "Tell me what is man and what is nature, that I can build an 'environmental control loop' which is satisfactory." Those who have worked in submarine medicine on problems of confinement in closed spaces are quite accustomed to wrestle with these basic issues. It is only logical that in a symposium of this kind we should take the opportunity to clarify our thinking on these basic problems and thereby fulfill some of the obvious needs in the present situation. In the following presentation I shall attempt to discuss basic problems in submarine medicine in connection with pertinent examples of research in this field. This is to review the background information which led to the formulation of the program for this symposium.

I. MAN AND NATURE

The scientific physiological concept of man and his relation to nature is expressed in Claude Bernard's principle "La fixité du milieu interieur est la condition de la vie libre" (1878). This principle has guided the lifework of many famous physiologists in the past and present. Among those who investigated a multitude of inner constants and steady states and their regulation are Henderson (1928), Cannon (1929), and Barcroft (1934). Cannon found it appropriate to coin the term "homeostasis," which gives a specific designation to the many steady states. Barcroft, in 1935, pointed out that nearly all physiologists were engaged in the study of the first part of Claude Bernard's principle, but that there was a noticeable silence in respect to the second part of his principle, the conditions of free life. In trying to answer the question, "What has the organism gained by the constancy of the inner environment?" he had to refer to the studies of man and produced the following table, data of which are based mostly on Cannon's work.

TABLE 1

Environment	Deficient	Excessive
Temperature	Inertia	Delirium
Oxygen	Unconsciousness	—
pH	Headache	Coma
Glucose	Nervousness; feeling of "goneness"; hunger	—
Water	(Weakness, Asher)	Headache; nausea; dizziness; asthenia; incoordination
Sodium	Fever	Reflex irritability; weakness; paresis
Calcium	Nervous twitchings; convulsions	Apathy; drowsiness verging in coma; general atonia

Barcroft could demonstrate that, under conditions in which the constancy of the inner environment (for example, the levels of temperature, sugar, oxygen, carbon dioxide, or water) is changed by excess or deficiency, symptoms of the CNS occur, resulting in loss of consciousness. He pointed out that none of the other bodily functions are affected to the same extent as the CNS, which led him to the conclusion that the constancy of the inner environment represents the necessary condition for intellectual activity or "free life." In this connection Barcroft makes two remarks which are very pertinent to the following discussion. He mentions that fine rhythmical processes probably are connected with the maintenance of intellectual activity and that he developed his interest in the second part of Claude Bernard's principle through his personal experiences of disturbances of intellectual activity in experiments in which the constancy of the inner environment was changed.

Following the suggestions of Barcroft, we found under high oxygen, as well as under increased carbon dioxide, a reduced responsiveness of the sympathetic system (Schaefer, 1955). Figure 1 shows the fixation of pulse rate which develops during underwater swimming while breathing oxygen. During the successive rest periods, changes in pulse rate following exercise become smaller and finally disappear. This fixation in pulse rate, indicating a predominant parasympathetic tone, occurs prior to the development of symptoms in 78% of the cases which developed symptoms and has, therefore, been recommended as

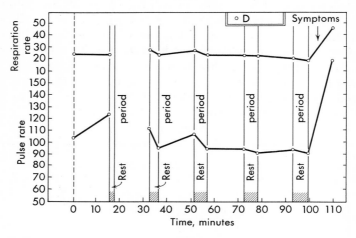

FIGURE 1.

Pulse rate and respiratory rate during subsurface swim (2 feet at constant speed 0.9 m.p.h.) while breathing oxygen. Run was stopped because of symptoms.

a warning sign for oxygen toxicity. The symptoms, convulsions which parallel a large increase in pulse rate, can be considered as a release phenomenon of the sympathetic system.

During prolonged exposure to increased CO_2 concentrations, for example 3% CO_2, a sympathicotonic phase is followed by a vagotonic phase. Symptoms of the CNS exist throughout the exposure. These phases correspond with periods of an uncompensated and compensated acidosis. The development of the vagotonia during prolonged exposure to 3% CO_2 is indicated by a decrease in pulse rate and an increase of the potassium/calcium ratio (Schaefer, 1949*b*). Associated with it is a decrease in neuromuscular excitability as shown in an increase of the chronaxia. Under these conditions, one finds a reduced response of the circulatory system to exercise and a reduction in the heat production in response to a cold load (Schaefer, 1948*a*). We call this condition a *fixed vagotonia*. Results of some dog experiments in which the blood sugar curve was determined after adrenalin injection may serve as a demonstration of the fixed vagotonia (Schaefer *et al.*, 1950).

After glucose infusions for 3 to 4 hours, adrenalin injections were made. It can be seen in Fig. 2, that the blood sugar level decreases during the CO_2 exposure and that the large increase in blood sugar after adrenalin injection, found under normal air and during the first few days under CO_2, practically disappears in the vagotonic phase. During CO_2 exposure a reduced and often prolonged response of the circulatory system to exercise is found. Figure 3 shows that the pulse rate, as well as the systolic blood pressure, increases less after twenty knee bends under conditions of CO_2 exposure. From experiments carried out during the Himalaya expedition, Brendel (1956) reported similar results during adaptation to altitude (4300 meters). This is shown in Fig. 4.

It appears that the normal relationship in the reactivity of sympathetic and parasympathetic systems which follows the day-night cycle as an expression of the diurnal cycles of the organism, as well as the cycle between activity and restoring rest, is generally affected or disturbed when the constancy of the inner environment is changed.

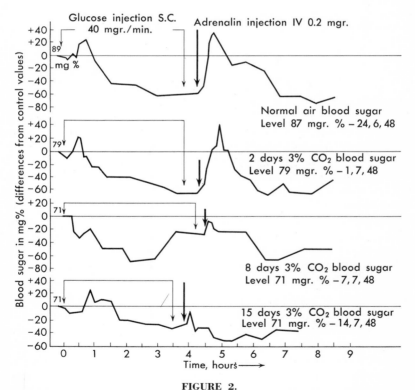

FIGURE 2.

Effect of prolonged exposure to 3% CO_2 on blood sugar responses in dogs to glucose infusion and adrenalin injection.

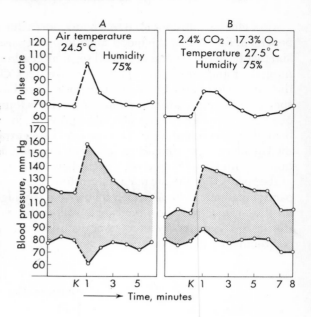

FIGURE 3 (*right*).
Reactions of pulse rate and systolic and diastolic blood pressure of subject prior to and after 20 knee-bends (K). A: during surface cruising: B: during submergence. (U-608 —1943)

FIGURE 4 (*below*).
Reactions of pulse rate and systolic and diastolic blood pressure of subject prior to and after 20 knee-bends (K).

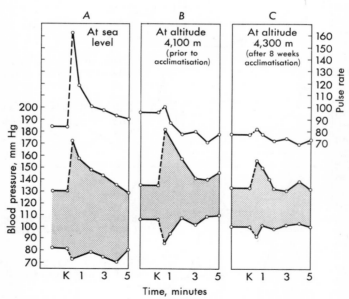

Differences in the adaptability of various functional systems

Studies in chronic CO_2 toxicity produced evidence of a significant difference in the adaptability of metabolism and circulation as compared with the nervous system. Figure 5 shows the oxygen utilization in liters/min at different workloads under normal conditions and acute and chronic exposure to 3% CO_2 (Schaefer, 1949b). It is quite apparent that oxygen utilization improves after prolonged exposure to CO_2 for three days. At this time a compensation of the CO_2 induced respiratory acidosis is usually reached. On the other hand, mental activity does not improve during prolonged exposure to CO_2. Results of attentiveness tests displayed in Fig. 6 indicate that initial values are not reached as long as the subjects are under CO_2 (Schaefer, 1949a). Measurements of chronaxia show similar results (Fig. 7). The chronaxia, which gives a measure of the speed of excitation processes underlying nerve conduction, is significantly prolonged during chronic CO_2 exposure and does not return to normal values until several days of recovery on air. These results seem to suggest that the nervous system cannot adapt to CO_2 and a great deal of practical experience in submarines can be cited to support this point.

This also can lead one to understand that different approaches in the study of adaptation in which the investigators concentrated on different functional systems produce different results and, consequently, different theoretical formulations. One of the best known students of homeostasis, Selye (1940), developed the concept of the "general adaptation syndrome" on the basis of studies of the endocrine glands and body fluids and tissues dependent on the regulation of hormones. He stated "that comparatively little evidence has come forward to prove that the nervous system plays a prominent role in regulating the course of the general adaptation syndrome."

The concept of the general adaptation syndrome has proved very successful for an understanding of patho-physiological processes. There is another monumental work in this field, the patho-physiology of the Russian pathologist Speransky (1935). According to Speransky's concept, the nervous system has a primary, absolute, dominating role in the development of most patho-

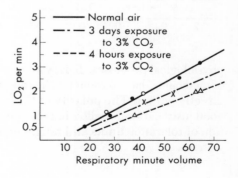

FIGURE 5.

Effect of acute and chronic exposure (3 days) to 3% CO_2 upon O_2 utilization and respiratory minute volume at different workloads.

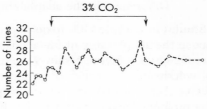

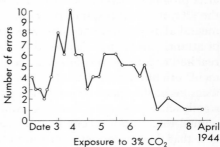

FIGURE 6 (*right*).
Attentiveness: tests prior to, during, and after exposure to 3% CO_2 for several days. (Subject: A.S.S.)

FIGURE 7 (*below*).
Strength-duration curves under normal air and short and prolonged exposure to 3–3.5% CO_2 for several days. (Subject: A.S.S.)

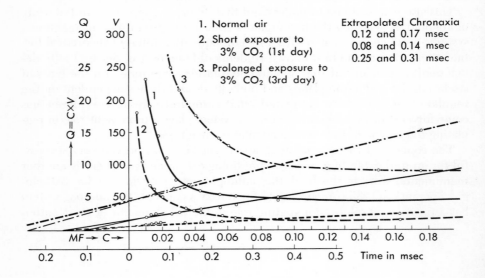

physiological processes. This system, which the author considers to be a "basis of medicine," has no room for the role of the blood and the processes connected directly with it. The polarity of these two approaches is striking and gives a good justification for allowing so much time in this program for the presentation of tolerance limits and ranges of adaptation of the individual functional systems.

Specificity of symptoms of the CNS

The findings of nonadaptability of the CNS under chronic CO_2 exposure drew attention to the symptoms of the CNS which develop when the tolerance limits to environmental changes are exceeded. Since Barcroft compiled his table in 1934, considerable evidence has been collected which attests to a specific characteristic of symptoms produced by various environmental changes. For example, under CO_2 intellectual changes occur rather early while motor coordination is still in good shape (Schaefer, 1958a).

Under low oxygen or at altitude, changes in motor function seem to occur prior to manifestations of intellectual impairment. I like to refer to the descriptions of the famous balloon ascents of the 19th century when men like Glaischer and Tissandier reached an altitude of nearly 30,000 feet without using oxygen. They reported that arms and legs were paralyzed, while they were still completely clear and conscious. Tissandier mentioned that he tried to take the mouthpiece of the oxygen tube, but was unable to move his arm. Symptoms of nitrogen narcosis were first described and cataloged by Behnke (1935). They include, beside changes of mood, "pressure-happiness"—a characteristic form of stupefaction and fixation of ideas.

These symptoms of nitrogen narcosis are quite distinct from symptoms of syncope and convulsive seizures caused by high oxygen tensions. It is obvious that these indications need to be more thoroughly investigated; and it is hoped that the symptomatology of environmental effects on consciousness included in the program of the symposium might provide a stimulus for further research in this direction. It might be permissible to incorporate the two additional characteristic features which we discussed so far in relation to Claude Bernard's principle into the scheme used by Barcroft (Table 2).

TABLE 2

I. *Constancy*	*Rhythmic*	*Normal consciousness* (Intellectual) activity and working efficiency
Of the inner environment O_2, CO_2, N_2	Activity of sympathetic and parasympathetic system	
II. *Excess* or deficiency in O_2, CO_2, (N_2)	*Fixation* (Damping) Loss of rhythmical activity of sympathetic and parasympathetic systems	*Specific disturbances of consciousness* Related to O_2 CO_2, N_2 and impairment of voluntary performance

It appears to be necessary to say a few words about the inclusion of problems of consciousness in a strict physiological program. For a number of physiologists it might be painful to hear discussions about consciousness. No one less than Sherrington (1933) warned about attempting physiological investigations of psychic phenomena. But the progress in clinical neurology in recent years produced a strong tendency to do research in this field. It is also noteworthy that attempts have been recently made to reintroduce consciousness into psychology. Nuttin stated in an article in 1955 that it is necessary to appeal to the concept of consciousness in order to formulate the problems of behavior and personality in a realistic fashion in spite of the fact that the concept of consciousness still remains associated with a traumatic experience in the life history of scientific psychology, i.e., introspectionism. The problems man faces under conditions of prolonged confinement in closed spaces such as the effect of sensory deprivation, among other problems, are certainly so great that the full cooperation of physiologists and psychologists is needed to solve them.

II. NATURE AND SUBNATURE
(NATURAL AND TECHNICAL ENVIRONMENT)

Underlying Claude Bernard's principle is the thought that during evolution man has incorporated bits of his natural environment and developed homeostatic regulation of the established inner levels of environmental components, thereby becoming independent of the environment. The fact that Na and Cl concentrations in the blood correspond with the salt concentration of the archetypal oceans is often cited in this connection. The natural environment is, therefore, included in the organism and receptors, and the regulation of various functional systems has been developed in connection with this environment. One can, therefore, *define nature* as the environment which consists of (1) tolerance limits and ranges of adaptation of man to atmospheric components like O_2, CO_2, and N_2; (2) cyclic environmental factors like light, temperature, humidity and electrical conductivity, air pressure, etc., which undergo rhythmical changes in connection with the earth's revolution. The latter act as timegivers for the organism which synchronizes the cycles of physiological functions with the environmental cycles. The adrenal cycle, according to Halberg (1953), is instrumental in this synchronization, because of its responsiveness to changes in the inner as well as the outer milieu.

In a closed space such as a submarine, a number of factors are artificially introduced into the environment. This technical environment consists, for example, of atmospheric impurities and a number of trace substances which change with the technical equipment used and are not normally present in the environment. A few of these substances are hydrocarbons, nitrites, sulfites, hydrogen, arsine, carbon monoxide, ozone, etc. We also found a 10- to 20-fold increase in

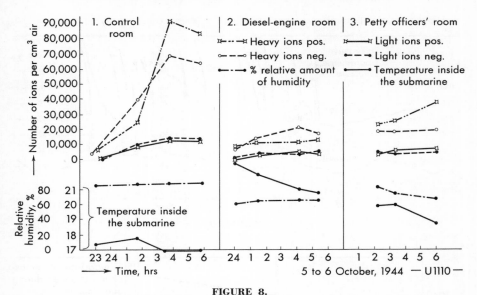

FIGURE 8.

Simultaneous measurement of the number of positive and negative ions and temperature and humidity in three different rooms of a submarine during submergence. Heavy ions: (K = 0.0075 cm² /V/s). Light ions: (0.05 cm² /V/s).

the number of positive and negative ions in the air of conventional submarines of the fleet type.

Figure 8 exhibits the results of simultaneous measurements of *positive* and *negative ions* as well as temperature and humidity in three compartments of a submarine during simulated submergence (Schaefer, 1959a). The largest increase of ions was found in the control room. This was caused by an accumulation of a large number of dials painted with a radioactive paint. Measurements of gamma radiation in the control room at the stations of the personnel demonstrated the presence of a sufficient amount of gamma radiation to account for the increase in ionization of the submarine atmosphere during submergence. A detailed account of these investigations is given elsewhere (Schaefer, 1959b). The calculated radiation exposure of the personnel at the control stations was 38 milliroentgen per week. This is below the presently accepted weekly permissible exposure of 100 milliroentgen, but significantly higher than the radiation exposure of the engineering personnel of the atomic powered submarine Nautilus, which amounts only to 9 milliroentgen equivalents per week according to Ebersole (1957). Results of two series of investigations of the ionization pattern in the submarine atmosphere under conditions of submergence up to 12 hours and simulated submergence in a closed submarine showed a 10- to 20-fold increase of ions in various compartments with the highest numbers in

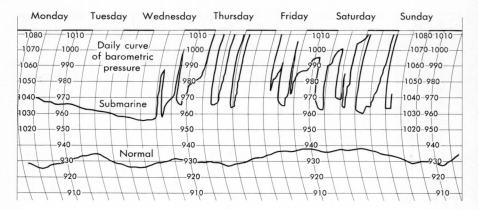

FIGURE 9

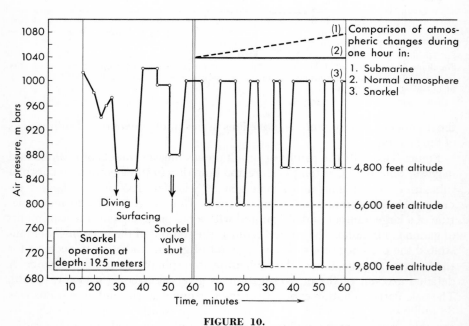

FIGURE 10.

Variations of atmospheric pressure in a submarine during snorkel operations.

the control rooms. In most of the cases a dominance of positive ions was found. Short time exposure to positive ionization in the observed range should not have any consequences, but long time exposure might pose a problem in view of the recent accumulation of evidence that positively charged air can precipitate symptoms of hay fever in patients who were asymptomatic at the time of treatment (Kornblueh *et al.*, 1958). It has also been reported that positive ions cause nasal obstruction, dryness of mucous membranes, and headaches (Winsor and Beckett, 1958; Yaglou *et al.*, 1933). Findings of Krueger *et al.* (1957), demonstrating a significant reduction in the movements of ciliae of the trachea during inhalation of positively charged air, lend considerable support to the view that positive ionization of the air can affect the well-being of personnel in an adverse manner.

A comparison of *atmospheric* pressures recorded during a period of a week under normal conditions and in a submarine during a war patrol in the Atlantic is given in Fig. 9 (Schaefer, 1948*b*). Note the contrast between the natural cycles of atmospheric pressure (lower curve) and the larger completely irregular variations of atmospheric pressure due to submergence and surfacing of the submarine (upper curve). With the introduction of the snorkels considerably larger pressure changes occurred. If the snorkel valve was shut under a wave and the diesel engines continued to run, the atmospheric pressure fell approximately 200–300 mb corresponding to altitudes between 6000–9000 feet. Figure 10 shows the large increase in frequency and amplitude of atmospheric pressure changes produced by the introduction of the snorkel. Under such conditions, Uffenorde (1948) found changes in the middle ear associated with a decrease of the hearing threshold.

I do not think that such jumps corresponding to 6000- to 9000-foot altitudes in 10- to 15-minute intervals will ever be encountered again in future submarines. But this is a good example to show how technical influences change the pattern of a natural environmental factor, from which is known that He acts as an important timegiver for biological cycles (Brown, 1957).

In Figure 11 average records of light, temperature, humidity, barometric pressure, and ionization extending over a 2-day period are compared under natural conditions (left) and aboard a fleet-type submarine operating in the Atlantic (right). The hatched areas represent the submerged periods, which generally covered the daytime. The natural environmental rhythms in form of sine waves are replaced on the submarine by arrhythmical processes which are determined by the schedule of submerging and surfacing. The resulting curves show, in general, a slow increase during submergence and an abrupt fall after surfacing, and may attain under certain conditions the "beat" of an engine. The environmental factors are shown in order of their importance as timegivers. The average crew member had no opportunity to see daylight; therefore, no changes in this most important timegiver have been indicated. Temperature, humidity, barometric pressure, and ionization all reach higher peak values than normal. The natural environmental timegivers, which serve as synchronizers between the endogenous physiological time and the natural environmental 24-hour time scale, have become timegivers of a new technical environment with a different periodicity of 12–18 hours (Schaefer, 1948*b*). Animal experi-

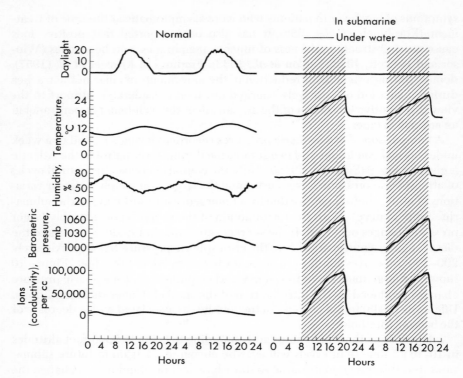

FIGURE 11

Daily course of light, temperature, humidity, air pressure, and ions in nature and on submarines.

ments indicate that the endogenous cycles are not quite 24 hours and can easily be brought in synchronization with the natural 24-hour cycles. The former can adapt to a certain extent to artificial days up to 28 hours and down to 21 hours according to Aschoff (1955), and Tribukeit (1956). However, they become independent of external cycles if the artificial day is further shortened. To what extent man's endogenous cycles can adjust to changing artificial time scales is not known. If the artificial days introduced by the technical environment are of such length that the organism cannot adjust, synchronization of inner and outer cycles cannot be achieved and a dissociation of the organism and environment would result. This could be a very important problem for the future of man living in confined spaces of machine systems.

It will be of help for an understanding of these problems if, for biological purposes, we abandon the notion of a general environment, which includes everything, and differentiate a *natural environment* from a *technical environment*. The natural environment is defined by its relation to man. It comprises all those components that have been incorporated *during evolution* into the organism. The latter was able to develop and stabilize an internal environment with these components and thereby achieved independence from external conditions. In the fast-changing world of today, we have to fall back to the still existing organismic heritage to find out what *nature* is really *like*. The *technical environment* is, on the other hand, characterized by its basic unrelatedness to man, by missing cycles or arrhythmical processes, and by deviations of natural components produced by the necessities of machine operations. To create more contrast to the newly regained *Nature* one could call the technical environment *Subnature*.

If nature is defined by its inherent relation to man and subnature by absence of this relation, it follows that man either has to adapt on a biological level to the laws governing the technical environment, which means departure from what he is now, or this technical environment has to be adapted to the principles embodied in man.

III. THEORETICAL ASPECTS OF OPEN AND CLOSED SYSTEMS

Man and all living organisms can be described as *open systems,* which take in material, digest it, and excrete it. In spite of a continuous breakdown and building up of their components they maintain themselves.

Characteristics of *open systems* have been developed by Bertalanffy (1950). They become clear when contrasted with closed reaction systems, which we generally use in chemistry. A process in a *closed system* leads to a chemical equilibrium, which is based on a reversible reaction. The closed system in equilibrium does not need energy for maintenance. It follows the second law of thermodynamics, eventually reaching a state of equilibrium with maximum entropy and minimal free energy.

An *open system* is also frequently characterized as a *dynamic equilibrium.* Another expression is the *steady states.* A steady state requires (1) transformation of free energy into effective work, and (2) energy for the maintenance of the steady state. The maintenance energy can account for the so-called low efficiency of *living machines.* It is also recognized more and more that the separation of maintenance energy from effective work is essential for a real understanding of biological processes; it probably represents also one of the knottiest problems—knowing what energy is used for maintenance of the cell machinery and what is used directly for growth, etc.

Prigogine (1947) worked out some of the thermodynamic aspects of open systems. In open systems, free energy is imported by taking in more complex molecules and releasing simpler end products back to the environment. The change in entropy in an open system consists therefore of two factors: (1) the import of frequently negative entropy (or free energy); and (2) the production of positive entropy through irreversible processes of heat transport, diffusion, etc., in the system. Steady states in open systems are, according to Prigogine

(1947), defined as tending toward minimum entropy production and are, in general, stable. Bertalanffy, on the basis of Prigogine's work, comes to the conclusion that the conventionally used *astronomical time* cannot be applied in open systems and that the concept of a *thermodynamic time* should be introduced. The thermodynamic time is *nonmetrical* and it is a *local time* because it is based on irreversible processes at a certain point in space (Bertalanffy). It is an open question whether the situation has advanced far enough to permit the successful introduction of a modification of time. While some physicists might agree that the current concept of time is not the proper concept corresponding to what it is really intending to represent, the feeling prevails that time is such a basic concept that any change is necessarily of a nature that must involve profound changes in physics which might come someday but for which the present state in physics offers little or no induction. (Katz, personal communication.)

The open systems theory of Bertalanffy (1952) avoids the fallacies of mechanistic interpretations as well as the pitfalls of the vitalistic viewpoint. The concept of thermodynamic time might provide a new basis to approach the problems of *physiological* time, to which men like Palagy (1901), Carrell (1939), Lecomte du Nouy (1937), and others have contributed. Using the Arrhenius equation which relates chemical reaction velocity to temperature, Hoagland (1936; 1950) could demonstrate a temperature characteristic for the human time sense and for the alpha-wave frequencies of subjects. This means that our time sense is somehow connected with the speed of certain chemical reactions in tissues, a finding which probably could have been predicted by the use of the concept of a thermodynamic time. With higher temperature the perception of time appears shortened; with lowered temperature, lengthened. A biological time presupposes a biological space. The phenomena of constancy of size of things we see when the distance is changed and the constancy of form when the visual angle is altered are demonstrations of the existence of the biological space. These considerations have recently found more interest with the evidence that the visual space of moving eyes has non-Euclidian characteristics [Luneburg (1947), Hardy (1953), von Schelling (1956), Zajaczkowska (1956), Squires (1956)]. The relation between biological time and biological space in regard to movements has been extensively investigated and discussed by Butendyk (1956) and von Weizsaecker (1946). According to these men movements can only be understood as directed meaningful performances if a unity of biological time and space is assumed.

The use of the homeostasis concept

In recent years the concept of homeostasis has been used extensively in connection with the negative feedback principle (Wiener, 1948) to describe biological systems and man-machine systems. A typical example is Ashby's (1952) homeostat for the brain, Grodins' (1954) homeostat for the respiration, etc. If the concept of homeostasis is rather loosely used and if one throws out adaptation, which Cannon (1929) had connected with it, one can get simple mechanistic models for almost everything in physiology and psychology. Ashby, for example, starts out by saying that homeostasis in the living organism is a mechanism to keep a few essential variables in physiological limits, variables which can be easily represented by a pointer of a dial. Homeostasis interpreted in such a way is a carry-over from the mineral sciences, where all laws have a form with a constant. If anything becomes really so constant in biology it is pathological. It is no wonder, therefore, that in the discussion of Ashby's homeostat, Heinrich Kluever compared Ashby's machine to a gas-poisoned patient without memory of time (1952). Grodins' homeostat is based on a number of assumptions and simplifications which eliminate essential variables of respiration such as breathing rate and tidal volume. We were able to demonstrate (1958) that these two variables, which together form the pattern of breathing, determine whether the subject is responding to inhalation of 7.5% CO_2 with a ventilatory response of 20 liters or 60 liters. These examples should only demonstrate that the use of these models involves usually an oversimplification of conditions which *eliminate the degrees of freedom* an organism has in response to environmental changes, as expressed in the different forms of adaptation of individual systems to changes of the environment.

IV. REQUIREMENTS FOR MAN-MACHINE SYSTEMS

In a submarine or a space ship, man, representing an *open system* is put into a *closed system.* Both systems have different characteristics and we have to find a compromise and a medium through which the compromise can be achieved.

1. The atmospheric conditions in the closed systems have to be kept in conformity with established tolerance limits and ranges of adaptation. For long periods of exposure the CO_2 concentrations should be kept as low as 0.5–0.8%. Oxygen should be maintained at appropriate concentrations depending upon the situation without increasing it to a level at which symptoms of oxygen toxicity could arise. These levels are not clearly defined since the effect of continuous O_2 breathing at pressures up to 1.0 atmosphere has been studied only for periods up to 24 hours (Comroe *et al.*, 1945). This symposium might bring to light more evidence for the notion that nitrogen in the atmosphere is essential for long exposure periods. The physiological significance of nitrogen in pulmonary gas exchange under these conditions is probably not limited to the prevention of atelectasis due to absorption of alveolar gas.

2. The imitation of natural cycles in closed systems is considered necessary.

(a) Environmental timegivers are essential for a synchronization of inner physiological cycles with the environmental time scale.

(b) The change or loss of cycles has been found to be connected with the beginning of pathological processes (Schulte *et al.*, 1955). Neglect of the role of cycles has been shown to impair the performance of work in shift workers (Bjerner and Swenson, 1953). Proposed cycles are: light, temperature, humidity, air pressure, and ionization.

(c) In the creation of special conditions, consideration should be given to the prevention of energy reduction by allowing or designing space in which man can actively move. Interior decorating of spaces should be considered for the purpose of creating perceptual values, and stimulation using various colors to create illusions of larger space, etc.

We hope that this symposium can contribute to the clarification of many aspects of basic physiological problems which are not really understood. It has been said (Benson, 1958) that in the space age we face a new "vertical frontier." This is certainly true, but associated with it is a new "inner" frontier which has come to the fore—the necessity to define the degrees of freedom man needs for a human existence in a man-machine system.

REFERENCES

Aschoff, J. 1955. "Exogenous and endogenous components of the 24-hour periodicity in man and animal," Naturwissenschafften *42:* 569.

Ashby, N. R. 1952. "Homeostasis," Trans. 9th Conf. on Cybernetics, J. Macy Jr. Foundation 73.

Barcroft, J. 1934. *Cambridge Comparative Physiology,* Cambridge.

Behnke, A. R., R. M. Thomson, and E. P. Motley. 1935. Am. J. Physiol. *112:* 554.

Benson, O. 1958. 26th Annual Meeting, Institute of the Aeronautical Sciences, New York.

Bernard, Claude, 1878. *Les Phenomenes de la Vie,* p. 113.

Bertalanffy, L. 1952. *Problems of Life,* John Wiley & Sons, Inc., New York.

——— 1950. "The theory of open systems in physics and biology," Science *111:* 23.

Bjerner, B., and A. Swenson. 1953. "Schichtarbeit und Rhythmus," International Transactions Third Conference, Society for the Study of Biological Cycles, Stockholm, p. 102.

Brendel, W. 1956. "Adaptation of respiration, hemoglobin, body temperature and circulation during prolonged exposure to high altitudes (Himalaya)," Pflueg. Arch. *263:* 227.

Brown, F. A., Jr. 1957. "Biological chronometry," Am. Naturalist *91:*129.

Butendyk, F. J. J. 1956. *Allgemeine Theorie der Menschlichcen Haltung und Bewegung,* Springer, Heidelberg.

Cannon, W. B. 1929. "Organization for physiological homeostasis." Physiol. Rev. *9:* 399.

Carrell, A. 1939. *Man, The Unknown,* Harper & Bros., New York.

Comroe, F. H., R. D. Dripps, D. R. Dunike, and Dening, 1945. "Effects produced in man by inhalation of high concentrations of oxygen for 24 hours," Am. J. Med. Sci. *209:* 814.

du Nouy, Lecomte. 1937. *Biological Time,* The Macmillan Company, New York.

Ebersole, J. H. 1957. "Radiation Exposure Patterns Aboard U.S.S. Nautilus, New England J. Med. *256:* 67.

Grodins, F. S., J. S. Gray, K. R. Schroeder, A. L. Norrins, and R. W. Jones. 1954. J. Appl. Physiol. *7:* 283.

Halberg, F. 1953. "Some physiological and clinical aspects of 24 hours periodicity," Lancet *73:* 20.

Hardy, Legrand H., G. Rand, M. C. Rittler, A. A. Blank, and P. Boeder. 1953. *The Geometry of Binocular Space Perception,* Institute of Ophthalmology, Columbia University, College of Physicians and Surgeons, New York.

Henderson, L. 1928. *Blood,* Yale University Press, New Haven, Connecticut.

Hoagland, H. 1950; 1936 (1) "Consciousness and the chemistry of time," Trans. of the First Conf. on Problems of Consciousness, J. Macy Jr. Foundation 64. (2) "Pacemakers of human brain waves in normals and general paretics," Am. J. Physiol. *116:* 604.

Hutchins, R. M. 1948. Lecture at the Centennial Celebration of the St, Paul's Cathedral in Frankfurt am Main, Germany.

Katz, E. Personal communication.

Kluever, H. 1952. Trans. 9th Conf. on Cybernetics, J. Macy Jr. Foundation 107.

Kornbleuh, J. H., G. M. Piewohl, and F. D. Speicher. 1958. "Relief from pollinosis in negative ionized rooms," Am. J. Physiol. Med. *37,* 18.

Krueger, A. P., and R. F. Smith. 1957. "Effects of air ions on isolated rabbit trachea," Proc. Soc. Exp. Biol. and Med. *96:* 807.

Luneburg, R. K. 1947. *Mathematical Analysis of Binocular Vision,* Dartmouth Eye Institute, Princeton University Press, Princeton.

Nuttin, J. 1955. "Consciousness, behavior and personality," Psychol. Rev. *62:* 349.

Palagy, M. 1901. *Neue Theorie des Raumes und der Zeit.*

Prigogine, J. 1947. *Etude Thermodynamique des Phenomenes Irreversibles,* Durrod, Paris.

Schaefer, K. E. (ed.) 1948*a*. *Heat Regulation Aboard Submarines,* 5, C VII German Monograph on Submarine Medicine. Translation prepared by Technical Section (Medical) U.S. Navy, Germany.

Schaefer, K. E. (ed.) 1948*b*. *Man and Environment in the Submarine (Bioclimatology of the Submarine),* 1, B I German Monograph on Submarine Medicine. Translation prepared by Technical Section (Medical) U.S. Navy, Germany.

Schaefer, K. E. 1949*a*. "Influence of prolonged exposure to 3% CO_2 on behavior and excitability of the peripheral nervous system," Pflueg. Arch. *251:* 726.

Schaefer, K. E. 1949*b*. "Respiration and acid base balance during prolonged exposure to 3% CO_2," Pflueg. Arch. *251:* 689.

Schaefer, K. E., 1955. "Studies of oxygen toxicity in underwater swimming," J. Appl. Physiol. *8:* 524.

Schaefer, K. E. 1958*a*. "Physiological effects of CO_2 as related to CO_2 therapy," in L. J. Meduna, *Carbon Dioxide Therapy.*

Schaefer, K. E. 1958*b*. "Respiratory pattern and respiratory response to CO_2," J. Appl. Physiol. *13:* 1.

Schaefer, K. E. 1959*a*. "Experiences with submarine atmospheres," J. Aviation Medicine *30:* 350–359.

Schaefer, K. E. 1959*b*. "Airborne condensation droplets, ions, may be major health factors in habitability of closed spaces," Heating, Piping, Air Conditioning, May, June, July.

Schaefer, K. E., H. Klein, and K. H. Zinck. 1950. "Experimental investigations about the functional relation of adrenal, medulla, and cortex during prolonged exposure to increased CO_2," Klin. Woch, *28:* 179.

Schulte, W., R. Gjemy, and K. Franke. 1955. Trans. Fifth Conf. of the Intern. Soc. Study Biol. Cycles.

Selye, H. 1940. "The general adaptation system and the diseases of adaptation," J. Clin. Endocrinol. *6:* 118.

Sherrington, C. S. 1933. *The Brain and its Mechanism,* Cambridge Univ. Press, London.

Speransky, A. D. 1935. *A Basis for the Theory of Medicine,* Intra-Cooperative Publishing Society.

Squires, P. C. 1956. "Luneburg theory of visual geodesies in binocular space preception," A.M.A. Arch. Ophthalmol. *56:* 280.

Tribukeit, B. 1956. "Periodicity of motor activity of white mice in artificial days from 16–29 hours," Z. F. Vergleich. Physiol. *38:* 479.

Uffenorde, H. 1948. *Otological Experiences with Snorkel Equipped Submarines,* D II German Monograph on Submarine Medicine, ed. K. E. Schaefer, Translation prepared by Technical Section (Medical) U.S. Navy, Germany.

von Schelling, H. 1956. "Concept of distance in affine geometry and its application in theories of vision," J. Opt. Soc. Am. *46:* 309.

von Weizsaecker, V. 1946. *Der Gestalt Kreis,* Georg Thieme.

Wiener, N. 1948. *Cybernetics.* John Wiley & Sons, Inc., New York.

Winsor, T. A., and J. C. Beckett. 1958. Am. J. Phys. Med. *37:* 83–89.

Yaglou, C. D., L. C. Benjamin, and A. D. Brandt. 1933. Heating, Piping, Air Conditioning, *5:* 422.

Zajaczkowska, A. 1956. "Experimental test of Luneburg's theory. Horopter and alley experiments," J. Opt. Soc. Am. *46:* 514.

PART ONE

Effects of Acute and Chronic Environmental Stress Conditions on Endocrine and Metabolic Functions

Chairman

DR. HUDSON HOAGLAND

Worcester Foundation for Experimental Biology
Shrewesbury, Massachusetts

General and Specific Characteristics of Physiological Adaptation

E. F. ADOLPH

University of Rochester School of Medicine and Dentistry, Rochester, New York

The old notion that animals adapt to influences from their environments is now assuming precise meaning. By experimentation we are seeing how organisms change their properties within hours or days in controlled directions. My aim here is to discuss certain characteristics of many sorts of adaptation within the individual, to describe some methods of studying them, and to evaluate their significance in environmental physiology.

The history of men's concepts about adaptation and acclimatization helps to grasp their diffuse nature. That animals and plants change their properties according to circumstances was believed in folklore. The hardy northerner, the desert pioneer, and the ranging mountaineer were considered to possess specialized physiological capacities. Further, it was noted that animals and plants had limited distributions, yet could gradually become inured to new boundaries. Experimental studies of adaptation began about 1815 with the placement of sea-water animals into fresh water and vice versa; it was found that gradual transitions through diluted sea waters often allowed survival (Beudant, 1816). In the period 1835 to 1875 came the realization that man adapts to high altitude, and specific physiological properties were explored during the transition (Bert, 1878). In the present century the genetic factors of adaptation became clearly distinguished from the modifications that occur within the individual. The latter are what I refer to as physiological adaptations. In the past decade or two the study of adaptations in bacteria, insects, viruses, and enzymes has come to the fore.

Genetic adaptation appears to be largely by natural selection among individuals that differ in their innate constitutions. But physiological adaptation is not a selection among individuals, and probably not among cells or response systems. Rather it consists in prearranged responses to particular influences. We may term the complex of influences to which the individual is exposed a

33

stressor, and term the complex of responses an adaptation or a set of adaptates. Each measured property that becomes modified is, then, an adaptate. These built-in response systems differ in their persistence from the prompter response systems that physiologists have more usually studied. Their slower onset and their longer persistence make adapted responses less obvious and somewhat more difficult to trace.

I wish to illustrate some general characteristics of adaptations, rather than analyze any one of them. But I will describe some specific adaptations in pointing out these characteristics. I will dwell largely on the responses to low oxygen pressures and confine my remarks to data on mammals. When one begins to look for adaptations he finds them at nearly every turn, for they are products of the tendency which characterizes all systems to shift toward new steady states.

STRESSOR-ADAPTATE SYSTEMS

Methods for the study of adaptations are indicated by the above concepts. The concepts evidently require that we expose individuals to some reproducible influence, perhaps an environmental complex, and measure some modifications in them. For the physiologist the chief stipulation often is that control individuals without exposure be simultaneously observed. Exposures may be continuous or intermittent.

Thus, men who go to high altitudes decrease the pressure of carbon dioxide in their alveolar airs (Fig. 1). The initial change was only a part of the total one; several days were required before alveolar pressure of carbon dioxide became minimal, and thereafter it slowly increased again. Evidently adaptation is far from complete in the few days represented.

A number of other changes are known to be related to the one measured here, for the decreased pressure of carbon dioxide reflects the increased ventilation of the lungs (Kellogg *et al.*, 1957), the respiratory alkalosis, the cation excretion, and a host of other modifications. Each is an adaptate that prevails over a period of many hours or days. Further, the adaptates persist for some time after men return from altitude to sea level, even though breathing is me-

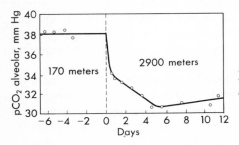

FIGURE 1.

Alveolar pressures of carbon dioxide in men who went to high altitude on day zero. (Data of Rahn and Otis, 1949)

chanically able to change instantaneously. Clearly the adapted responses outlast the stimulus, just as the adaptates gradually came to a new steady state many days or years after the stimulus or stressor first impinged.

In the case of man at altitude we are aware that the low oxygen pressure of the atmosphere becomes a low oxygen pressure in arterial blood (Hurtado *et al.*, 1945) and in many tissues. We like to think of low oxygen pressure as itself a stimulus, whether in specialized chemoreceptors or elsewhere. The sensitive tissue transmits information to its own reacting systems and probably to distant tissues; some of those tissues are effectors and execute the modifications which we observe. Probably all physiological adaptations can be fitted into this scheme of stressor → sensor → transmitter → effector → adaptate.

The search for the sensitive tissues and the communications that they broadcast is one direction in which the study of adaptation often proceeds. But it is also possible, as here, to bypass that search, and instead to establish quantitative relations between stressor and adaptate. For instance, at diverse altitudes progressively greater hemoglobin concentrations are found in the blood of resident men (Fig. 2). These concentrations may be said to be end products of effectors that are responding to stimuli closely connected with the oxygen desaturation of arterial blood.

Again, men exposed to atmospheres high in carbon dioxide modify their breathing in accordance with the concentration of carbon dioxide being breathed (Fig. 3). The responses after 5 to 8 days of exposure to 3% carbon dioxide in the atmosphere are consistently different from those after only 2 hours of exposure. Significant shifts in a number of factors in blood and other properties are known. No less than in altitude, in carbon dioxide caves, or submarines a complex of long-term modifications results in all individuals exposed to carbon dioxide as an environmental stressor (Schäfer, 1949). Adaptation has also been reported in men exposed to repeated experimental hyperventilations with consequent diminutions in carbon dioxide pressures of tissues (Balke *et al.*, 1958).

Adaptation may be aroused locally as well as in the whole body. This fact can be illustrated by another form of adaptation in man. Ito and Adachi, 1934, exposed one arm to heat on alternate days for one-half hour each (in 4 to 12 exposures), and measured the sweating rate. The rate on the exposed arm increased greatly, while that on the control arm did not. The effect persisted for 5 to 8 days after the last exposure. In the heat-adapted arm no more sweat glands were active, but each gland worked faster. Hence each gland modified its function independently. In contrast, the whole body adapted its sweat glands by modifying the concentration of electrolytes in the sweat in response to whole body exposures; the sweat became less concentrated with successive exposures to heat (Kuno, 1956). This modification occurred over the whole body and arose from general stimulation, not from local heating.

Results of adaptations are implanted in various tissues as well as in whole

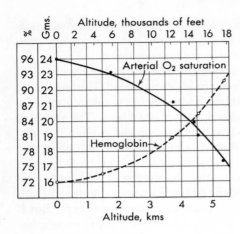

FIGURE 2.

Hemoglobin concentration of bloods and percentage oxygen saturation of arterial bloods of men permanently residing at various altitudes. (From Hurtado *et al.*, 1945)

FIGURE 3.

Alveolar ventilations (lower curves) and alveolar pressures of carbon dioxide in a man inhaling various CO_2 mixtures: after only two hours in an atmosphere of 3% CO_2 (dashed lines) and after three days in that atmosphere (solid lines).

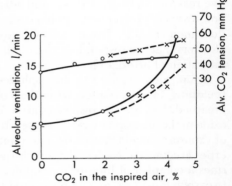

organisms, even when the whole body is exposed to the stressor. Thus the oxygen consumption of several tissues decreased (Ullrich *et al.*, 1956) and the myoglobin content of certain tissues increased (Vaughan and Pace, 1956; Tappan *et al.*, 1957) upon exposure of animals to altitude. Not just breathing, not just blood, not just synapses, not just hormone liberation is affected by the stressor, but many tissues are targets for the communications that are initiated by the stressor (Stickney and Van Liere, 1953). Perhaps every cell of the mammalian body adapts in one way or another to altitude or to carbon dioxide-rich atmospheres, and to scores of other stressors as well.

KINETICS OF ADAPTATES

A useful approach to the study of physiological adaptations is to compare the velocities of onset of the various modifications that are induced. Such comparisons can be made among the responses to stressors of like kind but of different intensities, or can be made among the responses to very dissimilar stressors. Suitable data exist for rats exposed to altitude and to half a dozen other stressors. Sometimes these stressors acted continuously, at other times intermittently.

First we compare various intensities of a single stressor, namely, altitude or decompression, using the blood hematocrit ratio as the adaptate (Fig. 4). An immediate response of limited amount was followed by a gradual increase that is known to be chiefly the result of accelerated hematopoesis. At the highest altitude not only the absolute rate of modification was greater, but also the time required for half the modification was shorter. The ultimate hematocrit ratio attained, however, had the same maximum for the three most intense stimuli, indicating that there is a ceiling to the hematocrit ratio tolerated in the circulating blood.

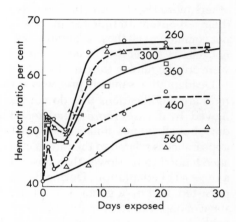

FIGURE 4.

Hematocrit ratios in bloods of rats exposed to various air pressures, mm Hg. Data of Sundstroem and Michaels (1942) as graphed by Adolph (1956).

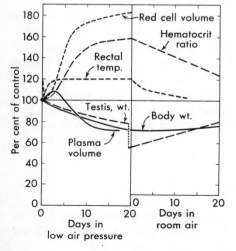

FIGURE 5.

Modifications during adaptations and deadaptations to air pressure of 380 mm Hg. Data from various sources cited in Fig. 3 (Adolph, 1956).

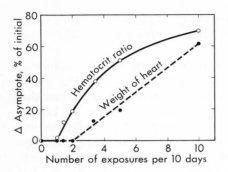

FIGURE 6.

Two modifications as ultimately produced by exposures to 282 mm Hg of air pressure with various frequencies. Data of Altland and Highman (1951) as graphed by Adolph (1956).

Next we compare several adaptates that respond to the single stressor of altitude (Fig. 5). Some adapted in the first day (as, rectal temperature lowering), others more slowly and continuingly (as, testis hypotrophy), others reversed their response with time (as, plasma volume). Part of the responding system is not common to all these adaptates, but whether only the effectors differ we cannot tell. At the end of 5 days some adaptates were in full force, while others were only beginning to be realized. Even at 20 days, adaptation was only partial.

Deadaptation similarly proceeds at various rates (Fig. 5). By definition, adaptates are modifications that do not disappear at once when the stressor is removed. In all cases represented here, the modifications diminished over many days, but all did not diminish at equal rates. Whether the adaptate's rate of disappearance is related to the rate of onset seems doubtful, except that disappearance tended to be slower than onset. In general, deadaptation was not merely a reversal of adaptation. During deadaptation varying degrees of adaptedness persisted, and on a given day not in the same combinations as at a selected stage of onset. Further, a suitable degree of reinforcement at an early stage will evidently maintain the partial state of adaptation and prevent deadaptation.

When intermittent exposures are given serially, the adaptation may be nil if the exposures are too infrequent (Fig. 6). But a unit of stressor that was inadequate to arouse one adaptate (as, increase of heart weight) was found adequate to arouse another (as, increase of hematocrit ratio). For one adaptate there was an asymptotic maximal response, for the other the response was proportional to the frequency of stimulation. Various rules can be found for the effectiveness of intensity × duration × frequency in diverse adaptates; but each response measured tells us the nature of the responding system of adaptation in the same degree as the arousal of nerve impulses tells us the nature of those systems.

SPECIFICITIES

We wish to know whether the same adaptates will appear in response to more than one stressor, and in what combinations. This information will tell us to what extent adaptation is general, and to what extent specific.

TABLE 1

Modifications (relative to controls) in rats continuously exposed to cold or hypoxia for 10 to 15 days.[*]

Adaptate	Air of 5°C	Air of pO_2 70 mm Hg
Resistance to cooling	+64%	−25%
Tolerance time hypoxia	−70%	+270%
Total O_2 consumption	+28%	0
QO_2 of liver slices	+43%	0
Thyroid weight	+13%	0
Adrenal weight	+95%	+108%
Heart weight	+14%	+21%
Body weight	−11%	−26%

[*] Data from various sources cited in Tappan *et al.*, Table 2.

When some of the data on rats exposed to decompression and on rats exposed to cold were placed side by side, little overlap of responses appeared (Table 1). Adaptates that showed an increase in one might show decrease in the other (as, resistance to cooling, tolerance to. hypoxia). Other adaptates showed no response at all to one of the two stressors. Several adaptates responded to both stressors (as, adrenal weight, heart weight). Evidently each stressor can be expected to arouse a different combination of adaptates; an animal in some respects responds with the same effectors in opposing directions. Communication is inferred to be sufficiently specific within the animal so that stressors are distinguished qualitatively as well as quantitatively.

Another type of study may be designated cross adaptation. Individuals are exposed to stressor A (perhaps cold air), and then exposed to stressor B (perhaps decompression). When these particular stressors were chosen, rats kept in cold air were unable to increase their tolerance to altitude (Fregley, 1954). In this case the daily test of the time required for the rats to lose their righting reflexes in rarified air was itself the second adapting influence. The reverse experiment was also done; rats kept in low oxygen (stressor B) for several weeks were subjected under restraint to cold air (stressor A), whereupon they cooled more rapidly than control rats not exposed to low oxygen (Fregley, 1954). Clearly, resistance to cooling is affected along with resistance to low oxygen in such a manner that gain in one accompanies loss in the other. The incompatibility of these two resistances could not be predicted on any theory that has been proposed.

A further point which indicates the specificity of adaptive responses is that all individuals show the same adaptates upon exposure to the same stressor. There is the usual quantitative variability among the individuals, but they all are evidently set to respond in a stereotyped or prearranged pattern. The origins of any adaptive pattern in the ontogeny of the individual have not yet been explored.

Often the particular modifications that occur are believed to be ones that favor the organism's operation or its survival. Often this belief turns out to be justified. The usual difficulty is to prove it, for most adaptates by themselves cannot be evaluated in terms of survival. Thus, an increased basal metabolism may or may not be an advantage in cold adaptation; a decreased metabolism might or might not be an advantage in altitude adaptation. But, we usually arrange to observe just those adaptates that we imagine will favor the organism's existence. More often we try to rationalize those that are found, and sometimes succeed in excusing both an increase and a decrease of the same adaptate. For this reason I recommend the study of adaptation as the study of modifications. This study frees us of the need for rationalizations. A modification that may or may not in itself be valuable to the organism is part of a large complex of responses. It probably is unfair to consider a single item in this complex as having positive or negative value to the organism.

NEED FOR THEORIES

The study of adaptations needs most a comprehensive theory that will allow us to predict what properties will be modified in an adapting individual. Now that we have reached the point where we expect the individual to modify in response to its present and past environments, we want guidance as to the likely directions of the modifications before we have tried each new stressor. The problem is larger than it seemed when only a few adaptates were known for each stressor.

Evidently each adaptation involves an extensive network of displacements. We might picture a mechanical model of such a network in terms of a flat bedspring. The location of each point in the spring, and the tension on each wire of the spring, depends on the location and size of the load. When the load shifts, tensions change not only immediately under the load but throughout the spring. Every shift modifies the tensions in all directions, achieving a balance very quickly. In the living individual, however, each wire becomes a physicochemical component, and there are many more components than in the mechanical model. These interconnected components are responsive and behavioral as well as mechanical, with the result that reactions are aroused that take varying lengths of time to arrive at a steady state. To physiologists a frustrating feature is that we know only a few components of the steady state, so that we can rarely tell whether the state observed is anywhere near completely described. Obviously our mechanical model of the bedspring is hopelessly inadequate. It is even an assumption that in the organism a steady state is being approached after each shift of a load.

Recognizing that each individual is physiologically malleable, we still need a theory to help us predict the direction in which modification will occur. So far the only one we have is the theory of fitness, that the adapted individual is more efficient or more economical or more able to survive than it was before. This theory has led to valuable observations and experiments. But what is fit in the organisms and what is unfit in it is not agreed among us. Hence the use-fulness of the theory is small at present.

Meanwhile we must define the limits of adaptation to each stressor, and learn how to manipulate individuals within those limits. Today operators manipu-late human individuals by propaganda; tomorrow they have the possibility of manipulating individuals by use of calculated stressors, with all the dangers that are involved when operators interfere in the lives of themselves and others.

SUMMARY

Adaptations in individual animals are represented by modifications that tend to persist. They are reproducible in all individuals. Usually many modifica-tions develop, partially in parallel. Rates of development vary even among the partially parallel adaptates. The combination of adaptates tends to be specific to the stressor and sometimes two stressors nullify one another's adaptive ef-fects. Each adaptate represents a shift of regulation, but the shift need not be permanent, for other adaptates of slower development may replace them. Later, deadaptation involves return to the original property. Adaptations add to the range of circumstances within which the self-regulating individual main-tains itself; possibly adaptations relieve some of the strains of maintenance.

REFERENCES

Adolph, E. F. 1956. Am. J. Physiol. *184:* 18–28.
Altland, P. D., and B. Highman. 1951. Am. J. Physiol. *167:* 261–267.
Balke, B., J. P. Ellis, Jr., and J. G. Wells. 1958. J. Appl. Physiol. *12:* 269–277.
Bert, P. 1878. *La Pression Barométrique,* Paris, 1178 pages.
Beudant, F. S. 1816. Ann. chim. et phys. *2:* (2), 32–41.
Fregley, M. J. 1954. Am. J. Physiol. *176:* 267–274.
Häbisch, H. 1949. Arch. ges. Physiol. *251:* 594–608.
Hurtado, A., C. Merino, and E. Delgado. 1945. Arch. Intern. Med. *75:* 284–323.
Ito, S., and J. Adachi. 1934. J. Oriental Med. *21:* 851–857.
Kellogg, R. H., N. Pace, E. R. Archibald, and B. E. Vaughan. 1957. J. Appl. Physiol. *11:* 65–71.
Kuno, Y. 1956. *Human Perspiration,* Springfield. 416 pages, pp. 321 and 325.
Rahn, H., and A. B. Otis. 1949. Am. J. Physiol. *157:* 445–462.
Schäfer, K. E. 1949. Arch. ges. Physiol. *251:* 689–715.
Stickney, J. C., and E. J. Van Liere. 1953. Physiol. Rev. 33: 13–34.
Sundstroem, E. S., and G. Michaels. 1942. Memoirs Univ. Calif. *12:* 409 pages.
Tappan, D. V., B. Reynafarje D., V. R. Potter, and A. Hurtado. 1957. Am. J. Physiol. *190:* 93–98.
Ullrich, W. C., W. V. Whitehorn, B. B. Brennan, and J. G. Krone. 1956. J. Appl. Physiol. *9:* 49–52.
Vaughan, B. E., and N. Pace. 1956. Am. J. Physiol. *185:* 549–556.

Unspecific Systemic Stress Reactions[*]

HANS SELYE

Institut de Médecine et de Chirurgie expérimentales, Université de Montréal, Montréal, Canada

The concept of stress and the "diseases of adaptation" have been reviewed in several monographs (Selye, 1950; Selye *et al.*, 1951–56) and, in a synoptic treatise (Selye, 1957a). The latest investigations of our Institute on the participation of the "stress hormones" in the development of lathyrism (Selye, 1957b) and cardiac necroses (Selye, 1958) have likewise been surveyed elsewhere; hence, it would be redundant to deal with these subjects in detail here. Instead, I should like to mention only a few of the key experiments upon which the concept of stress and the diseases of adaptation is based (with special reference to some of our latest findings on the prevention of stress-induced myocardial necroses), and then to discuss the most common misconceptions which interfere with the proper evaluation of this theory.

FUNDAMENTAL OBSERVATIONS FOR THE STRESS CONCEPT

Soon after the discovery of the "alarm reaction" as a stereotype response to nonspecific stress, it was noted that the principal manifestations of this reaction that were known at that time (adrenal hyperplasia with signs of hyperactivity, thymicolymphatic involution and eosinopenia, gastro-intestinal ulcers) tended to disappear after a few days, even if the organism continued to be exposed to the same degree of the same stressor agents. This second phase was called the "stage of resistance." Eventually, if the stressor was sufficiently severe, a third reaction-type to stress, the "stage of exhaustion," ensued. Thus it was learned that the standard reaction-type to stress is a triphasic response, the "General Adaptation Syndrome" (G.A.S.).

The striking hyperplasia and hyperactivity of the adrenal cortex represented a clue for a series of experiments designed to explore the value of corticoids

[*] Most of the experiments upon which this synopsis is based were subsidized by Grant No. H-3688 from the National Heart Institute and Grant No. A-1461 from the National Institute of Arthritis and Metabolic Diseases (U.S. Public Health Service).

in the body's *resistance* to potentially pathogenic agents. It was found that, although both glucocorticoids and mineralocorticoids can prolong the life of adrenalectomized animals, the former are much more effective than the latter in raising resistance to stressors (e.g., trauma, hemorrhage, toxic chemicals).

Although only very intense overdosage with corticoids produces manifestations of disease, even small amounts of these hormones can decisively influence the effects of certain nonhormonal pathogens. For example, the *experimental arthritis* produced by the injection of formalin into the paw of a rat can be prevented by relatively small doses of glucocorticoids and aggravated by mineralocorticoids.

The so-called "anaphylactoid inflammation" that ensues in rats, following the intraperitoneal or intravenous administration of egg-white, dextran, and other macromolecular substances, is similarly influenced by the same types of hormones. Both the antiphlogistic effects of glucocorticoids and the prophlogistic actions of mineralocorticoids are more evident in the adrenalectomized than in the intact animal, presumably because, in the latter, endogenous corticoids of the opposite type can interfere with the actions of the hormones that are injected.

Further investigations showed that heavy overdosage with mineralocorticoids (e.g., desoxycorticosterone) can, under certain conditions, produce a simile of the so-called *collagen diseases* in animals. For example, using desoxycorticosterone it is possible to induce nephrosclerosis with hypertension, periarteritis nodosa, and a myocarditis with intense hyalinization; but the development of this syndrome depends upon certain "conditioning factors." Unilateral nephrectomy and an excess of dietary NaCl proved to be especially effective in increasing sensitivity to this particular effect of the mineralocorticoids.

It was even possible to dissociate the individual actions of desoxycorticosterone overdosage by procedures of "selective conditioning." For example, partial constriction of certain mesenteric vessels can selectively desensitize that part of the vascular tree in which the pulse pressure is diminished so that here (unlike in the rest of the mesenteric arterial system) periarteritis will not develop. Thus, NaCl and unilateral nephrectomy act as positive conditioning agents, while a decrease in pulse pressure acts as a negative conditioning agent for mineralocorticoid hormones.

Although our first investigations were concerned with the actions of corticoids upon inflammatory diseases, it soon became evident that morbid lesions that are not inflammatory in character can likewise be aggravated or prevented by suitable treatment with stress hormones. Thus, the *skeletal lesions* induced by a diet containing the seeds of *Lathyrus odoratus* (or its active principles, the aminonitriles) are suppressed by pretreatment with cortisone or ACTH. Conversely, STH (the somatotrophic or growth hormone) induces severe deformities of the skeleton and joints in rats simultaneously treated with small amounts of *Lathyrus odoratus* seeds, in themselves inactive. Obviously here the hor-

mones exert a decisive influence upon the pathogenicity of a potentially dangerous diet.

Another instance of conditioning by corticoids for a noninflammatory disease
phenomenon was discovered in the course of studies on *muscular fatigue*. Oral
administration of $NaClO_4$ greatly increases the fatigability of skeletal muscles,
so that rats normally able to run for about 3 hours in our standard running
mill collapse with fatigue within 10 minutes when pretreated with this salt. Glucocorticoids (e.g., triamcinolone) restore working ability to essentially normal
levels, under similar conditions.

Perhaps the most interesting outcome of our investigations on stress was the
finding that corticoids can so condition the cardiac muscle that it develops
massive, *infarctlike necroses during nonspectfic stress*. Rats pretreated with
2α-methyl-9α-chlorocortisol (Me-Cl-COL) develop severe cardiac necroses
upon comparatively brief exposure to such stressors as forced restraint, surgical
trauma, hot or cold baths, electroshock, or the injection of various toxic chemicals. This is all the more noteworthy, because even fatal doses of Me-Cl-COL
alone or of the stressors alone fail to produce comparable cardiac damage. Apparently, here again, the hormones are not pathogens in the usual sense of the
word, but merely conditioning agents for the potentially pathogenic effects of
stressors. This conditioning action of Me-Cl-COL can be duplicated by corti-
sol, as well as by mixtures of pure glucocorticoids (e.g., triamcinolone, medrol)
and mineralocorticoids (e.g., desoxycorticosterone).

Certain sodium salts (e.g., Na_2HPO_4, Na_2SO_4, $NaClO_4$) given in conjunction
with Me-Cl-COL produce massive cardiac necroses, even in the absence of
stress. The lesions so produced have been referred to as the "Electrolyte-
Steroid-Cardiopathy with Necroses" (ESCN). Other sodium salts (e.g., NaCl
and most of the organic sodium salts) that do not possess any such sensitizing
effect under normal conditions become highly effective in this respect during
exposure to stress. Apparently, the metabolic changes induced by stress render otherwise inactive Na salts cardiotoxic.

From a clinical point of view, it is particularly noteworthy that other electrolytes, especially $MgCl_2$ and KCl, *are highly effective in preventing the cardiac
damage* normally induced either by corticoids plus stress or by corticoids plus
sensitizing Na salts. The possible value of these desensitizing electrolytes in
the treatment of spontaneous necrotizing cardiopathies is now under investigation.

COMMON ERRORS IN EVALUATION

The experiments just mentioned led to the concept that some diseases that
are not primarily due to an increased or insufficient corticoid secretion may, in
the final analysis, nevertheless be due to hypo- or hypercorticoidism, respectively. For example, a decreased resistance to infections may be viewed as due

to an increase in glucocorticoids (e.g., during stress), since overdosage with ACTH and cortisone does, in fact, diminish resistance to infections in experimental animals. Conversely, a diminished activity of prophlogistic hormones (e.g., STH) may have the same effect, as judged by the observation that injections of STH are highly effective in restoring towards normal the decreased resistance to infection that can be induced by antiphlogistic hormones. Furthermore, acute gastric ulcers—such as are characteristic of the alarm reaction— can be produced with an excess of glucocorticoids both in experimental animals and in man. This suggested the possibility that spontaneous gastroduodenal ulcers may likewise partly depend upon an increased antiphlogistic hormone activity. If this concept is correct, we shall have to consider certain maladies that tend to develop during stress as "diseases of adaptation," maladies which are not only due to the actions of the apparent pathogen, but largely also to changes in disease susceptibility induced by inadequate hormonal reactions to stress.

In the supposed diseases of adaptation of man, marked changes in the blood level or urinary elimination of hormones can rarely be observed. This fact led to the conclusion that endocrine factors do not play a decisive role in the pathogenesis of such maladies.

However, the theory of the diseases of adaptation does not postulate an *absolute* increase or decrease in hormone production, but rather a change in hormone activity. The latter may be due to faulty conditioning, and hence need not be reflected by any absolute change in hormone levels. Thus, a nearly "normal" glucocorticoid secretion, such as suffices to maintain homeostasis at rest, is grossly insufficient to maintain the life of an adrenalectomized animal exposed to stress. Such a "normal" secretion also fails to prevent inflammation in the presence of a special irritant (e.g., formalin, in the case of the experimental arthritis, or egg-white, in the case of the anaphylactoid inflammation). Here, the pathogenic factor would be precisely the maintenance of the normal hormone level when the situation calls for a considerable increase. Conversely, as we have seen, in themselves well tolerated amounts of desoxycorticosterone or STH can acquire severe pathogenic potencies, owing to changes in the metabolic conditioning factors which determine susceptibility to their toxic effects. Therefore, an increase in corticoid activity must not be equated with an increase in corticoid hormone secretion.

It was thought, furthermore, that, *if stress and the stress hormones were responsible for the development of the various diseases of adaptation, these should all be present simultaneously* whenever an individual is exposed to stress. This is not the case and, indeed, it was not to be expected in view of what we have just said about selective conditioning. Dietary factors (e.g., in the experiments just described, NaCl or *Lathyrus odoratus*), interference with the normal function of an organ (e.g., the kidney, as suggested by the unilateral nephrectomy experiments), hereditary predisposition, and many other factors can selectively increase or decrease the responsiveness of individual organs to the potentially pathogenic actions of stress or stress hormones. In the light of what we know about the widely different manifestations of infections with the same microorganism (e.g., tuberculosis of the lungs, skin, bones, miliary tuberculosis), it is not unexpected that exposure to the same stressor may affect various individuals in essentially distinct ways.

It has also been thought that *overdosage with a hormone, be it relative (e.g., owing to special conditioning) or absolute, should invariably be accompanied by clinical manifestations characteristic of an excess in this endocrine principle.* This is likewise not a valid assumption. For example, in rats kept on the *Lathyrus odoratus* diet and treated with small amounts of STH, the "growth hormone" produces pronounced skeletal and joint deformities, yet fails to stimulate growth. Apparently, the active principle in these seeds simultaneously sensitizes to the pathogenic actions and desensitizes to the normal physiologic growth effect of STH.

CONCLUSIONS

The fact that stress—no matter how produced—elicits a rather stereotyped nonspecific response, the General Adaptation Syndrome, has now been established with certainty. It is also clear that at least some manifestations of the G.A.S. do possess a defensive value, i.e., they facilitate adaptation to various stressors. We have learned, furthermore, that by suitable humoral conditioning disease susceptibility can be markedly altered; not only is it possible to increase or decrease resistance to stress (e.g., influence survival), but we can selectively direct the effect of stress against a certain organ (e.g., produce selective cardiac necroses by a cold bath).

Yet, it must be kept in mind that, up to now, in the clinical equivalents of what we call diseases of adaptation the existence of hormonal derangements (or of metabolic changes capable of conditioning for hormones) has only rarely been demonstrated with certainty. It is in this direction that future research is most urgently needed in order to test the applicability of these concepts to the problems of practical medicine.

PREVENTION OF CARDIOPATHIES BY SIMPLE OR CROSS RESISTANCE°

During the typical triphasic evolution of the G.A.S., resistance to diverse, potentially pathogenic stimuli undergoes considerable and largely predictable variations. In this connection, we have learned to distinguish: (I) simple (or specific) resistance, that is, increased tolerance, to only the particular kind of stimulus to which the body has been previously exposed; and (II) cross (or non-

° Addendum dated August 12, 1960.

specific) resistance, that is, increased tolerance, to a stressor qualitatively different from that to which the body has been adapted. Depending primarily upon the intensity and duration of the pretreatment, both these kinds of resistance can be either increased or decreased, as a consequence of previous exposure to stress (Selye, 1950).

Recently, it has been found that, in rats conditioned [with fluorocortisol (F-COL) + Na acetate] for the production, by stress, of infarctoid myocardial necroses, gradual adaptation to one stressor induced resistance to the cardiotoxic effect of subsequent treatment not only with the same but also with other stressors. Thus, the infarctoid-necroses-producing action of muscular exercise could be prevented by pretreatment with cold, that of cold by muscular exercise, that of noradrenaline by restraint, that of restraint by noradrenaline and that of bone fractures by muscular exercise (Bajusz and Selye, 1960a).

A similar cross resistance can also be induced in animals conditioned by dihydrotachysterol (DHT) + NaH_2PO_4, although here the character of the cardiovascular lesion is different, since DHT produces predominantly calcifying lesions (Bajusz and Selye, 1960b).

It may be argued that, even in the case of cross resistance between stressors, the nonspecificity of the induced tolerance is only apparent. Whatever the conditioning procedure (e.g., Na acetate + F-COL, or DHT + NaH_2PO_4), the prophylactic and the eliciting agents (e.g., restraint, cold, trauma) are comparable as regards their stressor effect, which is obviously the decisive factor in their pathogenicity. It was especially important to establish, therefore, that pretreatment with various stressors (e.g., restraint, cold, quadriplegia, bone fractures) can also protect the myocardium against such highly specific types of lesions as are induced by plasmocid or papain (Bajusz and Selye, 1960c).

REFERENCES

Bajusz, E., and H. Selye. 1960a. "Adaptation to the cardiac necrosis-eliciting effect of stress," Am. J. Physiol. *199:* 453.

Bajusz, E., and H. Selye. 1960. "How do nonspecific adaptive reactions alter susceptibility to renal and cardiovascular diseases? An experimental study on cross resistance," Folia Clin. Intern. *10:* 260.

Bajusz, E., and H. Selye. *1960c.* "Über die durch Stress bedingte Nekroseresistenz des Herzens. Ein Beitrag zum Phänomen der "gekreuzten Resistenz," Naturwissenschaften. *47:* 520.

Selye, H. 1950. "Stress," Acts Inc. Med. Publ. Montreal.

Selye, H., A. Horava, and G. Heuser. 1951–1956. "Annual Reports on Stress," Acts Inc. Med. Publ. Montreal.

Selye, H. 1957a. *The Stress of Life,* McGraw-Hill Book Company, Inc., New York, 5th printing.

Selye, H. 1957b. "Lathyrism," Rev. Can. Biol. *16:* 1.

Selye, H. 1958. *The Chemical Prevention of Cardiac Necroses,* The Ronald Press Company, New York.

Physiologic 24-Hour Rhythms:
A Determinant of Response to
Environmental Agents*

FRANZ HALBERG

Elsa U. Pardee Professor of Cancer Biology and Experimental Pathology, University of Minnesota Medical School, Minneapolis; and Director of Research, Cambridge State School and Hospital, Cambridge, Minnesota

I. PERIODICITY ANALYSIS AND EXPERIMENTAL METHOD

In this volume, glimpses at adaptive functional organization precede the agenda on more immediate problems of space and submarine medicine, such as respiration. A noted investigator of respiration, Karl E. Schaefer, dealt with integrative physiology as a whole in the preceding chapter. He emphasized, as did Haldane, that scientific medicine develops with studies of the manner in which the body responds to environmental changes—that is, the manner in which the body reasserts itself in the face of disturbance and injury (Haldane, 1922). The important underlying assumption may be reemphasized. Physiologic regulation must be understood if disturbances of health are to be recognized and interpreted and thus prevented or corrected.

Physiologic regulation, in turn, has been viewed as of the body's provisions for supplying and transporting the "right material" in the "right amount" to the "right place." This view seems incomplete unless we also consider the "right time" (Kalmus, 1957). Among the sciences basic to medicine, biochemistry deals with the right compound, pharmacology with the right dose, and the morphologic sciences with the right organ or cell. Physiology has to find out how the various tasks of organic regulation are accomplished and integrated with one another as well as with the environment. The physiologist thus builds upon the details of other sciences, including morphology, bio-

* Supported by Elsa U. Pardee Foundation; American Cancer Society; U.S. Public Health Service; Dept. of Public Welfare, Minnesota; and Graduate School, University of Minnesota.

chemistry, and pharmacology. In his past outlook, however, the recognition of rules governing provisions for the "right time" as a function of physiologic state and ecologic condition (as well as age) took second place to his concern for compounds, doses, sites of action, etc.

We shall now examine the extent to which an understanding of several important body functions depends upon detection of the right time. We shall approach functional integration and adaptation by dealing specifically with time-varying behavior along a 24-hour scale. The biologic significance of 24-hour periods was stated, of course, a long time ago (Hufeland, 1797); physiologic 24-hour periodicity has indeed fascinated many biologists (Kleitman, 1939; Park, 1940; Brown, 1956; Halberg, 1953, 1960. The significance of the phenomenon, nonetheless, is hardly recognized in current physiologic theory and practice.

Concepts of environmental adaptation, for instance, were highlighted without reference to rhythms in the preceding papers by Adolph and Selye (see also Adolph, 1956; Selye, 1950; Selye, 1951; Selye and Horava, 1952; Selye, 1953; Selye and Heuser, 1954; Selye, 1955); they focused upon several specific or unspecific and systemic or local effects exerted upon the body by environmental agents. In their classical approach to homeostasis (left arrow in Fig. 1), a given agent under study was experimentally varied; the organism, in turn, was approached as a more or less constant entity.

Physiologic periodicity—a source of variation?

From experimental practice we all realize, of course, that concepts of the body's "constancy" are not to be accepted literally. One accounts instead for existing variability by referring to the so-called range of normal values, a time-honored reference standard. This is the abstraction which allows for variability without analysis of its sources.

The parameters of the normal range are set by the distribution of values in samples from "normals," collected without consistent concern for physiologic variation, genetics (Williams, 1953; Williams, 1956), diet, or other factors (Brown, 1930). Despite such limitations, much useful information on favorable or unfavorable adaptations to environmental agents has been derived from the recognition of gross deviations from normal—by those following the left arrow in Fig. 1. What can one expect by comparison from following the right

Is it fruitful to start by singling out for analysis in physiologic terms one periodic component of normal variations over many other periodic and random components?[1] Rhythms with periods of about 24 hours [briefly, circadian rhythms (L.*circa*-about, + L. *dies*-day)] contribute largely to normal variations, but this does not set them apart from other contributing factors such as genetic or dietary. What does set them apart is their dimension in time, which

[1] A discussion of all the important sources of normal variability is desirable but remains beyond our scope.

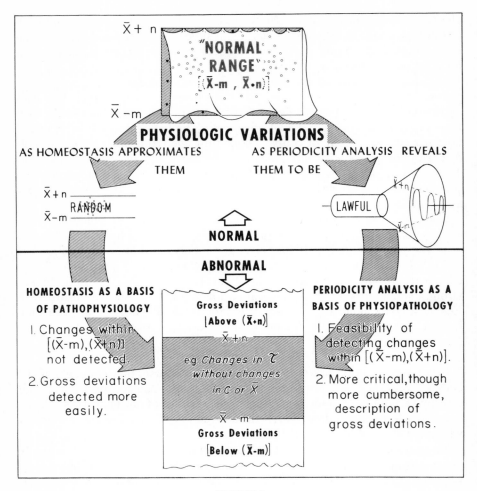

FIGURE 1.

Periodicity analysis, a tool for exploring the "normal range."

they share with adaptive response (the phase, but not necessarily the period, of circadian rhythms being an adaptive response in itself). Because of their time dimension, circadian rhythms either hinder or further studies on adaptive responses, as a function of our experimental attitude and approach.

It is not uncommon to regard circadian rhythms simply as a source of variation—as another factor. One may then ignore rhythms as trite or attempt their control by fixed sampling times usually chosen for convenience rather than pertinence. Some pitfalls in such experimental procedure will be discussed later, but at this point one might draw an analogy to corresponding considerations in genetics or nutrition.

The mere recognition of variability brought about by genetic factors does not constitute the discipline of genetics, just as cognizance of dietary contributions to normal variations cannot be confused with the science of nutrition. By the same token, the laws and methods of circadian periodicity analysis cannot be confused with awareness of variability as a simple function of time of day.

Periodicity analysis—a basic physiologic method

It is true that by comparison to genetics or nutrition, reliably established information on circadian rhythms seems meager. Rules governing such rhythms recognized thus far are few in number. The penalty for ignoring these rules may nonetheless be heavy if life or death from exposure to a given agent can be recognized experimentally as a function of circadian rhythm. Information derived from periodicity analysis may already meet Selye's (1958) three desiderata of basic research, i.e., that it be true, surprising, and generalizable.

Figure 2 shows the extent of reproducibility of the rhythm in blood eosinophils [(Halberg and Visscher, 1950; Halberg and Visscher, 1952; Panzenhagen and Speirs, 1953; Brown and Daugherty, 1956; Louch *et al.*, 1953) and liver glycogen (Barnum *et al.*, 1958) (cf. also Forsgren, 1928; Ågren *et al.*, 1931; Holmgren, 1931; Higgins *et al.*, 1932; Higgins *et al.*, 1933; Jores, 1939, Jores, 1940; Ekman and Holmgren, 1947; Boutwell *et al.*, 1948; Beringer, 1950; Sollberger, 1954, Sollberger, 1955*a*, Sollberger, 1955*b*; and Halberg in 1958)]. These functions are known to be variable in the hands of different investigators or even in the same laboratory—when they are studied by the "homeostatic" approach. Rhythms that are reproducible as the data in Fig. 2 suggest may be regarded as "true." What seems important, is that many discrepancies existing in literature on the timing of rhythms can be resolved by synchronized periodicity analysis (Halberg, 1960), and can thus be eliminated.

Figure 3, at first view at least, provides the element of surprise by revealing the drastic as well as reproducible extent to which 24-hour changes in physiologic state affect the resistance to a toxin. In this symposium it will be desirable to recognize the critical manner in which circadian rhythms affect our ability to withstand damage.

Figure 4 suggests that circadian rhythms are generalizable: circadian adaptive *functional organization in time* seems as basic as *cellular structural organization in space*. Examples of such rhythms are available for forms of life ranging from unicellular to mammals; in the latter, periodic functions include the incidence of births (Knapp, 1909; DePorte, 1932; Guthmann and Bienhüls, 1936; Malek, 1952; Malek, 1954; King, 1956; Points, 1956) and deaths (Schneider, 1859; Jusatz and Eckardt, 1934) and range from the metabolism of cytoplasmic fractions to the behavior of the body as a whole, such as its motor activity or its susceptibility to environmental agents. The number of observations on circadian periodicity over such ranges may be relatively small, when compared to the stock of classical physiologic knowledge. One might postulate, however, that rhythmicity is the rule rather than the exception in physi-

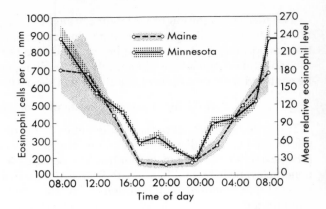

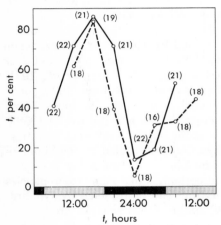

FIGURE 2 (*above*).

Eosinophil rhythm (mouse), showing extent of reproducibility under slightly different conditions, in different laboratories. The author is indebted to Dr. Robert S. Speirs for the data from Maine (1953).

FIGURE 3 (*left*).

Circadian rhythm in susceptibility to i.p. injection of *E. coli* endotoxin. Reproducibility in separate experiments.

ologic behavior by assuming as a working hypothesis that superficial lack of periodicity might have been recorded when the rhythms of individuals consti-tuting a given population studied were not synchronized.

Results on physiologic rhythms thus are true, surprising, generalizable, and as a fourth characteristic, they are significant entities (Fig. 3). One might expect, therefore, to find that circadian periodicity has quite a bearing upon experimen-tal method in general.

Hormone effects in the light of circadian periodicity analysis

Under certain conditions, the detection of a hormone effect is feasible at one time but not at another; effects of pituitary growth hormone (STH) upon mitotic counts on histologic sections of immature intact mouse liver are a case in point. Figure 5 summarizes a study on mouse livers that were removed after a 3-day course of either saline or STH (Litman *et al.*, 1958). Some of the animals were killed during the middle of the daily dark period (~00:30), others during the middle of the daily light period (~12:30). At these two times, mitotic counts on sections from mice given saline were not the same. Spot-checks (at only two times) had sufficed to suggest the operation of a physiologic rhythm in hepatic mitoses (Fig. 5). The rhythm comes more clearly to the fore in Fig. 6 [samples on separate but comparable groups of mice, at 4-hour intervals; effects of sampling are discussed elsewhere (Barnum *et al.*, 1958)].

For the moment, we are not concerned with rhythms as such but with the effect of STH. Figure 5 shows that the STH count (of mitoses) was significantly higher than the corresponding saline count in samples from mice killed at about 12:30 (right half of figure). This effect was not detected, however, in samples removed at 00:30 (left half of figure). (Colchicine was not used for

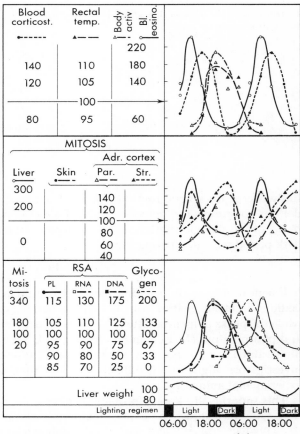

FIGURE 4.

Time relations among physiologic rhythms at several levels of organization.

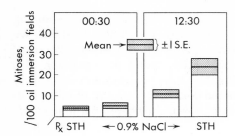

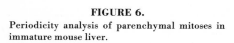

FIGURE 5.

Hepatic mitotic activity in mice given a three-day course of pituitary growth hormone (STH) daily at about 16:30 is significantly higher than that in controls given saline if liver is removed at noon on the day following last injection (right-hand section of figure). This effect is not apparent in materials removed at midnight (left-hand section). (Light from 06:00 to 18:00, alternating with darkness.)

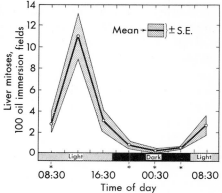

FIGURE 6.

Periodicity analysis of parenchymal mitoses in immature mouse liver.

*Point based on examination of 500 oil immersion fields

this work, or for several replications that confirmed the results in Fig. 5.) Under our conditions the detection of STH effect depended critically upon the phase of physiologic rhythm; for our purposes, then, the middle of the daily dark period was the "wrong time."

Practicability

For peak mitoses in growing mouse liver (under conditions of light from 06:00 to 18:00 alternating with 12 hours of darkness), noon is the "right time," while the peaks of incorporation of P_{32} into hepatic microsomal RNA (M-RNA) and phospholipid (M-PL) on one hand and DNA on the other are found at 8 P.M. and 4 A.M., respectively (Barnum *et al.*, 1958). In these latter instances, investigators might find it difficult to adjust their schedules to that of their experimental animals.

This superficially knotty problem is amenable, however, to an easy solution. One may adjust the experimental animals' schedule to one's own, instead of vice versa (Halberg *et al.*, 1953), as shown by Halberg and others during 1957, 1958, and 1959. The feasibility of resetting a rhythm removes a first objection to many periodicity analyses, namely that they *always* involve work at odd hours, by instituting an appropriate lighting regimen in the animal room and by maintaining the same schedule (and several other precautions shown by Halberg and others in 1957 and 1959) for an appropriate time period, one may shift the timing of rhythms in the mouse to any desired clock hour.

Circadian periodicity versus age effects

Many problems in research obviously involve several questions as to "when." In the instance of hepatic mitoses, there is a rapid drop in count during the second month of life, even in samples removed at the "right hour." Age effects are generally recognized, however, and they would not deserve belaboring for their own sake. We cite them only as reference standards in evaluating another physiologic "when," namely the "when" along the 24-hour scale. The data in Fig. 6 provide indeed an opportunity to compare the methodologic significance of the two "whens:" e.g., their contribution in providing a higher or lower mitotic count in immature mouse liver. A study of the figure reveals, e.g., that the wrong hour at the right age (Fig. 6) may involve a drop to values that are below those obtained at the wrong age and right hour (Halberg, 1960).

Physiologic "programs": circadian maps-in-time

It may have become apparent that periodicity maps (e.g., Fig. 4) are important; one might object, though, that they are costly in effort and time, if each investigator must map along a 24-hour scale each variable studied. Diverse nonphysiologic programs, however, are thoroughly planned and each checked, sometimes at great cost, before they are posted; rocket shoots are pertinent examples. But once non-physiologic programs are printed, they can be distributed and used at minimal cost by all interested persons.

Why then have physiologists in the past, more often than not, shied at the same approach? Its desirability is obvious, its feasibility challenging. Time-of-day effects have been recognized in practice on innumerable occasions; most often they are dismissed as trite (coincidental); only rarely are they actually segregated from other sources of variation operating in the same data; much more often, they are written up without analysis and submitted for publication; all too often such papers are published.

The description of rhythm as time-of-day effects without further qualifications as to conditions (e.g., lighting regimen, or daily routine) has done more harm than good; such programs are so unreliable as to defeat their purpose. Only to the extent to which physiologic maps-in-time can be reproduced reliably can periodicity analysis develop into an analytic tool of medical research.

If, as is the case, conditions can be found showing 24-hour rhythms in metabolizing structures as reliably reproducible as well as ubiquitous phenomena (Figs. 2–4), maps along a 24-hour scale must interest students of different functions, at various levels of organization. The standardization of genetic background, sex, age, past history, and experimental conditions then becomes desirable to evaluate the full significance of circadian rhythms; it is then that we are dealing not only with *statistically significant* differences, but also with such *physiologic significance* that the phase of rhythm critically affects the ability to withstand damage (Fig. 3).

Controls and periodicity

Experimental methods are based upon appropriate controls. Physiologic controls, in turn, may show circadian periodicity. It seems to follow that controls of periodic variables are appropriate only if their rhythms are rigorously evaluated, rather than casually thought to be "eliminated." The search for controls then implies a search for periodicity.

As soon as maps-in-time have been obtained, however (e.g., Figs. 2–4), and checked for a given variable, species, sex, age, and set of other conditions, one need not repeat the entire labor of mapping in each experiment. The rhythm of controls may be assessed from spot-checks against the known times of peak and trough, just as a trail may be followed by checking landmarks encountered en route against appropriate maps.

II. THE CIRCADIAN PERIOD—ITS IMPLICATIONS

Strange as it may sound, the periods of 24-hour rhythms are not always of exactly 24-hour length (Aschoff, 1952a; Aschoff, 1952b; Aschoff, 1953; Aschoff, 1954; Aschoff, 1955; Aschoff, 1958; Aschoff and Meyer-Lohmann, 1954; Aschoff and Meyer-Lohmann, 1955a; Aschoff and Meyer-Lohmann, 1955b; Halberg, 1954; Halberg in 1957; Halberg and Visscher, 1953; Halberg and Visscher, 1954; Halberg et al., 1954; Halberg in 1959; Hastings and Sweeney, 1957; Pittendrigh and Bruce, 1957; Szymanski, 1920; Tribukait, 1954; Tribukait, 1956; Wagner, 1930). A given period may differ from 24 hours by a few hours or only by a few minutes, yet the difference may be highly significant statistically. By using the term circadian one implies that certain physiologic periods, individually or on the average, may be in the neighborhood of 24 hours, if not exactly that length (Halberg, 1959). "Circadian" thus describes rhythms under several conditions. It applies to rhythms that are desynchronized from the local day; that are "free-running" from the local clock-time, since they have periods that are slightly yet consistently different from 24 hours. It also describes rhythms that are frequency-synchronized with acceptable environmental schedules, whether or not they are strictly 24-hour periodic.

Frequency desynchronization of rhythm from environmental schedule: free-running periods

In the past decade, we have studied rather extensively the desynchronization of temperature rhythm, first in the mouse and more recently in certain hu-

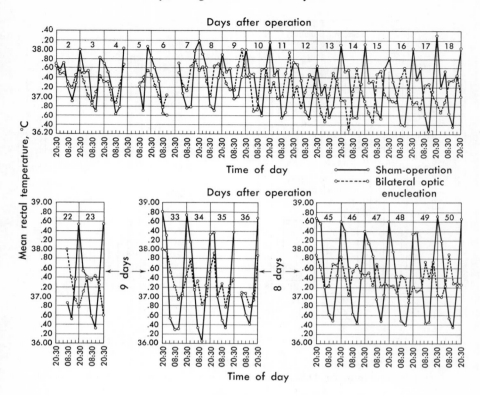

FIGURE 7.

Rectal temperature rhythm in mice subjected to blinding or to a sham-operation. Group-means (see text).

man subjects. Rectal temperatures of mice were measured at 4-hour intervals after blinding or sham-operation on several groups, each composed of over 20 singly housed animals (Fig. 7) (Halberg, 1954; Halberg, in 1959; Halberg and Visscher, 1953; Halberg and Visscher, 1954; Halberg *et al.*, 1954). They were kept at 24.5 ± 1°C, in light from 06:00 to 18:00, alternating with 12 hours of darkness.

In blinded mice a lead in phase of temperature rhythm was hardly detectable during the first few days after operation. Figure 7 shows that with the 4-hourly sampling interval used, data collection during the first few days following blinding did not suffice for the detection of free-running periods. Thereafter, a lead in phase of rhythm in blinded mice became more apparent with each day; by day 22, the rhythms had passed through temporary antiphase; temperatures were higher in blinded mice at the time of the low in sham-operated mice and vice versa.

By day 33, in turn, the two rhythms were roughly back in phase again. Thereafter, the curve for mean temperatures in blinded mice was affected by the

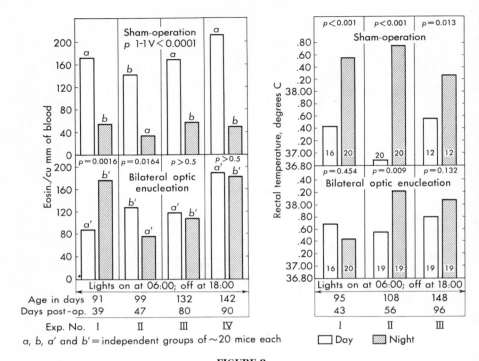

FIGURE 8.

Spot-checks of the behavior of blood eosinophils and rectal temperature after blinding (mouse).

desynchronization of individual rhythms from each other. Finally a resynchronization among individual rhythms, on one hand, and their environment on the other, became apparent at late time points post-operation (Fig. 7).

Spot-checks (Fig. 8) suggest further that free-running circadian periods characterize the rhythms in blood eosinophils, tissue mitoses, and body activity of blinded mice as well as their temperature rhythm as shown by Halberg in 1959. The changes brought about by blinding are statistically significant in all of these variables.

Periods that are free-running from the local time scale have been most frequently recorded for activity rhythms studied under conditions of environmental constancy and their proper significance has been demonstrated in particular by the studies of Aschoff (1958). The operation of free-running periods under conditions, e.g., of alternating light-dark and in variables other than activity, i.e., in variables that we often measure in medical research, brings us, however, to another methodologic point. It has been suggested earlier and elsewhere (Halberg, 1960) that it is not necessarily a scientific method for studies of rhythms to collect observations "at different times of day." Free-running periods, in turn, may be cited to suggest further that one may be confronted with pitfalls in attempts to "control" (or to eliminate) rhythms by working always at the same time of day. The frustrations derived from the collection of observations at different times of day, without standardization of conditions such as an artificial lighting regimen, can actually be surpassed by those derived in making observations at the same time of day with rigorously controlled conditions of constant light, for instance.

Thus, as has been the case, a meticulous investigator may have become used to thinking that experiments begin where periodicity ends. Accordingly, why waste time in dealing with periodicity in appropriate experimental terms? Instead, one can assume a superficially safe attitude. One institutes constant light in the animal room housing the rats, unaware of the likelihood that under such conditions the rhythms of the animals may be "free-running" from the local time scale, with unknown, unmeasured periods (probably longer than 24 hours). Under these circumstances, it is bad enough if one samples at random at different clock hours of the working period, but the chances of encountering similar physiologic states on consecutive days may be better with such random sampling, as compared to those associated with sampling repeatedly at the identical clock hour.

Free-running rhythms in constant light are likely to glide out of phase with the local clock hour and eventually their peak will occur at the same clock hour at which a trough had occurred earlier (temporary antiphase). The intention to control effects of circadian changes in physiologic state thus is almost certainly defeated—defeated, actually, by the decision to sample at the *same* clock hour! If one remains unaware of such possibilities, the fixed clock hour chosen for sampling will be cited as a major argument for acceptance of the data as results in which periodicity could not have been a factor.

Whenever we are uncertain whether or not we are dealing with free-running periods, the methodology for controlling rhythms may be more difficult than would appear on the surface. The methodology for evaluating rhythms, in turn, also poses problems (Halberg, 1960) among which we may allude to those of data analysis. In certain instances, such as the daily onset of gross motor activity in rodents, one may rely upon the study of plots of the data. Inspection used alone is elegant by virtue of its simplicity and satisfactory when it is applied to selected time series. Any time series must be examined, of course, for eventual trends and other features that may be superimposed upon possible circadian rhythms. Inspection can hardly be recommended, however, as the sole choice of analysis; the decision as to the site of a peak or trough (or perhaps even of an onset of activity, in the records of certain animals) may be a rather subjective venture. Therefore, we often need computational procedures that reduce "biologic noise." More often than not in medical research, exclusive reliance on the inspection of the data may prove to be unsatisfactory; it is costly in terms of length of the time series needed for achieving persuasiveness, and in certain cases, unreliable in terms of the subjectivity involved in judging, e.g., the length of a given period.

Computational procedures: autocorrelogram, periodogram and variance spectrum

The reliability of two computational procedures, the periodogram (Schuster, 1898; Schuster, 1900; Schuster, 1906a; Schuster, 1906b; Schuster, 1906c; Whit-

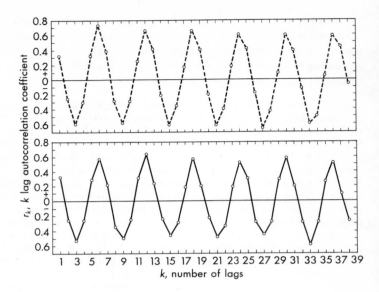

taker and Robinson, 1924; Stumpff, 1937; Stumpff, 1939; Kendall, 1948; Koehler *et al.*, 1956) and the autocorrelogram (Kendall, 1948) has been checked against data which by inspection alone provided a satisfactory estimate of period. The autocorrelogram on data from Fig. 7 showed peaks of comparable amplitude at the numbers of lags corresponding to the circadian period and to its multiples (Fig. 9a). These results suggested that in our particular time series we were dealing with an additive model of periodicity rather than with an auto-regressive one.[1] Periodograms, in turn, showed well-defined maximum points, the abscissas of which can be taken as the estimate of the period and the ordinates as the estimate of the amplitude.

Figures 9b and 9c are periodograms for rectal temperature series from intact mice and human beings respectively, the maxima pointing to an average period of exactly 24-hour length. Figure 9d, in turn, shows periodograms on the data from six individual mice, obtained during the first month after blinding. In five of these mice the period had shortened. For the sixth mouse a well-defined circadian peak was not apparent.

[1] In the additive model one assumes the operation of two components (added together), one of which is periodic and the other random, while the auto-regressive model of a periodicity depends mostly upon a system's immediate past history. To additive models, periodograms may be applied (Koehler *et al.*, 1956). Professors Hurwicz, Koehler, Savage, and Johnson, all of the University of Minnesota, guided the application of these computational procedures to physiologic data, and Doctor Rao worked out a method for computing the lower bound of the period (Halberg *et al.*, 1959*a*; Lehman, 1950). More recently, variance spectrum analysis, according to Blackmann and Tukey (1958), has proved to be a useful method for the detection of frequency shifts in physiological time series. This technique of generalized harmonic analysis reduces some of the statistical uncertainties associated with earlier direct methods of harmonic analysis.

FIGURE 9

a (*left*). Correlogram of rectal temperature data (mouse).

b (*top right*). Periodogram of rectal temperature data (mouse).

c (*center*). Periodogram of rectal temperature (man).

d (*below*). Periodogram of rectal temperature data after blinding (1st month post-operative). Analysis of individual time series (mouse).

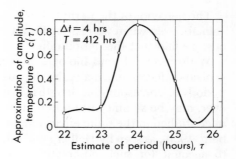

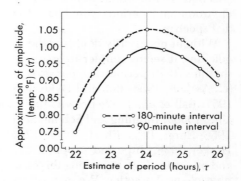

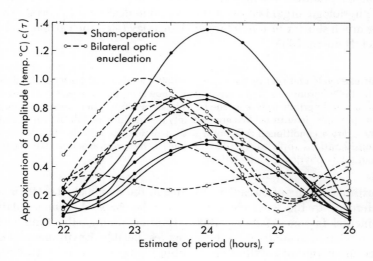

The behavior of the period after blinding thus is not the same in a group of animals; even when we restrict our attention to those mice with shortened periods, we find that the period differed among the individuals studied.

With these different biologic circadian periods, at various physiologic organization levels, one may raise the question of the operation of environmental periods of corresponding lengths (Brown, 1958). The biologic periods, however, may be significantly different from each other for the same variable in mice studied in the same environment and at the same time (Fig. 9d) (cf. Halberg, 1959), as seen by Halberg and others in 1959. It seems difficult, therefore, to account for such observations by periodic environmental factors alone (Aschoff, 1952), different mice exposed to an as yet hypothetical spectrum of environmental periods would have to respond to different and specific parts of that spectrum.

Without necessarily doubting the operation of as yet ill-defined cosmic periodicities, it seems simpler to assume that the periodic character of circadian rhythms (their periodicity, *per se*) is more largely endogenous than exogenous (cf. Aschoff, 1958; Ball and Dyke, 1954; Ball and Dyke, 1956; Ball and Dyke, 1957; Ball *et al.*, 1957; Brown, 1956; Brown, 1958; Brown *et al.*, 1958; Bünning, 1958a; Bünning and Schöne-Schneiderhörn, 1957; Cloudsley-Thompson, 1956; Ehret, 1953; Ehret, 1955a; Ehret, 1955b; Halberg, 1959; Harker, 1956; Harker, 1958; Hupe and Gropp, 1957; Pittendrigh, 1954) as shown by Halberg and others in 1959. In making this assumption, we are in keeping with accepted physiological practice. We may accept circadian periodicity as an intrinsic aspect of physiologic organization, just as we do in dealing with certain rhythms that are much shorter or much longer than a day (e.g., the cardiac and estrus cycles (cf. Halberg, 1953).

The cardiac cycle and that of the ovary are both variable and both can be drastically affected by the environment. They are periodic, however, in the absence of corresponding environmental periodicities (e.g., the heart beat, *in vitro*). Therefore, we regard them as intrinsic physiologic entities. We are certainly not inclined to call the cardiac cycle or that of the ovary a conditioned reflex or a stress reaction. Admittedly, to a lesser extent, similar considerations apply to circadian periods, if these represent genetic adaptations rather than solely physiologic adaptations.

The external timing of circadian rhythms in the mammal—i.e., their timing with reference to the local clock hour—can be changed by manipulation of environmental factors (Halberg, 1960). Internal timing—the timing of one rhythm in relation to another—is, however, less flexible. Environmental effects influence the period of rhythms only within limits, as shown by Halberg and others in 1959 (Aschoff, 1958; Tribukait, 1954; Tribukait, 1956; Fleeson *et al.*, 1957): these are limits within which a circadian rhythm is amenable to frequency synchronization with an environmental periodicity.

Period of rhythms in human beings on unusual schedules

The above considerations are likely to apply to human beings as well as experimental animals. Kleitman and Jackson (1950) have studied, among other schedules, a routine providing for the uninterrupted succession of four hours of duty and eight hours of leisure. Nine Navy recruits, 17 to 25 years of age, followed this "four-on, eight-off" schedule for two test periods, each of two weeks' duration. Concerning the results of a schedule with hours of duty, 0 to 4 and 12 to 16, the authors state that the shape of the diurnal temperature curve did not reveal any bimodality, such as was previously found in the diurnal curves of submarine crews operating on a "four-on, eight-off" watch schedule (Kleitman, 1949; Utterback and Ludwig, 1949). With respect to the second experience with the "four-on, eight-off" schedule (but hours of duty 8 to 12 and 20 to 24) they state: "Again there was no bimodality in the group diurnal temperature curve." Thus, it would appear that "four-on, eight-off" schedules, in the study cited, were unable to synchronize the temperature rhythms of healthy human beings. It would be interesting to examine suitably collected data on such schedules for possible free-running periods (e.g., by periodograms).

Lewis and Lobban (1954; 1957a; 1957b) also raised the question as to the period of rhythms in human beings living on unusual schedules. They employed less extensive modifications of schedule than the "12-hour day" of Kleitman and Jackson (1950). Their subjects carried specially adjusted wrist watches showing 12 hours either during 10½ ordinary hours or 13½ ordinary hours; thus they lived on a 21-hour day or a 27-hour day. These routines were maintained for several weeks, while the subjects lived in two isolated communities in Spitzbergen under unusual conditions of environmental constancy. Moreover, this study is of methodologic importance since data were examined by a modified form of Fourier analysis.

In Lewis and Lobban's subjects, initial adaptation of certain excretory rhythms to a 21-hour routine or to a 27-hour routine was uncommon. Such adaptation progressively improved, however, with time. It was seldom complete, even after six weeks on the new environmental routine.

The same investigation by Lewis and Lobban brought to the fore a most important point, namely, a dissociation among different daily rhythms on a given unusual routine. Thus the temperature rhythm adapted almost immediately to the experimental routines in most subjects, while for excretory rhythms the reverse held true. Moreover, rhythms in the excretion of water, chloride, and potassium also revealed dissociations, that in potassium excretion usually being out of phase with those in water and chloride.

Such dissociation among different rhythms in a given individual may occur on "24-hour day" routines as well. The rhythms in blood eosinophils and serum iron may dissociate in healthy human beings (Howard, 1952; Halberg and Howard, 1958) (Fig. 10). This was noticed in changing from a 3-meal-a-day rou-

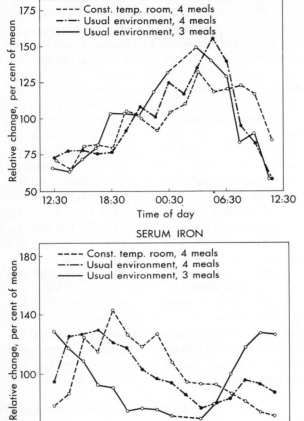

BLOOD EOSINOPHILS

---- Const. temp. room, 4 meals
---·-- Usual environment, 4 meals
—— Usual environment, 3 meals

Relative change, per cent of mean

Time of day

SERUM IRON

---- Const. temp. room, 4 meals
---·-- Usual environment, 4 meals
—— Usual environment, 3 meals

Relative change, per cent of mean

Time of day

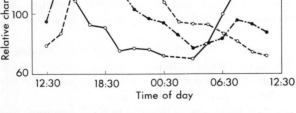

FIGURE 10

a (*top*). Roughly comparable timing of eosinophil rhythm in man on three different regimens.

b (*right*). Significantly different timing of serum iron rhythm in man on three different regimens.

tine to the consumption of 4 iso-caloric meals at 6-hour intervals, while continuing to live in the usual environment, and by changing then again to the 4-meal routine in a constant temperature room with its additional effects of confinement and detachment.

Do free-running periods also characterize circadian rhythms in human beings? One might wish to study for this purpose subjects allowed to choose their own periodicity under conditions of detachment and confinement and in an environment which is devoid of periodicities from both the physical and mental viewpoints. Mental dissociation from a 24-hour clock seems desirable for such studies in man: the question whether rhythms in human beings free-run from a local time scale is difficult to explore when the subject has (1) a 24-hour clock (to which he can adjust) or (2) any clock (e.g., one showing 24 hours in 21 regular hours from which he may compute time on a 24-hour basis).

In social man the physical constancy of the environment actually is not essential to bring about free-running periods; mental detachment in itself seems to suffice. Certain psychoses separate indeed an individual from the real world around him to an extent which is as drastic as it is nonphysiologic. This separation is particularly dramatic in patients given intensive electro-shock treatment (Glueck *et al.*, 1957). While regressed, these patients are mute and doubly incontinent. Treatment is actually applied until neurological changes associated with extrapyramidal tract activity appear, until the Babinski sign becomes positive.

Three schizophrenics were studied during and after, as well as before, regression by electro-shock, to examine the behavior of the period of rhythms under conditions of mental dissociation from the environment seldom achieved in man otherwise (Fleeson *et al.*, 1957). Figure 14 summarizes data from two paranoid patients and one catatonic, all females, while they were given two electro-shocks at a time, at 12-hour intervals until regressed. The findings seem pertinent to the problem of the plasticity of the human 24-hour period. The rhythms in temperature and eosinophils were only initially driven by the shock schedule. The 12-hourly shock schedule did not ultimately bring about a predominating 12-hour period in the rhythms studied. It had failed to do so when it might have been most effective, namely during the week or two of electro-shock administration.

In periodograms on data obtained during the administration of 12-hourly shocks (Fig. 11a), the highest peak occurs at trial periods around 24 hours rather than around 12 hours. The rhythms were almost certainly desynchronized from the shock schedule while the shocks were applied. Moreover, in each case the periods of the rhythms in blood eosinophils and body temperature differ slightly from each other, as far as one may judge by periodograms: in all three cases, the temperature peak lies to the left of the 24-hour line on the graph; the eosinophil peak in two cases is on that line and in one case to its right. These rhythms may have desynchronized not only from the artificial 12-hour shock schedule but also from each other. The latter conclusion is tentative, in view of limits to the reliability of the periodogram when it is applied to relatively short time series (lower bounds for the standard error of the period were from about 30 minutes to about 60 minutes).

Figure 11b shows in more detail periodograms on the body temperature data of the same patients. The shock period is broken down into two halves, each of these being analyzed separately. Periodograms are also shown for body temperature before and after the shock period. The three patients are described as R_1, R_2, and R_3 in this figure. In each case at the end of study (post-regression) the period had shifted to the right of the vertical line corresponding to the 24-hour trial period. In cases R_1 and R_3 this apparent lengthening of period

Franz Halberg

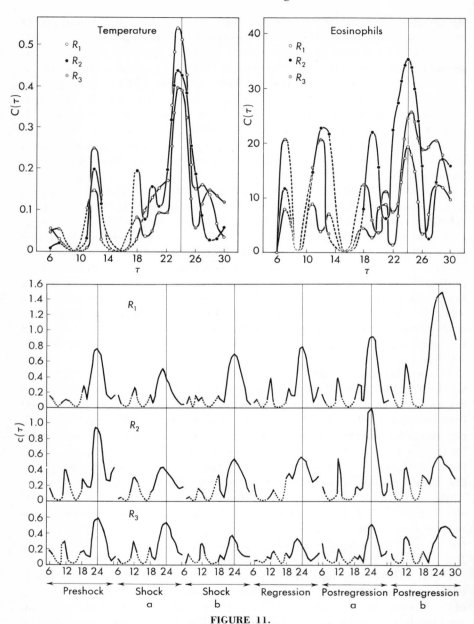

FIGURE 11.

a (*top*). Periodogram on eosinophil and temperature data of three patients, each given two electro-shocks every 12 hours, until regressed.

b (*below*). Periodogram of temperature data on three patients, before, during and after regressive electro-shock therapy.

seems considerable. Is this simply a compensatory lengthening of the period, in response to an earlier shortening, or are these periods that are free-running from the environmental 24-hour schedule? These questions await further study in additional cases, but the fact seems established that certain circadian rhythms of man exposed to 12-hourly shocks cannot be shortened by 12 hours.

The question as to the extent to which the circadian period "is, as it were, the unit of our natural chronology" was raised in 1797 (Hufeland, 1797). It seems germane in 1958, while one considers the adoption of drastically unusual schedules for long periods in atomic submarines or future space ships; it is pertinent to the methodology for gauging the effects, e.g., of the lighting regimen which we are to use or those of the planned schedule of activity and rest (Shcherbakova, 1937; Shcherbakova, 1938). Important in this symposium is the methodology required for standardized and quantitative work on rhythms (Halberg, 1959). By such methods much additional information may be gained in future work which will have to analyze further the limits of plasticity of circadian periods, particularly in man. Thus, periodicity analysis will bear on the success or failure to be encountered in adaptation to various long-continued modifications of schedule. The relevance of this problem to space and aviation medicine has recently been noted by Hauty (1958) and earlier by Strughold (1952), while its relevance to problems of the submariner was considered by Kleitman (1949), Kleitman and Jackson (1950), and Behnke (1951). We can anticipate with interest an authoritative discussion at this symposium, by Aschoff.

Those interested in various aspects of the modifiability of mammalian rhythms by exogenous factors may be referred particularly to publications by Aschoff and his school (Aschoff, 1958) for controlled data and important interpretations, and to an authoritative book by Bünning (1958b) [among others by Reinberg and Ghata (1957) and Bykow (1954)].

Circadian rhythms have been further extensively studied in lower animal forms and plants, including unicellulars. Pertinent are studies by Pittendrigh (1954), Pittendrigh and Bruce (1957), Brown (1956; 1958), Ehret (1953; 1955a; 1955b), Cloudsley-Thompson (1956), Harker (1958), Bünning (1958b), Bünning et al. (1957), Ball and Dyke (1954; 1956; 1957), Ball et al. (1957), and Hastings and Sweeney (1957). Controlled work refers even to rhythms in tissue culture (1957). These various approaches reveal external-internal interactions: differing numbers and types of intermediate steps are involved in the mechanisms of different rhythms and/or species. Accordingly, models of rhythms will differ in complexity in various forms of life (Fig. 12).

At the two ends of their scale, comparative physiologists are dealing with the unicellular, devoid of conventional nerves and hormones and the Strategic Air Command aviator, devoid of conventional daily routines. Including these extremes, a variety of organisms may possess common features in their controls of circadian rhythms (Fig. 12).

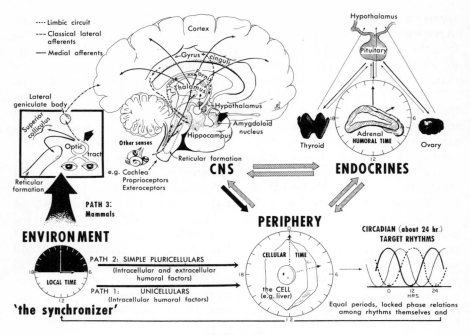

FIGURE 12.

Sketch of factors and pathways known or hypothesized to participate in frequency synchronization *among* circadian rhythms themselves, as well as in synchronization *between* rhythm(s) and environmental synchronizer(s) (see Halberg, 1957 *a*; Halberg *et al.* 1959).

III. PHASE CONTROL OF RHYTHMS: ENVIRONMENT— THE SYNCHRONIZER

In each case rigorously studied, rhythms may be synchronized with certain periodic environmental schedules. Under appropriate conditions, an alternating regimen of 12 hours light and 12 hours darkness, for instance, may "lock in phase" a variety of rhythms, in many species. The lighting regimen may be called a primary synchronizer of rhythms in the mouse (Halberg, 1959; Halberg *et al.*, 1953; Halberg *et al.*, 1954). Sociologic factors, according to which we adjust our watches, may synchronize rhythms in civilized human beings. Changes in daily routine of human beings thus may be instituted and maintained in order to shift the phase of their rhythms (Fig. 13). In each case, a particular environmental schedule (e.g., of lighting) and a variety of physiologic rhythms equalize their periods, within certain limits.

One may call frequency synchronization the preponderance of equal periods between an organism's rhythm and its environment's periodicity. We are here dealing with a preponderance of *similar* periods rather than with a strict *equal-*

ity. The time relations between physiologic rhythm and environmental schedule are plastic rather than rigid. One adaptive value of circadian rhythms lies in their plasticity on any one day (another, in the limits to their abrupt modifiability, as we shall see below).

Frequency synchronization between a rhythm and the lighting regimen, for instance, does not imply that rhythms are not responsive to factors other than lighting; times of feeding, of exposure to aggressors, actually any changes in sensory inflow exert effects upon phase and/or form of rhythms. These factors, among others, are potential secondary synchronizers; their effects on a given organism vary in degree, if not in kind, among different rhythms, particularly at various physiologic organization levels. But if such effects are not exerted day after day at a fixed time, they will be modulating, rather than synchronizing; these effects, interacting with the primary synchronizer, bring about phase changes only if they are exerted in a 24-hour periodic fashion.

Such interaction among synchronizers (Aschoff's competition of time-givers) occurs in time as well as in intensity of effect. Synchronizer interaction is positive in time if the phase difference of effects approaches zero; e.g., if the effect of a primary synchronizer, such as the lighting regimen for fully fed mice, coincides with another effect, such as that of the feeding time; feeding then merely reinforces lighting. Interaction in time is negative when the primary

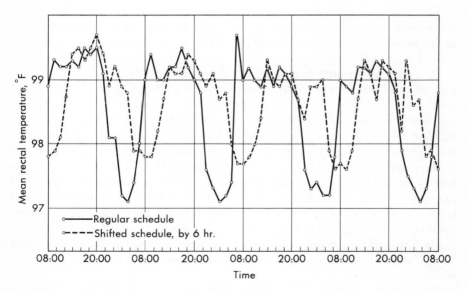

FIGURE 13.

Shifts in phase of rhythms following a 6-hour shift in schedule during second month after initiation of shifted schedule (Man: 12 subjects per group)

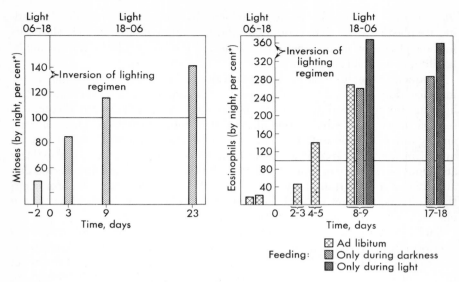

FIGURE 14.

Gradual shift of rhythms in pinnal mitoses and blood eosinophils following abrupt inversion of lighting regimen (mouse). Note difference in "synchronization-time," suggestive of transient "desynchronization."

and secondary synchronizers act with a significant phase difference at different hours. Some oversimplified rules apply to the environmental phase control of several mammalian rhythms.

(1) There is the superficial equivalent to a refractory period. Even if the shift of synchronizer is sudden, extensive phase shifts are gradual. A transient refractoriness of rhythms to extensive changes in timing of synchronizer(s) seems equal in adaptive value to a certain degree of modifiability (see above). At least for a while, the exigencies of the temporal integration of diverse functions within the organism may override claims of new schedules, particularly at the cellular level (Fig. 14). It is only with a lag that the organism will ultimately be able to supply and transport the "old compounds," in the "old amounts," to the "old places"—at "new times." For this purpose, essential steps in a sequence of periodically integrated metabolic events may be shortened or lengthened, rather than eliminated or reversed in order.

(2) The shift time usually increases with the complexity of the species, other things being comparable (for a given variable, synchronizer, and degree of shift).

(3) Shift time also is a function of the synchronizer(s) involved. Shifts are fastest under control of the primary synchronizer, slower if controlled by secondary synchronizers.

(4) Shifts also depend upon factors other than the synchronizer being dom-

inant at a given time; shift time may be several weeks longer following an inversion of the feeding time of mice severely restricted in calories, as compared to the shift time in response of fully fed mice to shifts in lighting. In this instance, the secondary synchronizer had to override the effect of lighting persisting on the old schedule.

Thus, if other environmental interaction with a given shifted schedule is positive, it will reinforce the shift and shorten shift time; if it is negative, it will delay the shift or prevent it. In exploring the effects of new schedules one must, therefore, examine the number and the nature of those factors possibly persisting with the old timing.

(5) The shift time further depends upon the plasticity of the organism's particular rhythm; in the same species and individual, shift times may differ from one rhythm to another. In the mouse, inversion times (by lighting reversal) differ for rhythms in blood eosinophils and tissue mitoses (Halberg and Howard, 1958). The same may apply for the same species and synchronizer with respect to the same function in different tissues. Thus, inversion of mitotic rhythm in liver parenchyma was detected at nine days after initiation of lighting reversal by Halberg and others in 1959; in the same animals at the same time the mitotic rhythm in pinnal epidermis was not yet reversed.

(6) If different rhythmic functions of the same organism shift with different speed, optimal time relations among such functions might be disturbed at some time during the shift. Shifts may therefore involve a transient reversible frequency-desynchronization. Such acute desynchronization, per se, may have no obvious ill effects, under usual conditions.

Susceptibility to trauma, however, might change during the shift time. Thus, at nine days following inversion of the lighting regimen, peak susceptibility to audiogenic convulsions occurred at the time of trough in mice on the opposite schedule and vice versa; the within-day difference in convulsions was statistically significant, whether or not the mice had been subjected to a change in schedule. Irrespective of circadian periodicity, however, over-all susceptibility to convulsions and death from convulsions had increased significantly, Halberg showed in 1958. A decrease in resistance to trauma (during transient frequency-desynchronization of rhythms) may be an unspecific aspect of shifts. There may be an equally unspecific subsequent increase in resistance, which overshoots the initial levels, once all shifts are completed (during optimal resynchronization).

IV. PHYSIOLOGIC ASPECTS OF CIRCADIAN PERIODICITY

Despite absolute phase-control by synchronizers, these stimuli do not account for the periodicity, *per se*, of circadian rhythms. Circadian periods persist when food and water are continuously available to animals isolated as far as feasible from environmental fluctuations with corresponding periods. It seems useful to distinguish those factors which (so to speak) set the clocks from the clocks themselves. Snychronizers (or "time givers," cf. Halberg *et al.*, 1959a; Aschoff, 1958) belong to the former category. In turning to the experimental analysis of intrinsic factors, however, one may go beyond the stimulating analogies of clocks or oscillators, as Halberg showed in 1959.

Cellular cycles—temporal organization of metabolism

In unicellular forms as well as in mammals, cellular cycles may be the common denominator of periodicity. "Cellular time" along the 24-hour scale may result from the integration of periodic metabolic phenomena into circadian-repetitive sequences.

As a first approximation, one may delineate three metabolic stages by the leads and lags in phase of various cellular processes in mammalian liver as Halberg stated in 1957 and 1959 (Barnum *et al.*, 1957; Barnum *et al.*, 1958; Jardetzky *et al.*, 1956). Stage A starts with the mitotic peak. We thus begin the cellular cycle at the time when most new daughter cells enter the population. This stage ends with peaks in relative specific activity (RSA) of microsomal phospholipid and RNA. Stage A thus started with an event involving largely the nucleus and it ended with metabolic peaks more characteristic of the cytoplasm. Stage A may be subdivided into Stages A_1 and A_2, preceding and following the peak in blood corticosterone (occurring normally $\approx$ 4 hours prior to the peak in RSA of phospholipid; cf. Fig. 15). A_1 then precedes the corticosterone peak, while A_2 follows. Stage B follows Stage A. It lasts until the peak time in RSA and DNA. Stage C, in turn, extends from the DNA peak to that in mitosis. Stage C may be subdivided into substages C_1 and C_2, preceding or following the glycogen peak.

Such a classification is provisional, restricted to the organ studied and limited, among other things, by the number of processes studied and the sampling interval used. Of interest, at any rate, is the observation that certain metabolic functions decrease in rate significantly at the time of mitotic high, even though mitosis takes place only in a very small fraction of the total cell-population.

Moreover, the changes in rate of cellular events are sequential only with respect to the time when they reach a peak along the 24-hour scale. Such a temporal sequence of peaks (or troughs, or slopes) cannot be regarded as being necessarily causal, i.e., the sequence of periodic events does not imply that each peak results from the preceding one. Without collateral evidence, one cannot even presuppose which peak leads the other, time-wise. In some instances, however, some collateral information is available, since parts of the metabolic sequence can be started almost anew.

Discounting (for our specific purpose) the low levels of mitotic activity in mature liver, one may say that one started anew, in mature liver regenerating, e.g., after partial hepatectomy (Barnum *et al.*, 1957; Podwyssozki, 1886; Jaffe, 1954). Studies on regenerating mouse liver reveal periodicity in the RSA of DNA as well as in mitosis, and in the first cycle the DNA peak precedes the

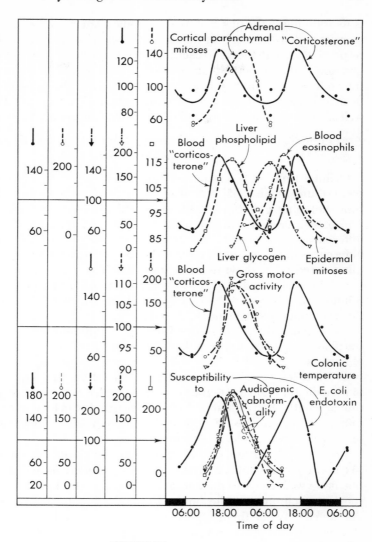

FIGURE 15.

Time relations among circadian physiologic rhythms associated with adrenal cycle but not all causally related to it.

mitotic peak and does so with an interval (8 hours) which is roughly comparable to that observed in intact growing liver. That similar intervals between DNA formation and mitosis were reported for plants (without periodicity analysis) also seems interesting (Pelc and Howard, 1952; Taylor and McMaster, 1954).

These sequences of periodic intracellular processes are ultimately adaptable in their timing to the phase of those periodic changes prevailing in their milieu, internal and/or external (as the case may be in unicellulars and pluricellulars, respectively). But the key reactions involved are unknown. One might suggest only that such periodicities constitute basic problems, characterizing DNA, transmitting information from one generation to the next, RNA, which has been associated with enzyme-forming systems (Potter, 1957; Potter, 1958) as well as enzymes (Greenberg and Glick, 1958; Glick *et al.*, in press).

Periodic physiologic regulations—their integration by frequency synchronization

Cellular time, in the same mammal, may vary within organs and among them (Blumenfeld, 1942) as well as among physiologic organization levels. The timing of mitotic rhythms in adrenal cortical parenchyma and stroma, for instance, seems roughly synchronous; with the sampling schedule used the phase differences appear to be zero. In the immature pancreas, in turn, important differences in phase among mitotic rhythms were detected with 4-hourly sampling in recent work with Runge and Pass. The peaks of mitoses in exocrine tissue, in α cells and in β cells were dissociated from one another by about 8 hours. In this instance, circadian peaks for the same function, mitosis, in different units of a given organ do not coincide.

More generally, for the same function in different units of a given organ, the phase difference may be either plus or minus or zero. Moreover, in instances of apparent synchrony (phase difference $= 0$), more frequent sampling might well reveal lesser differences in timing. Therefore, the general characteristic of periodic functional integration within organs, as well as among them, is the similar length of circadian periods, rather than the coincidence in time of certain peaks or troughs. Frequency synchronization cannot be mistaken as implying always "in phase" synchronization.

Frequency synchronization among organs or tissues can sometimes be seen. We may compare mitotic rhythms in liver parenchyma and skin epidermis on one hand with those in the adrenal cortex. The rhythms in liver and skin are roughly synchronous at the "magnification" (sampling interval) used; the phase difference between them appears to be zero. But mitoses in either liver parenchyma or in skin epidermis show an important phase difference in relation to adrenal cortical mitoses (in the frequency-synchronized state!).

In Fig. 15, frequency synchronization of periodic functions from different levels of organization also is illustrated. Periodicity analysis in different parts of the body thus resolves a new facet in time of the mutually coordinated activities in different organs; the phase relations of various periodic events shown on circadian temporal maps are the trails leading to the exploration of a *partium consensus in tempore*. Questions arise as to how these internal phase relations among rhythms are maintained and as to how the periods themselves are being controlled.

Adrenal cycle

In Fig. 12, the adrenal gland has been circled as a critical control of certain circadian rhythms in the mammal. My interest in adrenal mechanisms of periodicity arose during studies of blood eosinophil cells, which were known to be depressed by cortical adrenal hormones.

In the mouse, blood eosinophil cells show rather drastic spontaneous numerical changes along the 24-hour scale (Halberg and Visscher, 1950; Halberg and Visscher, 1952; Panzenhagen and Speirs, 1953; Brown and Dougherty, 1956; Louch et al., 1953). Under standardized conditions, such changes exceed in extent and in regularity the corresponding variations previously found by others and ourselves in human subjects (Halberg, 1953; Halberg et al., 1951). It seemed likely that the eosinophil count, depressed by exogenous cortical hormone, changed periodically as a result, at least in part, of cyclic endogenous hormone secretion. Corresponding changes were known for other indices of cortical adrenal function (Fig. 16a) (Halberg, 1953; Brown and Dougherty, 1956; Halberg et al., 1953; Pincus, 1943). Moreover, with the advent of chemical methods for cortical hormone determinations, it was subsequently shown in 1959 by Halberg and others that adrenal hormones in blood and gland indeed show 24-hour periodicity (Fig. 18b) Appel and Hansen, 1952; Doe et al., 1954; Migeon et al., 1955; Tyler et al., 1954; Forsham et al., 1944).

In the adrenals themselves, Engstrom et al. (1938) described a maximum at night for the red-blood-cell content of the fasciculata in rats and mice. Bänder (1950), working with mice, noted a maximum for the lipid content of the fasciculata in the morning and a minimum at night. Mühlemann et al. (1955) established under standardized conditions the occurrence of significant day-night differences in mitoses of the adrenal cortex in male rats. These findings were then extended to the mouse by Halberg and others in 1957.

Figure 15 shows periodicity in several other functions that have been associated with the adrenal. Circadian periodicity in variables affected by adrenal hormones, cortical or medullary, indeed seems to be the rule rather than the exception. Pioneering work on epinephrine and periodicity was reported in 1943 by Lehmann (Lehmann and Michaelis, 1943), whose chapter appears later in this volume. The critical questions as to the role of the adrenal in maintaining rhythms and their phase relations differ, however, from inquiries as to whether or not a given function is periodic.

Of interest, first, is the question of the extent to which the periodicity of the adrenal cortex may underlie circadian periods elsewhere in the body. The rhythm in serum iron, for instance, might change its phase relation to other rhythms but it persists under conditions of verified cortical adrenal insufficiency (Fig. 16b) (Halberg and Howard, 1958; Howard, 1952). Under such conditions, the eosinophil rhythm, however, is obliterated in man (Halberg

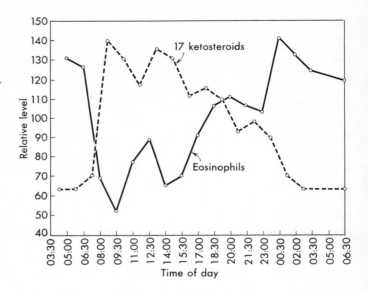

et al., 1951; Kaine *et al.*, 1955), dog (Halberg and Nahas, 1955), or mouse (Brown and Dougherty, 1956; Halberg *et al.*, 1953) (Fig. 16c) and similar findings have been reported for some excretory rhythms in man (Reinberg and Ghata, 1957). The rhythms of mitoses in skin epidermis and of the RSA of phospholipid in hepatic microsomes (Fig. 16d) (Halberg, 1955; Halberg and Howard, 1958; Halberg *et al.*, 1956; Vermund *et al.*, 1956) also appear to be critically dependent upon an adrenal cycle. This cycle seems to be an essential (though probably not a sufficient) condition for mammalian circadian periodicity, particularly at the cellular level; its dependence, among other things, upon the supportive role of the thyroid has been noted (Flink and Halberg, 1952).

Of particular interest is a comparison of the phase relations of rhythms in blood corticosterone on one hand and in gross motor activity on the other, in mice studied under standardized circumstances by Halberg in 1959. Will the daily rise in blood corticosterone of mice lead the onset of gross body activity, as an endocrine entity may do (Halberg, 1953; Halberg, 1955) Halberg asked in 1959, or will it lag behind as a mere "reaction to the activities" of daily life? The suggestion that an adrenal cycle is preparatory for daily activity and that its period does not depend directly or solely upon environmental control (Halberg, 1953) differs from unqualified references (1) to daily changes in corticoid levels as responses to the stresses of daily life, and (2) to a basal level of adrenal cortical activity as a characteristic of rest and/or sleep. Figure 16e, showing that the corticosterone rhythm normally leads the onset of gross motor activity, suggests indeed that we are dealing with an endocrine entity in its own right.

The adrenal cycle is modulated by superimposed and juxtaposed endocrines

FIGURE 16.

a *(left).* Circadian rhythms in circulating eosinophils and in excretion of 17-ketosteroids. Relative eosinophil curve computed from data obtained by author on 17 medically normal males. Relative 17-ketosteroid curve computed from data of O. Mickelsen, E. V. O. Miller, and Ancel Keys on four medically normal males, one of them studied over two 24-hour periods (E. V. O. Miller, O. Mickelsen, and A. Keys, 1947, Fed. Proc. *6*: 279).

b *(top, right).* Persistence of serum iron rhythm in man, in verified adrenocortical insufficiency.

c *(center, right).* Obliteration of eosinophil rhythm in man in verified adrenocortical insufficiency: Group 2, unlimited activity; Group 1, limited activity; Group 3, limited activity, adrenal insufficiency.

d *(below).* Alteration of rhythms in blood eosinophils, epidermal mitoses, and hepatic phospholipid metabolism in verified adrenocortical insufficiency.

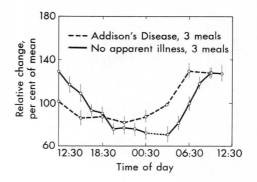

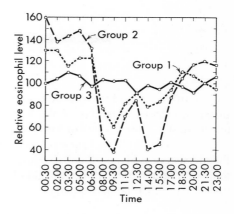

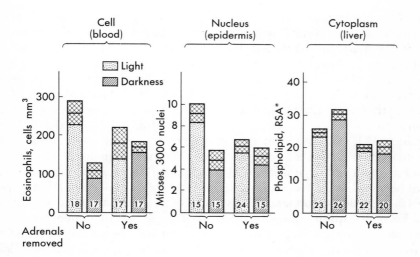

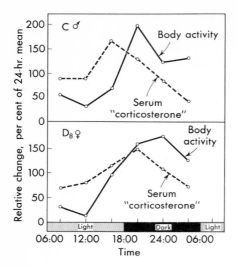

FIGURE 16e.

Circadian rhythms in gross motor activity of two populations of mice and changes in serum corticosterone (mouse). The latter rhythm appears to lead the former; almost certainly, it does not lag. (D_8 mice had the Bittner—i.e., mammary tumor—agent.)

and neurocrines and the interactions involved await further study. The pituitary participates, of course, in this modulation of rhythm, as may be suggested on the basis of late effects of hypophysectomy upon the temperature rhythm (Ferguson *et al.*, 1957). Since pituitary removal is compatible, however, with the persistence of circadian rhythms in body temperature and in epithelial mitoses (Zander *et al.*, 1954), the gland is not indispensable for the maintenance (as such) of circadian periodicity.

Central nervous system

Peripheral circadian rhythms are subject to central nervous as well as endocrine regulation. Neurohumoral and neural regulations, however, serve primarily the more immediate adaptations of the body in emergency reactions and circadian periodicity modify only via the integration of their shorter term effects. The role of the nervous system might be visualized by discussing the way in which lighting schedules exert their effect upon the phase of 24-hour rhythms (Fig. 12). Stimuli such as light or sound received by transducers such as the eye or ear evoke potentials that are transmitted corticipitally by conductors (1) via classical lateral pathways to the special sensory areas of the cerebral cortex such as the striate area, and (2) via medial pathways to the reticular formation and hypothalamus. A multitude of impulses reaching the brain must be mixed, weighted, and combined, after "biologic noise removal"—perhaps in the reticular formation. This tentative localization of a "logic control" is in keeping with the characteristics of potentials recorded medially, which show lack of modality segregation, interaction and attenuation of responses upon successive stimulation, as well as diffuse cortical spread (Magoun, 1952; French *et al.*, 1952; French *et al.*, 1953a; French *et al.*, 1953b).

Moreover, somewhere in the brain and somehow, a "comparison" must be made between the composite phase information from within the body and that from without, COPI and CEPI, respectively. The composite *organismic* phase information (COPI) may be yielded by the mixing, weighting, and combining of information from various feedbacks, psychogenic, neurogenic, hormonal, and metabolic. The composite *environmental* phase information (CEPI), in turn, may schematically be subdivided into the potentials evoked by stimuli originating in the physico-chemical environment (EPIp) (light and food, for instance), and into those evoked by other signals, arbitrarily designated as "socio-ecological" (EPIs).

Most likely, EPIs, our social schedule, and our emotional response to it, are more critical in determining the timing of bodily rhythms in urbanized human beings, while EPIp might be more pertinent for humans living in the setting of an isolated farm. But to separate experimentally the effects of EPIp and EPIs constitutes no minor undertaking in the case of man. This same task seems more amenable to study in certain experimental animals, even though in the latter EPIs also has dramatic and often unexpected effects.

The electroencephalographic changes occurring, for instance, in the unanesthetized rabbit when it is confronted with the investigator, probably involve emotional components and these alerting responses are actually more striking than the corresponding changes evoked by light in itself (Gangloff and Monnier, 1956). Moreover, such emotional EPIs interfering with EPIp, involves not only brain waves, with their short periods, but also the rhythm in body temperature and even the periodic sequence of cellular metabolic events and mitoses (Halberg, 1957; Barnum *et al.*, 1958). Unless we anticipate these varied effects, their contribution via EPIs to CEPI will remain uncontrolled.

In studying the effect of a change in EPIp (e.g., in the lighting schedule), we must evaluate for experimental animals, as well as for human beings, possible concomitant changes in EPIs. Ambiguous results obtained in studies of effects of EPIp can quite easily be brought about by our failure to evaluate inadvertent yet critical changes in EPIs. At any rate, changes either in EPIp or in EPIs (or in both) can alter CEPI. Accordingly, a physiologic mechanism [a neural phase comparator(s) (?)] is now confronted with a new CEPI and an old COPI: it will compare the two and if the phase relations of COPI and CEPI are found to be altered, an appropriate message will be sent to various bodily rhythms to speed up or to slow down, as need be. Moreover, the phase comparator will continue to send messages until the rhythms are again in step with the environment, i.e., until the abnormal relations between CEPI and COPI have been corrected.

The medical researcher in viewing the above hypotheses might raise the question of diseases of "synchronization." Psychoses are often defined as illnesses that separate the individual from the realities of the environment. Can some of them result from abnormal phase relations of COPI and CEPI? Can the psychogenic component of the former and/or the latter arrive at the wrong time, e.g., because of some delay under way? The possibility that a failure of synchronization, particularly if chronic, can characterize a disease seems real and the question whether the same failure of synchronization may, in addition, underlie disease awaits further study.

Periodicity defects after blinding concern "phase comparing" and have been recorded for mice (Halberg, 1954; Halberg and Visscher, 1953; Halberg and Visscher, 1954; Halberg *et al.*, 1954) and man (Landau and Feldman, 1954). Such an alteration of synchronization is not a clinically important aspect of blindness since CEPI consists of more than one modality, and thus the loss of one transducer is eventually compensated by activation of others as far as the phase of 24-hour rhythms is concerned. The data after blinding are of value, however, since they reveal the occurrence of free-running periods in an illness. The same data also demonstrate a methodologic point of importance (Ingle, 1951): since a change in period of temperature rhythm after blinding is not necessarily associated with changes in amplitude or level (Fig. 9d), we are here dealing with an alteration which periodicity analysis can describe but the study of gross deviations from a normal range may not detect.

From the ill-defined physiologic equivalents of a neural "phase comparator" and, perhaps, from an as yet hypothetical neural "oscillator" (Halberg, 1959a) "information" is channeled neurally to the periphery (Fig. 12), but in addition, some of it also travels from the hypothalamus to the pituitary. In the pituitary, messages from above may be again "compared" with hormonal feedbacks from target glands; at any rate, if the phase relations of CEPI and COPI are altered, the pituitary will send appropriate messages to the generators of rhythms, until the alteration of phase is corrected. The messengers are the pituitary tropic hormones; the generators of rhythms appear to be (in part) the appropriate target glands (as shown by Halberg and others in 1959); the latter are stimulated by their tropins to speed up or they are slowed down by throttling of tropin secretion until normal phase relations are re-established.

The path from the central nervous system via the pituitary gland seems to be obligatory (Halberg, 1959a) for the transmission of phase information to the target glands (Halberg, 1959). Of interest in this connection is ample direct evidence as well as indirect evidence of continued aldosterone secretion by the adrenal cortex in the absence of pituitary function (Müller, 1958). Whether or not, under such circumstances, aldosterone is periodic will have to be reinvestigated with more frequent sampling along the 24-hour scale, a problem which remains difficult in view of the exigencies of currently available methods.

In the field of central nervous mechanisms of rhythmicity, promising work has already begun (Mason, 1958) on problems that are important to the topic of this symposium. Is it useful to approach sensory isolation by periodicity analysis as a CEPI deficiency at its extreme? Data on human rhythms in confinement, detachment, and sensory deprivation will be of interest. CEPI deficiency in the face of an intact COPI seems deleterious and periodicity analysis might reveal how such damage might come about and what may be needed to prevent or correct it.

For exploring other problems of adaptation as well, rigorous periodicity analysis awaits applications as an instrument for functional resolution in time, just as the microscope serves for structural resolution in space. The method has proved itself already in revealing how critically circadian periodic changes in the "preparedness" of the body determine the outcome of its exposure to environmental agents.

V. CIRCADIAN RHYTHMS IN SUSCEPTIBILITY TO ENVIRONMENTAL AGENTS

People are more apt to die from one or the other disease at one or the other hour of the day; such claims are supported by extensive statistics, several of them reviewed already a century ago (Schneider, 1859, cf. also Jusatz and Eckardt, 1934; Frey, 1929). But the differences in mortality reported for different clock hours were often small; they were probably obscured by ill-defined diagnoses and other complicating factors, e.g., heterogeneity of sample studied in terms of genetic background, physical and social environment.

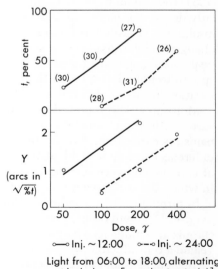

FIGURE 17.
Different "potency" of samples from same batch of *E. coli* endotoxin tested at different times.

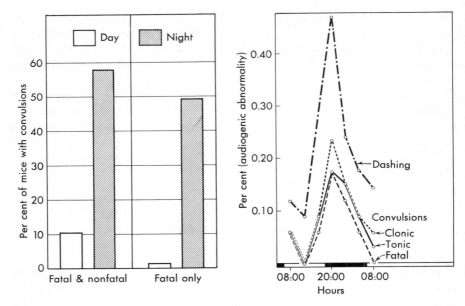

FIGURE 18.

a (*left*). Different effects of exposure to the same noise at different times (mouse).
b (*right*). Periodicity analysis of various abnormal audiogenic responses (D_8 mice, five weeks of age).

In more standardized work on the mouse, Ågren, Wilander, and Jorpes (1931) showed an increased resistance to insulin in the afternoon and particularly during the night: the percentage of convulsions in animals treated with insulin was regarded as a function of time of day and attributed to the daily changes in liver glycogen; a susceptibility rhythm to insulin with a defined peak and trough was not mapped. Variations along the 24-hour scale in response to gonadotropins in the mouse (Lamond and Braden, 1959) and to sedation in the rat (Everett and Sawyer, 1950) also are established.

Mottram (1945) reported on a statistically significant, and striking diurnal variation in the production of tumors in the mouse. In two experiments on hamsters carried out thus far by Doctor Chaudhry in Minnesota, important differences in tumor yield, at three months after one intraglandular injection of carcinogen, were seen as a function of the phase of circadian periodicity in which the carcinogen was injected.

In turning to susceptibility rhythms, this discussion will be restricted, however, to (1) agents that were repeatedly studied by standardized light-synchronized periodicity analysis (by Halberg in 1957), and to (2) data that revealed a reproducible well-defined peak and trough in susceptibility; [in tests carried out at 4-hour intervals during a 24-hour period]. In such tests, one starts out by keeping constant the kind, amount, and conditions of administration of an agent studied. One administers this fixed stimulus to separate groups of comparable subjects at different times, allowing only the physiologic state to vary along a 24-hour scale, as it does, whether or not we wish to evaluate such variations. Eventually, one should vary both the agent, e.g., the dose, and the organism's physiologic state, and we shall illustrate this approach with one example, endotoxin, Fig. 17.

Noise

Individual D_8 mice are exposed for 60 minutes to the ringing of electric bells (~104 db above 0.0002 dyne/cm² rms pressure) either between 08:00 and 10:00 or between 20:00 and 22:00 [light daily from 06:00 to 18:00 (Halberg *et al.*, 1955a; Halberg *et al.*, 1955b)]. Figure 18a shows that the number of mice with convulsions is significantly higher at one time as compared to the other, in response to the same noise. Another experiment summarized in Fig. 18b also showed significant within-day differences in audiogenic abnor-

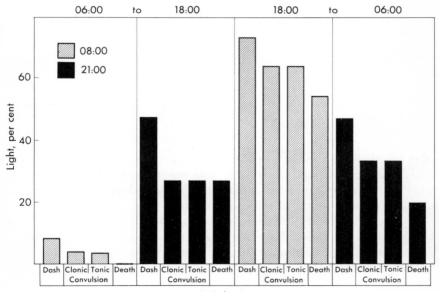

FIGURE 18c.

Abnormal audiogenic responses in D_8 mice, on two schedules of light and darkness, alternating at 12-hour intervals. Note the difference in incidence of abnormality at 08:00 and at 21:00, on each lighting regimen. Note also the difference in time of high abnormality, in mice exposed to light from 18:00 to 06:00, as compared with that in mice exposed to light from 06:00 to 18:00 (102 mice, about 5 weeks of age, of both sexes).

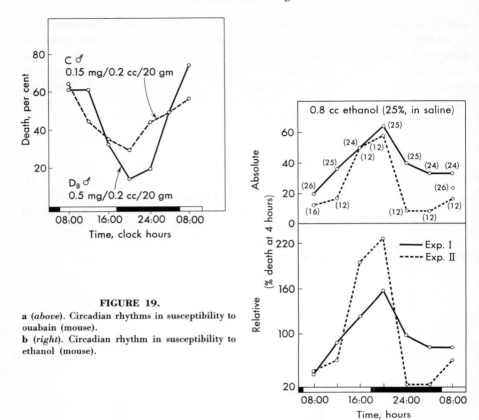

FIGURE 19.

a (*above*). Circadian rhythms in susceptibility to ouabain (mouse).
b (*right*). Circadian rhythm in susceptibility to ethanol (mouse).

mality whether one used as an end point the occurrence of convulsions or the more dramatic end point, death. In these experiments, dashing (abnormal racing) consistently preceded convulsions; such dashing also constituted a circadian-periodic abnormal response to noise.

The susceptibility rhythm to noise does not depend upon the clock hour, as such. As shown earlier for many functions, one may reset the timing of rhythms in audiogenic abnormality by an appropriate shift of the lighting regimen (Fig. 18c) (Halberg, 1958).

Ouabain

In several experiments on D_8 mice, each involving about 140 animals, mortality from ouabain was much higher early during the daily light period than at other times (Fig. 19a) (Halberg *et al.*, 1959*b*); resetting of this rhythm is feasible by manipulation of lighting. Moreover, peak susceptibility to ouabain differs in timing from peak susceptibility to audiogenic convulsions, when tested in mice of the same stock, sex, and age, and at the same time.

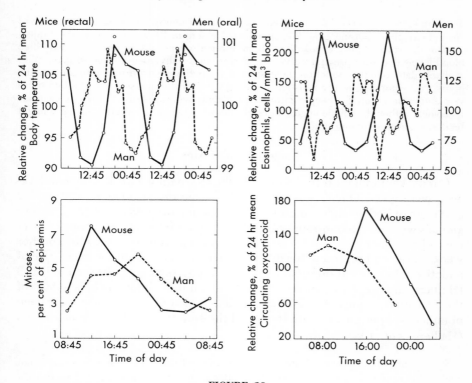

FIGURE 20.

Species difference in mode of synchronization of circadian rhythms in man and mouse. Light from 06:00 to 18:00, alternating with 12 hours of darkness, in experiments on mice only.

Ethanol

During work on susceptibility to drugs available in ethanol solution, periodic changes were found in the animals' reaction to the solvent itself (Haus and Halberg, 1959). Figure 19b shows the percentage of deaths at 4 hours after ethanol injection in two experiments (top) as well as the same data expressed as per cent of their day-mean (bottom). The latter way of plotting serves for comparisons of the temporal changes in variables studied at different operating levels.

In studies of alcohol, one need not always attempt "to eliminate rhythms by repeated measurements." In addition to the important differences among individuals in their genetic susceptibility to alcohol (Williams, 1953; Williams, 1956), attention may also be paid to critical physiologic, intra-individual changes in susceptibility.

The highest death rates from ethanol were consistently recorded for the subgroup injected 2 hours after start of the daily dark period, i.e., 20:00. Inferences from these and other data on a nocturnal rodent to the corresponding aspects of ethanol toxicity in usually diurnal human beings, however, are to be qualified. One must take into account, first, the known species difference between man and mouse concerning the timing of several circadian rhythms (Fig. 20), shown by Halberg in 1959. Also, the ethanol injections of this study (0.8 cc of a 25% solution, intraperitoneally) were associated with high blood levels that rose precipitously—conditions not usually encountered in man. With available data, one may sanction the custom of restricting heavy drinking to the evening hours, corresponding to the resistant morning hours of the mouse, only in a humorous vein and even so only for people with diurnal activity habits. Finally, from smaller, pharmacologic rather than toxicologic, doses of ethanol a greater (desired?) response might be derived at the "wrong time."

Bacterial endotoxins

C mice kept in light from 06:00 to 18:00, alternating with 12 hours of darkness, were given Difco's *E. coli* lipopolysaccharide, in doses of 100 μg/0.2 cc/20 gm of body weight; in each of two experiments, seven groups of mature animals were injected intraperitoneally, at 4-hour intervals. Mortality was recorded at 4-hour intervals for two days after injection and daily for another week. Large and reproducible differences in mortality from the same dose of endotoxin, injected at different hours, into separate groups, are seen in Fig. 3 (Halberg and Stephens, 1958). The same amount of endotoxin kills ~80% of the mice at one time and ~20% at another. Similar differences also have been obtained by spot-checks with the use of the endotoxin of *Brucella melitensis* (Halberg *et al.*, 1955*d*).

Such results are of practical interest to users of the LD_{50} which conventionally is not qualified as to physiologic periodicity. By standardization for periodicity analysis in 1957 Halberg showed intra-assay, inter-individual variability will be reduced; circadian changes in susceptibility to endotoxins may also account for a good share of the vexing problem posed by inter-assay variability. In two assays done 12 hours apart, the same material, *E. coli* endotoxin (Difco), was tested in mice that were comparable in terms of genetic background, sex, age, past history, and that were kept in identical experimental environments: a relative potency of 3.22 was obtained in the two assays of samples from the identical batch (Halberg *et al.*, 1960).

Hours of diminished resistance

Changes along the 24-hour scale probably characterize the organism's ability to withstand damage from a wider variety of agents. Among the susceptibility rhythms cited there were significant differences in the time periods elapsed between application of stimulus and recording of harmful response. Death from noise-induced convulsions occurred within seconds, death from doses of ouabain or ethanol tested occurred within a few minutes or a few hours, respectively. But death from endotoxin usually did not occur for many hours or days after injection; tumor induction, in turn, takes several months. In all these instances, however, conditions can be standardized so that the circadian change in physiologic state of the organism determines the difference between death and survival.

Changes in vulnerability with time, the "hours of diminished resistance," have their spatial counterpart in certain vulnerable spots of the body, recognized by the revered concept of *loci minoris resistentiae*. In terms of experimental documentation the "hours" (Fig. 21) may not compare unfavorably with the "spots." Moreover, differences in the timing of peak and trough in susceptibility to different agents suggest differences in the underlying factors. These factors are probably complex but the resulting differences in susceptibility are dramatic and reproducible. Whatever their heuristic value may be, the *horae minoris resistentiae* or *horae variae resistentiae* (one may wish to emphasize the change in resistance rather than its drop) dramatically emphasize the significance of circadian changes in physiologic state.

The temporal placement of a susceptibility peak depends, of course, upon many factors in addition to circadian rhythms. Pertinent are the dose administered, the rates of absorption, breakdown, and excretion of a given agent; the location of a peak may change with any of these or other factors.

Circadian changes in susceptibility cannot casually be accounted for by variations solely in activity, feeding, or drinking. In mice deprived of food or water for several days, the susceptibility rhythm to ethanol persists. In the absence of gross motor activity in the anesthetized animal, significant differences in electrocorticographic abnormalities were recorded (Harner and Halberg, 1958) at times when differences corresponding in sign are seen in the convulsive response of the unanesthetized animals.

The coincidence of two peaks or troughs, e.g., in susceptibility to audiogenic convulsions and gross motor activity, thus need not imply a causal relation. A significant phase difference between two peaks or troughs, in turn, contributes only to ruling out a direct, immediate, and exclusive effect of one of the two peaking variables upon the other.

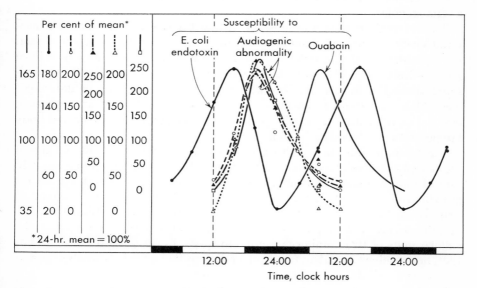

FIGURE 21.
Hours of diminished resistance (mouse).

At any rate, a new domain, the normal range, for old methodologic avenues is opened by the recognition of reproducible circadian changes in resistance. The problem of the possible relation between body activity and audiogenic abnormality was a pertinent example. If one suspects a relation between two periodic variables, one may examine the extent (if any) to which the experimental abolition of the rhythmic change in one variable affects the behavior of the other. This approach as such is not new but periodicity analysis enables us to apply it while we work at levels which are within the normal range (Fig. 1).

A spectrum of peaks and troughs in susceptibility to different agents seems useful to bio-assayists interested in restricting their sources of variation and, more important, in selecting the sensitive phase of rhythm for their tests (Fig. 5). Pharmacologic studies are warranted on possible periodic changes in therapeutic-toxic ratios; if these ratios also change periodically, some of the customary practices of drug administration might be reconsidered.

VI. SUMMARY AND CONCLUSIONS

In studies of adaptation, it is both desirable and feasible to quantify physiologic rhythms with periods of about 24 hours. From appropriate physiologic time series such circadian rhythms can be described by numerical estimates of the period and the amplitude, computed, for instance, by periodograms.

Circadian periods may be slightly, though consistently and significantly, different from 24 hours, by a few hours or a few minutes. Such periods characterize functions at several levels of mammalian organization and have no known environmental counterpart; with qualifications they may be regarded as endogenous.

The external timing of rhythms, rather than their periodicity, *per se*, is mastered solely by the environment. Exogenous mastery of phase depends upon some plasticity of the period, but period control by the environment does have limits—limits beyond which the intrinsic periodicity cannot be frequency-synchronized (with noncircadian, hence unacceptable, environmental schedules). Thus, in patients subjected to 12-hourly shocks until they are regressed, circadian, rather than 12-hourly, periods predominate in the rhythms of body temperature and blood eosinophils.

Circadian periods may originate at the cellular level in the leads and lags of sequential chemical processes, subservient to the periodic preponderance in rate of energy metabolism alternating with that in rate of metabolism for growth and/or repair. Whether or not this assumption is correct, circadian periods constitute units of integrated functional organization in time; their recognition as such is as important as that of their morphologic counterpart, the cellular units of structural organization in space. In carrying this analogy further, one resolves circadian functional relations by periodicity analysis just as one resolves cellular structural relations by microscopy.

The physiologist's circadian temporal maps may be compared to the morphologist's atlas. Illustrative interrelations among circadian functions have already been mapped-in-time at several levels of physiologic organization. Such maps describe adaptive functional integration as it involves frequency synchronization of circadian rhythms; cellular cycles thus are locked in phase by humoral and neural controls (with phase differences that are plus, minus, or zero). The adrenal cycle, as an endocrine entity, is one such control and it is synchronized, in turn, with the environment by superimposed and juxtaposed controls, awaiting further study.

The circadian rhythms themselves appear to be ubiquitous. At the one extreme one finds circadian behavior in work on compounds that have been related to the transmission of genetic information or to enzyme-forming systems and in enzyme studies as well. At the other extreme, the survival of the organism as a whole may be shown to be a function of the phase of its circadian rhythms.

Other things being comparable, death from exposure to bacterial endotoxins, ethanol, ouabain, or noise does or does not occur—as a function of predictable circadian changes in physiologic state. Moreover, in certain cases, such hours of diminished resistance differ for the response of the same animals to different agents. We may be dealing with genetic adaptations critically underlying physiologic responses, rather than with conditioned reflexes or stress reactions; this suggestion is supported by the limited modifiability of the period of rhythms.

The *horae variae resistentiae* may be counterposed as a concept to the *loci minoris resistentiae*. Their experimental documentation may further toxicology, pharmacology, and experimental pathology as well as bioassay work in general.

The problems of frequency desynchronization of rhythms at various levels of bodily organization await further study. The reality of such desynchronization has been ascertained for one illness, blinding. It seems important to ask whether disturbances of the normal time relations among the circadian rhythms themselves are signals of the temporal limits to functional integration and adaptability and whether they might underlie disease. If so, recognition of disturbances in time relations among rhythms will contribute to understanding of temporal maladaptations and diseases and thus to their eventual prevention or correction.

VII. ACKNOWLEDGMENTS

The author is indebted to Dr. John J. Bittner, George Chase Christian Professor of Cancer Biology at the University of Minnesota, for sympathetic interest and continued help and cooperation in several of the studies reported in this manuscript; Dr. Solon Gordon of the Argonne National Laboratory, Lemont, Illinois, and Dr. Robert Galambos of the Walter Reed Army Institute for Medical Research, Washington, D. C., kindly read the manuscript and provided helpful comments.

REFERENCES

Adolph, E. F. 1956. "General and specific characteristics of physiological adaptations," Am. J. Physiol. *184:* 18–28.

Ågren, G., O. Wilander, and E. Jorpes. 1931. "Cyclic changes in the glycogen content of the liver and the muscles of rats and mice: their bearing upon the sensitivity of the animals to insulin and their influence on the urinary output of nitrogen," Biochem. J. *25:* 777–785.

Appel, W., and K. J. Hansen. 1952. "Lichteinwirkung, Tagesrhythmik der eosinophilen Leukocyten und Hypophysennebennierenrizindensystem," Deut. Arch. klin. Med. *199:* 530–537.

Aschoff, J. 1952*a.* "Aktivitätsperiodik von Mäusen im Dauerdunkel," Pflügers Arch. *255:* 189–196.

Aschoff, J. 1952*b.* "Frequenzämderungen der Aktivitätsperiodik bei Maüsen im Dauerlicht und Dauerdunkel," Pflügers Arch. *255:* 197–203.

Aschoff, J. 1953. "Aktivitätsperiodik bei Gimpeln unter natürlichen und künstlichen Belichtungsverhältnissen," Z. vgl. Physiol. *35:* 159–166.

Aschoff, J. 1954. "Zeitgeber der tierischen Tagesperiodik," Naturwissenschaften *41:* 49–56.

Aschoff, J. 1955. "Exogene und endogene Komponente der 24-Stundenperiodik bei Tier und Mensch," Naturwissenschaften *42:* 569–575.

Aschoff, J. 1958. "Tierische Periodik unter dem Einfluss von Zeitgebern," Z. Tierpsychol. *15:* 1–30.

Aschoff, J. 1952*b.* "Frequenzämderungen der Aktivitätsperiodik bei Mäusen im Dauerlicht und künstlichen Belichtungswechsel," Z. Tierpsychol. *11:* 476–484.

Aschoff, J., and J. Meyer-Lohmann. 1955*a.* "Die Aktivitätsperiodik von Nagern im künstlichen 24-Stunden-Tag mit 6-20 Stunden Lichtzeit," Z. vgl. Physiol. *37:* 107–117.

Aschoff, J., and J. Meyer-Lohmann. 1955*b.* "Die Aktivität gekäfigter Grünfinken im 24-Stunden-Tag bei unterschiedlich langer Lichtzeit mit und ohne Dämmerung," Z. Tierpsychol. *12:* 254–265.

Ball, N. G., and I. J. Dyke. 1954. "An endogenous 24-hour rhythm in the growth rate of the *Avena* coleoptile," J. Exptl. Bot. *5:* 421–433.

Ball, N. G., and I. J. Dyke. 1956. "The effects of indole-3-acetic acid and 2:4-dichlorophenoxyacetic acid on the growth rate and endogenous rhythm of intact *Avena* coleoptiles," J. Exptl. Bot. *7:* 25–41.

Ball, N. G., and I. J. Dyke. 1957. "The effects of decapitation, lack of oxygen, and low temperature on the endogenous 24-hour rhythm in the growth rate of the *Avena* coleoptile," J. Exptl. Bot. *8:* 323–338.

Ball, N. G., I. J. Dyke, and M. B. Wilkins. 1957. "The occurrence of endogenous rhythms in the coleoptiles in various cereal genera," J. Exptl. Bot. *8:* 339–347.

Bänder, A. 1950. "Die Beziehungen des 24-Stunden-Rhythmus vegetativer Funktionen zum histologischen Funktionsbild endokriner Drüsen," Z. ges. exper. Med. *115:* 229–250.

Barnum, C. P., C. D. Jardetzky, and F. Halberg. 1957. "Nucleic acid synthesis in regenerating mouse liver," Texas Reports Biol. & Med. *15:* 134–147.

Barnum, C. P., C. D. Jardetzky, and F. Halberg. 1958. "Time relations among metabolic and morphologic 24-hour changes in mouse liver," Am. J. Physiol. *195:* 301–310.

Behnke, A. R. 1951. "Physical agents and trauma," Ann. Rev. Med. *2:* 243–272.

Beringer, A. 1950. "Ueber das Glykogen und seinen Einfluss auf den Stoffwechsel der Leber beim Gesunden und Diabetiker," Deut. med. Wochnschr. *75:* 1715–1719.

Blackman, R. B. and F. W. Tukey. 1958. *The Measurement of Power Spectra,* Dover Publications, New York.

Blumenfeld, C. M. 1942. "Normal and abnormal mitotic activity; comparison of periodic mitotic activity in epidermis, renal cortex, and submaxillary gland of the albino rat," Arch. Pathol. *33:* 770–776.

Boutwell, R. K., M. K. Brush, and H. P. Rusch. 1948. "Some physiological effects associated with chronic caloric restriction," Am. J. Physiol. *154:* 517–524.

Brown, F. A., Jr. 1956. "Studies of the timing mechanisms of daily, tidal, and lunar periodicities in organisms," Perspectives in Marine Biology (Symposium) Univ. California, pp. 269–282.

Brown, F. A., Jr. 1958. "An exogenous reference-clock for persistent, temperature-independent, labile, biological rhythms," Biol. Bull. *115*: 81–100.

Brown, F. A., Jr., M. F. Bennett, and H. M. Webb. 1958. "Monthly cycles in an organism in constant conditions during 1956 and 1957," Proc. Natl. Acad. Sci. *44*: 290–296.

Brown, H. E., and T. F. Dougherty. 1956. "The diurnal variation of blood leucocytes in normal and adrenalectomized mice," Endocrinol. *58*: 365–375.

Brown, W. H. 1930. "Constitutional variation and susceptibility to disease," *in: The Harvey Lectures*, Williams and Wilkins Co., Baltimore, pp. 106–150.

Bünning, E. 1958a. "Cellular clocks," Nature *181*: 1169–1171.

Bünning, E. 1958b. *Die Physiologische Uhr*, Springer-Verlag, Berlin, p. 99.

Bünning, E., and G. Schöne-Schneiderhörn. 1957. "Die Bedeutung der Zellkerne im Mechanismus der endogenen Tagesrhythmik," Planta, Berlin *48*: 459–467.

Bykow, K. M. 1954. *Studien über periodische Veränderungen physiologischer Funktionen des Organismus*, Akademie-Verlag, Berlin.

Cloudsley-Thompson, J. L. 1956. "Diurnal rhythms of activity in terrestrial arthropods," Nature *178*: 215.

DePorte, J. V. 1932. "The prevalent hour of stillbirth," Am. J. Obst. and Gynecol. *23*: No. 1.

Doe, R. P., E. B. Flink, and M. C. Flint. 1954. "Correlation of diurnal variations in eosinophils and 17-hydroxycorticosteroids in plasma and urine," J. Clin. Endocrinol. Metab. *14*: 774–775.

Ehret, C. F. 1953. "An analysis of the role of electro-magnetic radiations in the mating reaction of Paramecium bursaria," Physiol. Zool. *26*: 274–300.

Ehret, C. F. 1955a. "The effects of pre- and post-illumination on the scotophilic recovery phase of the Paramecium busaria mating reaction," Anat. Rec. *122*: 456–457.

Ehret, C. F. 1955b. "The photoreactivability of sexual activity and rhythmicity in Paramecium bursaria," Radiation Research *3*: 34.

Ekman, C. A., and Hj. Holmgren. 1947. "An investigation of the rhythmic metabolism of the liver with help of radio-active phosphorus," Acta Med. Scand., Suppl. *196*: 63–74.

Engstrom, H., Hj. Holmgren, and G. Wohlfart. 1938. "Untersuchungen über 24-stunden-rhythmische Veränderungen in der Blutkörperchenmenge der Leber, der Nebennieren und der Schildrüse," Anat. Anz. *86*: 129–149.

Everett, J. W., and C. H. Sawyer. 1950. "A 24-hour periodicity in the 'LH release apparatus' of female rats, disclosed by barbiturate sedation," Endocrinology *47*: 198–218.

Ferguson, D. J., M. B. Visscher, F. Halberg, and L. M. Levy. 1957. "Effect of hypophysectomy on the 24-hour rectal temperature rhythm in the mouse," Am. J. Physiol. *190*: 235.

Fleeson, W., B. C. Glueck, Jr., and F. Halberg. 1957. "Persistence of daily rhythms in eosinophil count and rectal temperature during 'regression' induced by intensive electroshock therapy," The Physiologist *1*: 28.

Flink, E. B., and F. Halberg. 1952. "Clinical studies on eosinophil rhythm," J. Clin. Endocrinol. *12*: 922.

Forsgren, E. 1928. "On the relationship between the formation of bile and glycogen in the liver of rabbit," Scand. Arch. Physiol. *53*: 137–151.

Forsham, P. H., V. DiRaimondo, D. Island, A. P. Rinfret, and R. H. Orr. 1944. "Dynamics of adrenal function in man," In: Ciba Fdn. Colloq. on Endocrinology *8*: 279–308.

French, J. D., M. Verseano, and H. W. Magoun. 1953a. "An extralemniscal sensory system in the brain," Am. Med. Assoc. Arch. Neurol. Psychiat. *69*: 505–518.

French, J. D., M. Verseano, and H. W. Magoun. 1953b. "A neural basis of the anesthetic state," Am. Med. Assoc. Arch. Neurol. Psychiat. *69*: 519–529.

French, J. D., F. K. Von Amerongen, and H. W. Magoun. 1952. "An activating system in brain stem of monkey," Am. Med. Assoc. Arch. Neurol. Psychiat. *68*: 577–590.

Frey, S. 1929. "Der Tod des Menschen in seinen Beziehungen zu den Tages- und Jahreszeiten," Deut. Z. Chirurgie *218*: 366–369.

Gangloff, H., and M. Monnier. 1956. "Electrographic aspects of an "arousal" or attention reaction induced in the unanesthetized rabbit by the presence of a human being," Electroencephalog. and Clin. Neurophysiol. 8: 623–629.

Glick, D., R. B. Ferguson, L. J. Greenberg, and F. Halberg. "Succinicdehydrogenase, panthothenate and biotin of rodent adrenal in different stages of circadian corticosterone rhythm," Am. J. Physiol., in press.

Glueck, B. C., H. Reiss, and L. E. Bernard. 1957. "Regressive electric shock therapy," Psychiat. Quart. 31: 117–136.

Greenberg, L. J., and D. Glick. 1958. "Quantitative histochemical distribution of coenzyme A in the rat adrenal in various functional states," Endocrinology 63: 909–915.

Guthmann, H., and M. Bienhüls. 1936. "Wehenbegin, Geburtsstunde und Tageszeit," Monatssch. Geburtschülfe u. Gynäkologie 103: 337–348.

Halberg, F. 1953. "Some physiological and clinical aspects of 24-hour periodicity," Lancet 73: 20–32.

Halberg, F. 1954. "Beobachtungen über 24-Stundenperiodik in standartisierter Versuch sanordnung vor und nach Epinephrektomie und bilateraler optischer Enukleation," 20th meeting of the German Physiologic Society, Homburg/Saar, 1953. In: Ber. über die ges. Physiol. 162: 354–355.

Halberg, F. 1955. "Experimentelles zur Physiologie des Nebennierenzyklus," Acta Med. Scand., Suppl. 307: 117.

Halberg, F. 1957. "Young NH mice for the study of hepatic mitoses in intact liver," Experientia 13: 502–503.

Halberg, F. 1959. "Physiologic 24-hour periodicity; general and procedural considerations with reference to the adrenal cycle," Z. Vitamin- Hormon- und Fermentforschung 10: 225–296.

Halberg, F. 1960. "The 24-hour scale: a time dimension of adaptive functional organization," Perspectives in Biology and Medicine. 3: 491.

Halberg, F., C. P. Barnum, R. H. Silber, and J. J. Bittner, 1958. "24-hour rhythms at different levels of integration in the mouse and the lighting regimen," Proc. Soc. Exptl. Biol. & Med. 97: 897–900.

Halberg, F., J. J. Bittner, and R. J. Gully. 1955a. "24-hour periodic susceptibility to audiogenic convulsions in several stocks of mice," Fed. Proc. 14: 67–68.

Halberg, F., J. J. Bittner, R. J. Gully, F. Albrecht, and E. L. Brackney, 1955b. "24-hour periodicity and audiogenic convulsions in I mice, Proc. Soc. Exptl. Biol. & Med. 88: 169–173.

Halberg, F., J. J. Bittner, and D. Smith. 1957. "Belichtungswechsel und 24-Stundenperiodik von Mitosen im Hautepithel der Maus," Z. Vitamin- Hormon- und Fermentforschung 9: 69–73.

Halberg, F., M. J. Frantz, and J. J. Bittner. 1957. "Phase difference between 24-hour rhythms in cortical adrenal mitoses and blood eosinophils in the mouse," Anat. Rec. 129: 349–356.

Halberg, F., E. Halberg, C. P. Barnum, and J. J. Bittner. 1959a. "Physiologic 24-hour periodicity in human beings and mice: the lighting regimen and daily routine." In: Photoperiodism and Related Phenomena in Plants and Animals, Ed. Withrow, R. B., Publ. 55, Amer. Assoc. Adv. Sci. Washington, D.C., pp. 803–878.

Halberg, F., 0. Haus, and A. Stephens. 1959b. "Susceptibility to ouabain and physiologic 24-hour periodicity," Fed. Proc. 18: 245.

Halberg, F., and R. B. Howard. 1958. "24-hour periodicity and experimental Medicine," Postgrad. Med. 24: 349–358.

Halberg, F., E. Jacobsen, G. Wadsworth, and J. J. Bittner. 1958. "Abnormal audiogenic response spectrum in mice," Science 128: 657–658.

Halberg, F., E. A. Johnson, W. Brown, and J. J. Bittner. 1960. "Susceptibility rhythm to E. coli endotoxin and bioassay," Proc. Soc. Exptl. Biol. & Med. 103: 142–144.

Halberg, F., and G. Nahas. 1955c. "Observations sur l'eosinopenie matinale chez le chien," Rev. belge path. med. exp. 24: 287–294.

Halberg, F., R. E. Peterson, and R. H. Silber. 1959. "Phase relations of 24-hour periodicities in blood corticosterone, mitoses in cortical adrenal parenchyma, and total body activity," Endocrinology 64: 222–230.

Halberg, F., W. W. Spink, P. G. Albrecht, and R. J. Gully. 1955*d*. "Resistance of mice to Brucella somatic antigen, 24-hour periodicity and the adrenals," J. Clin. Endocrinol. and Metab. *15:* 887.

Halberg, F., and A. N. Stephens. 1958. "24-hour periodicity in mortality of C mice from E. *coli* lipopolysaccharide," Fed. Proc. *17:* 439.

Halberg, F., H. Vermund, E. Halberg, and C. P. Barnum. 1956. "Adrenal hormones and phospholipid metabolism in liver cytoplasm of adrenalectomized mice," Endocrinology *59:* 364–368.

Halberg, F., and M. B. Visscher. 1950. "Regular diurnal physiological variation in eosinophil levels in five stocks of mice," Proc. Soc. Exptl. Biol. & Med. *75:* 846–847.

Halberg, F., and M. B. Visscher. 1952. "A difference between the effects of dietary caloric restriction on the estrous cycle and on the 24-hour adrenal cortical cycle in rodents," Endocrinology *51:* 329–335.

Halberg, F., and M. B. Visscher. 1953. "The dependence of an adrenal cycle in the mouse upon lighting," XIX International Physiological Congress, 1953. Therien Freres Limited, Montreal.

Halberg, F., and M. B. Visscher. 1954. "Temperature rhythms in blind mice," Fed. Proc. *13:* 65.

Halberg, F., M. B. Visscher, and J. J. Bittner. 1953. "Observations on the eosinophil rhythm in mice; range of occurrence, effects of illumination feeding and adrenalectomy," Am. J. Physiol. *174:* 313–315.

Halberg, F., M. B. Visscher, and J. J. Bittner. 1954. "Relation of visual factors to eosinophil rhythm in mice," Am. J. Physiol. *179:* 229–235.

Halberg, F., M. B. Visscher, E. B. Flink, K. Berge, and F. Bock. 1951. "Diurnal rhythmic changes in blood eosinophil levels in health and in certain diseases," Lancet *71:* 312–319.

Haldane, J. S. 1922. *Respiration*, Yale University Press, New Haven, pp. vii, viii, ix.

Harker, J. E. 1956. "Factors controlling the diurnal rhythm of activity of *Periplaneta americana*," J. Exptl. Biol. *33:* 224–234.

Harker, J. E. 1958. "Experimental production of midgut tumours in *Periplaneta americana*," J. Exptl. Biol. *35:* 251–259.

Harner, R. N., and F. Halberg. 1958. "Electrocorticographic differences in D_8 mice at times of daily high and low susceptibility of audiogenic convulsions," The Physiologist *1*(4): 34–35.

Hastings, J. W., and B. M. Sweeney. 1957. "On the mechanism of temperature independence in a biological clock." Proc. Natl. Acad. Sci. (U.S.) *43:* 804–810.

Haus, E., and F. Halberg. 1959. "24-hour rhythm in susceptibility of C mice to a toxic dose of ethanol," J. Appl. Physiol. *14:* 878–880.

Hauty, G. T. 1958. "Human performance in the space travel environment," Air Univ. Quart. Rev. *10:* 89–120.

Higgins, G. M., J. Berkson, and E. Flock. 1932. "The diurnal cycle in the liver: I. Periodicity of the cycle, with analysis of chemical constituents involved," Am. J. Physiol. *102:* 673–682.

Higgins, G. M., J. Berkson, and E. Flock. 1933. "The diurnal cycle in the liver: II. Food, a factor in its determination," Am. J. Physiol. *105:* 177–186.

Holmgren, Hj. 1931. "Beitrag zur Kenntnis der Leberfunktion," Z. mikr.-anat. Forsch. *24:* 632–642.

Howard, R. B. 1952. "Studies on the metabolism of iron," Thesis, Ph.D. Univ. of Minn. Graduate School, p. 125.

Hufeland, C. W. 1797. *The Art of Prolonging Life*, J. Bell, No. 148, Oxford-Street, London, pp. 331. and 201.

Hupe, K., and A. Gropp. 1957. "Ueber den zeitlichen Verlauf der Mitoseaktivität in Gewebekulturen," Z. Zellforsch. *46:* 67–70.

Ingle, D. J. 1951. "Parameters of metabolic problems," Rec. Prog. in Hormone Research *6:* 159–194.

Jaffe, J. J. 1954. "Diurnal mitotic periodicity in regenerating rat liver," Anat. Rec. *120:* 935–954.

Jardetzky, C. D., C. P. Barnum, and F. Halberg. 1956. "Physiologic 24-hour periodicity in nucleic acid metabolism and mitosis of immature growing liver," Am. J. Physiol. *187:* 608.

Jores, A. 1940. "Rhythmusstudien am hypophysektomierten Tier. Verh. int. Ges. Biol. Rhythmusforschung," Utrecht, 1939. Stockholm, Aktiebolaget Fahlcrantz' Boktryckeri, Acta Med. Scand. Suppl. *108*, pp. 114–120.

Jusatz, H. J., and E. Eckardt. 1934. "Die häufigste Todesstunde," Mün. Med. Wochenschr. *81*(1): 709–710.

Kaine, H. D., H. S. Seltzer, and J. W. Conn. 1955. "Mechanism of diurnal eosinophil rhythm in man," J. Lab. & Clin. Med. *45*: 247–252.

Kalmus, H. 1957. "Space and time in animal life," Proc. 1957 Conf. Intern. Soc. Biol. Rhythms. Semmering, cf. Biological rhythms. Nature *180*: 1100–1102.

Kendall, M. G. 1948. *In: The Advanced Theory of Statistics*, Charles Griffin & Co., Ltd., London, Vol. II, pp. 363–439.

King, P. D. 1956. "Increased frequency of births in the morning hours," Science *123*: 985–986.

Kleitman, N. 1939. *Sleep and Wakefulness*, University of Chicago Press, Chicago, p. 638.

Kleitman, N. 1949. *In: Human Factors in Submarine Warfare*, Williams & Wilkins, Baltimore, p. 329.

Kleitman, N., and D. P. Jackson. 1950. "Body temperature and performance under different routines," J. Appl. Physiol. *3:* 309–328.

Knapp, C. B. 1909. "The hour of birth," Bull. Lying-In Hospital *6:* 69–74.

Koehler, F., F. K. Okano, L. R. Elveback, F. Halberg, and J. J. Bittner. 1956. "Periodograms for study of daily physiologic periodicity in mice and man," Exptl. Med. and Sur. *14:* 5–30.

Lamond, D. R., and A. W. H. Braden. 1959. "Diurnal variation in response to gonadotropin in the mouse," Endocrinology *64:* 921–936.

Landau, J., and S. Feldman. 1954. "Diminished endogenous morning eosinopenia in blind subjects," Acta Endocrinol. *15:* 53–60.

Lehman, E. L. 1950. *Notes on the Theory of Estimation*, Associated Students' Store, University of California, Berkeley, Chap. II, pp. 1–20.

Lehmann, G., and H. Michaelis. 1943. "Adrenalin und Arbeit IV. Mitteilung, Adrenalin und Leistungsfähigkeit," Arbeitsphysiologie *12:* 305–312.

Lewis, P. R., and M. C. Lobban. 1954. "Persistence of a 24-hour patern of diuresis in human subjects living on a 22-hour day," J. Physiol. *125:* 34–35.

Lewis, P. R., and M. C. Lobban. 1957*a*. "The effects of prolonged periods of life on abnormal time routines upon excretory rhythms in human subjects," Quart. J. Exptl. Physiol. *42:* 356–371.

Lewis, P. R., and M. C. Lobban. 1957*b*. "Dissociation of diurnal rhythms in human subjects living on abnormal time routines," Quart. J. Exptl. Physiol. *42:* 371–386.

Litman, T., F. Halberg, S. Ellis, and J. J. Bittner. 1958. "Pituitary growth hormone and mitoses in immature mouse liver," Endocrinology *62:* 361–364.

Louch, C., R. K. Meyer, and J. T. Emlen. 1953. "Effect of stress on diurnal fluctuations in eosinophils of the laboratory mouse," Proc. Soc. Exptl. Biol. & Med. *82:* 668–671.

Magoun, H. W. 1952. "The ascending reticular activating system," Proc. Assoc. Research Nervous Mental Disease *30:* 480–492.

Malek, J. 1952. "The manifestation of biological rhythms in delivery," Gynaecologie *133:* 365–372.

Malek, J. 1954. "Der Einfluss des Lichtes und der Dunkelheit auf den klinischen Geburtsbeginn," Gynaecologie *138:* 401–405.

Mason, J. W. 1958. *In: Reticular Formation of the Brain* Little, Brown, and Co., Boston, p. 645.

Migeon, C. J., A. B. French, L. T. Samuels, and J. Z. Bowers. 1955. "Plasma 17-hydroxycorticosteroid levels and leucocyte values in the Rhesus monkey, including normal variation and the effect of ACTH," Am. J. Physiol. *182:* 462–468.

Mottram, J. C. 1945. "A diurnal variation in the production of tumors," J. Pathol. and Bacteriol. *57:* 265–267.

Mühlemann, H. R., T. M. Marthaler, and P. Loustalot. 1955. "Daily variations in mitotic activity of adrenal cortex, thyroid and oral epithelium of the rat," Proc. Soc. Exptl. Biol. & Med. *90:* 467–468.

Panzenhagen, H., and R. Speirs. 1953. "Effect of horse serum, adrenal hormones, and histamine on the number of eosinophils in the blood and peritoneal fluid of mice," Blood 8: 536–544.

Park, O. 1940. "Nocturnalism—The development of a problem," Ecological Monographs 10: 485.

Pelc, S. R., and A. Howard. 1952. "Chromosome metabolism as shown by autoradiographs," Exptl. Cell Research, Suppl. 2: 269–278.

Pincus, G. 1943. "A diurnal rhythm in the excretion of urinary ketosteroids by young men," J. Clin. Endocrinol. 3: 195–199.

Pittendrigh, C. S. 1954. "On temperature independence in the clock system controlling emergence time in Drosophila," Proc. Natl. Acad. Sci. (U.S.) 40: 1018–1029.

Pittendrigh, C. S., and V. G. Bruce. 1957. "An oscillator model for biological clocks," In: Symposium, Soc. for the Study of Development and Growth, Princeton University Press, Princeton, New Jersey.

Podwyssozki, W. v., Jr. 1886. "Experimentelle Untersuchungen über die Regeneration der Drüsengewebe," Beitr. path. Anat. 1: 259–360.

Points, T. C. 1956. "Twenty-four hours in a day," Obst. & Gynecol. 8: 245.

Potter, V. R. 1957. "Introductory remarks on nucleic acid metabolism," Texas Repts. Biol. and Med. 15: 127–133.

Potter, V. R. 1958. "The biochemical approach to the cancer problem," Fed. Proc. 17: 691–697.

Reinberg, A., and J. Ghata. 1957. Rhythmes et cycles biologiques, Presses Universitaires de France.

Schneider, C. F. 1859. "Ein Beitrag zur Ermittelung der Sterblichkeits-Verhältnisse in Berlin nach den Tageszeiten," Archiv. path. Anat. u. Physiol. u. klin. Med. 16: 95–119.

Schuster, A. 1898. "On the investigation of hidden periodicities with application to a supposed 26-day period of meteorological phenomena," Terrestr. Magn. 3: 13–41.

Schuster, A. 1900. "The periodogram of magnetic declination as obtained from the records of the Greenwich Observatory during the years 1871–1895," Trans. Cambridge Phil. Soc. 18: 107–135.

Schuster, A. 1906a. "The periodogram and its optical analogy," Proc. Roy. Soc. London A 77: 136–140.

Schuster, A. 1906b. "On sun-spot periodicities. Preliminary notice," Proc. Roy. Soc. London A 77: 141–145.

Schuster, A. 1906c. "On the periodicities of sun-spots," Phil. Trans. Roy. Soc. London A 206: 69–100.

Selye, H. 1950, Stress. The Physiology and Pathology of Exposure to Stress, Acta Inc., Montreal.

Selye, H. 1951. First Annual Report on Stress.

Selye, H. 1955. "Specific Alarm Syndromes," Postgrad. Med. 17: 336–338.

Selye, H. 1958. "What is basic research," Metabolism 7: 387–397.

Selye, H., and G. Heuser. 1954. Fourth Annual Report on Stress. Acta Inc., Montreal.

Selye, H., and A. Horava. 1952. Second Annual Report on Stress.

Selye, H., and A. Horava. 1953. Third Annual Report on Stress.

Shcherbakova, O. P. 1937. "Studies on the diurnal periodicity of physiological processes in higher mammals. I. Communication: The normal diurnal periodicity of physiological processes," Bull. biol. med. exp. 4: 327–329.

Shcherbakova, O. P. 1938. "Contributions to the study of diurnal and seasonal periodicity of physiological processes in higher vertebrates. II. Communication," Bull. biol. med. exp. 5: 159–162.

Sollberger, A. 1954. "A study of biological variation," Acta Anat. 22: 127–143.

Sollberger, A. 1955a. "Statistical aspects of diurnal biorhythm," Acta Anat. 23: 97–127.

Sollberger, A. 1955b. "Diurnal changes in biological variability," Acta Anat. 23: 259–287.

Strughold, H. 1952. "Physiological day-night cycle in global flights," J. Aviat. Med. (Am.) 23: 464–473.

Stumpff, K. 1937. Grundlagen und Methoden der Periodenforschung, J. Springer Verlag, Berlin.

Stumpff, K. 1939. *Tafeln und Aufgaben zur Harmonischen Analyse und Periodogrammrechnung,* Julius Springer Verlag, Berlin.

Szymanski, J. S. 1920. "Aktivität und Ruhe bei Tieren und Menschen," Z. Allgen. Physiol. *18:* 105–162.

Taylor, J. H., and R. D. McMaster. 1954. "Autoradiographic and microphotometric studies on desoxyribose nucleic acid during microgametogenesis in lilium longiflorum," Chromosoma *6:* 489–521.

Tribukait, B. 1954. "Aktivitätsperiodik der Maus im künstlich verkürzten Tag," Naturwissensahaften *41:* 92–93.

Tribukait, B. 1956. "Die Aktivitätsperiodik der weissen Maus im Kunsttag von 16–29 Stunden Länge," Z. vergl. Physiol. *38:* 479–490.

Tyler, F. H., C. Migeon, A. A. Florentin, and L. T. Samuels. 1954. "The diurnal variation of 17-hydroxycorticosteroid levels in plasma," J. Clin. Endocrinol. Metab. *14:* 774.

Utterback, R. A., and G. D. Ludwig. 1949. Report No. 1, Project NM 004 003, Naval Medical Research Institute, March. A comparative study of schedules for standing watches aboard submarines, based on body temperature cycles.

Vermund, H., F. Halberg, C. P. Barnum, G. W. Nash, and J. J. Bittner. 1956. "Physiologic 24-hour periodicity and hepatic phospholipid metabolism in relation to the mouse adrenal cortex," Am. J. Physiol. *186:* 414–418.

Wagner, H. O. 1930. "Ueber Jahres- und Tagesrhythmus bei Zugvögeln," Z. vergl. Physiol. *12:* 703–724.

Whittaker, E. T., and G. Robinson. 1924. *In: The Calculus of Observations,* Blackie & Son, Ltd., London, p. 343.

Williams, R. J. 1953. *Free and Unequal,* University of Texas Press, Austin, p. 171.

Williams, R. J. 1956. *Biochemical Individuality,* John Wiley & Sons, Inc., New York, p. 209.

Zander, H. A., J. Waerhaug, and F. Halberg. 1954. "Effect of hypophysectomy upon cyclic mitotic activity in the retromolar mucosa of rats," J. Clin. Endocrin. & Metab. *14:* 829.

DISCUSSION

Dr. Carlo: Dr. Laborit would like to comment and I will translate his remarks from French into English.

Dr. H. Laborit (through interpreter): If I may bring some clinical confirmation to the very good report of Dr. Halberg, I may say that for just about ten years now we have used an oscillating or diurnal rhythm form of therapy with what we believe to be good results. It always seemed illogical to administer catabolizing agents in the evening and anabolizing agents in the morning. Therefore, when we administer somatotrophic hormone, we do it in the evening; and when we give cortisone or ACTH, we do it in the morning. We were led to this idea from the observation that in certain pathological cases and in older patients, the variations between day and night of metabolic rhythms were not as great as in healthy persons and in younger persons. If in the morning you administer to these patients catabolizing agents such as ACTH, cortisone, or calcium salts, sodium salts, epinephrine, or norepinephrine, and in the evening if you administer potassium, glucose, or insulin, you can observe that the more normal metabolic fluctuations between day and night, particularly in temperature and diuresis, will reappear.

Chairman Hoagland: I would like to ask Dr. Selye in connection with the extensive work that he has done with the pro-inflammatory hormone desoxycorticosterone, how it compares in potency against anti-inflammatory hormones such as aldosterone.

Dr. Selye: Yes, we have studied aldosterone effects, although the amounts we have been able to obtain for use have been small. We find a ratio of aldosterone actively to DOC of about 10 to 1 in the sort of experiments here discussed. That is, it is only ten times as active as DOC. In some other types of tests it is thirty times as active.

Captain Vogel: I would like to ask Dr. Selye whether he has done any work with tranquilizing drugs in connection with his steroid work.

Dr. Selye: We have not. The only perhaps relevant work I could mention is that we have studied steroids as tranquilizers, but we have not studied the effect of steroids upon tranquilizers. At certain dose levels, many steroids can produce generalized anesthesia sufficiently intense to permit major surgical operations; and at lower doses they act something like tranquilizers, but I would not like to say they are identical in their application.

Chairman Hoagland: I was interested in Dr. Adolph's discussion of how very general adaptation is in cell systems and in organ systems throughout the body. It occurred to me that this is what one might expect if some of the geneticists are right in their views of how cells got going in the first place and of the role of natural selection in evolving defenses. One may think of molecular aggregates which have the property of reproduction, such as DNA molecules, and consider that such reproductive cells, possibly in the early phylogenetic, prelife stages became associated by chance with systems of other molecules that could yield energy for their reproduction. The very process of survival of these primitive aggregates by natural selection would necessitate the associated aggregates to possess adaptive functions. Thus, even at the pre-cell level of evolution one would find adaptive processes of survival value which, by natural selection, would become more varied and complex as the reproductive units became associated with more elaborate mechanisms to ensure against environmental vicissitudes. Survival of any form of organism in time would depend upon the effectiveness of the reproductive units in becoming associated with interlocking systems of adaptive mechanisms. From the point of view of survival by natural selection, it is inevitable that in any highly developed organism we would encounter a wealth of interrelated adaptive and homeostatic processes, since without them we would not be here at all. These would range all the way from chemical buffering systems of selectively permeable cell membranes to the elaborate neuromuscular homeostatic mechanisms of mammals.

Captain Behnke: I want to emphasize the importance of Dr. Halberg's study to people interested in space medicine. I find it difficult to believe his results. I don't question them, but I find it difficult to believe them.

In submarines or aboard ship it is possible to abolish the diurnal variation in temperature by rotating the watch. That is to say, it has been a practice for individuals to dog the watches, in which case men will be on watch and off for short repetitive intervals over 24 hours. As a rule in such men their temperature lines are practically straight and flat. As a result of this, we find that certain individuals may be less efficient. They may be more sleepy when the temperature is low, when they are supposed to be on watch, and vice versa; and this has been correlated with coffee drinking and all that sort of thing. I would like to know if these diurnal rhythms may be changed experimentally to see if the effects that Dr. Halberg gets, particularly with the injection of endotoxin and the ingestion of alcohol and other agents, may change the basic cycles such as that of the diurnal temperature variations.

Dr. Halberg: First, one should realize that periodic changes in physiologic states predictably account for the surprising difference between life and death from the same trauma only if other sources of variation are standardized. These include the genetic background and history of the test-mice, physical environmental factors, and sampling conditions. Second, the temperature rhythm, although altered, is not readily abolished in men living on usual schedules in submarines or aboard ships. This was shown in more recent work by Dr. Kleitman, cited in my paper.

In reply to Captain Behnke's last question, the timing of temperature rhythm is clearly shifted in mice given endotoxin (Laboratory Invest. 5:283, 1956). This alteration—*not* abolition—of temperature rhythm can be the only recognizable effect of low doses of endotoxin, and it is the earliest recorded effect with lethal doses. Thus, on the one hand, mild or severe injury alters circadian rhythms; on the other hand, the effects of traumata depend on the phase of the circadian system at the time of exposure. These are related facets of periodic functional integration, as it affects resistance to injury. Involved in such integration is the adrenal gland, long known to be periodic, but only recently recognized as an intrinsically cyclic entity.

Fundamental work by Pincus and others suggests that rhythms in adrenal function are merely reactions to the activities of daily life. However, since periodic adrenal activation normally occurs during sleep, an adrenal cycle can be regarded as underlying our preparation for activity rather than solely as a reaction thereto. The adrenal cycle adjust metabolic sequences of periodic events and, thereby, is integrative. The same cycle is modulated, in turn, neurally and neurohumorally. Thereby, it is adaptive, adjusting the internal timing of organisms to outside influences. However, available evidence suggests that the manipulation of external factors can not impose any arbitrary period and phase upon all rhythms at all levels of physiologic organization—not even in the rather drastic case of so-called "regressive electric shock." Apparently, one can not live efficiently without temporal physiologic considerations for scheduling rest and activity, or for enhancing other adaptations.

Chairman Hoagland: Dr. Pincus, in the early 1940's, made a study of the diurnal rhythms of adrenocortical secretion in normal men. He studied groups of factory workers who changed their shifts from day to night. He was the first to show a diurnal rhythm of 17-ketosteroid excretion as a reflection of adrenocortical function. Later he and others have confirmed these findings using such measures as lymphocyte and eosinophil changes, electrolyte, and 17-hydroxycorticoid output. Low levels of adrenocortical activity occur at night with a rise of 50% in the output an hour or two after getting up in the morning.

As some of us had long suspected, getting up acts as a stress. During an average day the adrenocorticoid output declines progressively from the morning peak in most of us. Pincus found, however, that there was a tendency for these diurnal rhythms to become reversed in persons who went from day to night shifts of work. He was able to change his own rhythm by staying up nights and sleeping in the daytime. The change may be sluggish, requiring a few days, as I recall it. But this is only one of many rhythms, as Dr. Halberg points out, and there are many interesting rhythms. One does not know what significance this adrenocortical rhythm may have in relation to the efficiency of performance.

Dr. Adolph: I would like to comment on what Dr. Hoagland said concerning the biological nature of adaptations. There seems to be a tendency to lump a whole lot of phenomena under the term of adaptation, and I would like to put in a plea for trying to separate these phenomena rather than lumping them together. In connection with cellular types of innate adaptation, I would suggest that there may be many types, and you cannot jump to the conclusion that just because there are adaptations in the uses of enzymes that, therefore, these are the kinds of adaptations which are being exhibited by organisms as a whole.

Also I would like to distinguish between adaptations which represent selections among possible processes, and where we have to assume that maybe 90% of the cells are doing one thing and 10% another under one circumstance, while under other conditions this ratio of cells and their activities may be reversed. This is quite different from the kind of adaptation where probably every cell is ready to respond just like every other cell. It seems to me only when we have reduced the study of adaptations to this sort of basis will we be able to straighten out the confusion.

Epinephrine, Norepinephrine, and Aldosterone: Release and Excretion[*]

FRED ELMADJIAN

Worcester Foundation for Experimental Biology, Shrewsbury, Massachusetts, and Worcester State Hospital, Worcester, Massachusetts

Responses of the adrenal gland to physical and emotional stress have been the subject of much research (Selye, 1950). The more recent developments have been concerned with the measurement of the excretion of epinephrine and norepinephrine which are the hormones secreted by the sympathico-adrenal system, involving the adrenal medulla; and aldosterone which is secreted from the zona glomerulosa of the adrenal cortex. Both portions of the adrenals are under the control of the central nervous system and are implicated in stress reactions and emotional expression.

EPINEPHRINE AND NOREPINEPHRINE

Unlike the adrenal cortex, where emphasis is on the response to nonspecific stress, the adrenal medulla as a part of the sympathetic nervous system is intimately connected with specific emotional expression (Gellhorn, '1943). With infusion techniques the metabolism of epinephrine (E) and norepinephrine (NE) was studied using unlabeled and C_{14} labeled compounds. Stress studies included human subjects in (a) anticipatory states, (b) subjects performing on the Hoagland-Werthessen pursuitmeter under normal and hypoxic conditions, (c) athletes and coach during sports events, i.e., professional hockey players, amateur boxers, professional basketball players, and college baseball team, (d) psychiatric patients in disturbed states, and (e) psychiatric patients at staff interviews.

Diurnal variations of normal subjects were studied for purposes of establishing normal excretion rates.

[*] This work has been aided by grants from the U.S. Army Medical Research and Development Board, the U.S. Public Health Service, the Ford Foundation, and the National Association for Mental Health.

Method

Urine was extracted by the alumina absorption method of von Euler and Hellner (1951). The maximum efficiency of this method is 70–80% based on recovery data. The bioassay was performed by a modification of the method described by Gaddum and Lembeck (1949). This method consisted of testing the sample on the rat colon for NE, and rat uterus for E. The bioassay is based on the quantitative inhibition by the catechol amines of the contractions induced *in vitro* in a 2 cc bath with acetycholine. The inhibitions of NE and E are approximately equal when tested on the colon, but when tested on the uterus, E is 75 to 300 times more potent than NE. The colon assay was used when rapid estimates of total (NE + E) were desired.

Diurnal variation

In Table 1 (Study A) are data on the NE and E excretion during sleep and waking states on ten normal subjects (Elmadjian *et al.*, 1958). Night samples of urine were collected from approximately 10:00 P.M. to 6:30 A.M., and day samples were collected from 6:30 A.M. to noon. All subjects had breakfast and conducted their usual activities, consisting of laboratory routines. Table 1 (Study B) contains additional data on six normal subjects, consisting of physicians and laboratory personnel who were conducting their usual daily activities. Each collected a sample representing the period of sleeping, a second sample from the time of waking to about 10:00 A.M., and a third sample from 10:00 A.M. to the time of retiring at night. There was an increase in the excretion of E and NE during morning and day samples over that observed during sleep. The NE increases were not as large percentagewise, as for E values.

TABLE 1

Diurnal variation of norepinephrine (NE) and epinephrine (E) excretion in normal subjects.*

Sample period	NE (µg/hr)	E (µg/hr)
	Study A (10 subjects)	
Sleep:	1.2	0.02
	±0.12	±0.002
Morning:	2.9	0.40
	±0.48	±0.10
	Study B (6 subjects)	
Sleep:	1.2	0.02
	±0.14	±0.01
Morning:	2.3	0.10
	±0.49	±0.02
Day:	2.4	0.21
	±0.60	±0.07

* Elmadjian *et al.* (1958).

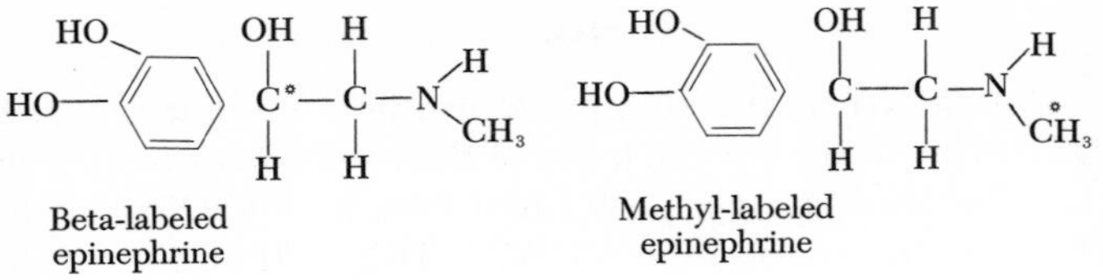

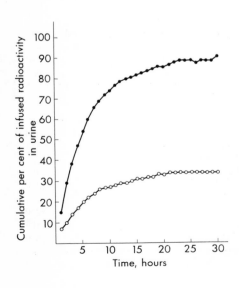

Beta-labeled
epinephrine

Methyl-labeled
epinephrine

FIGURE 1.

Structures of isotopic epinephrine used (Resnick and Elmadjian, 1958).

Infusion experiments

As indicated from our previous studies (Elmadjian *et al.*, 1957) only 0.5 to 2% of the E infused could be accounted for in the one-hour post-infusion urine, and 3.0 to 6% of the NE in a similar experiment. This posed the question regarding the fate of the unaccounted material. Dr. Oscar Resnick of our laboratories has undertaken the study of the metabolism of E, labeled at the beta position with C_{14}, as well as with E, labeled at the methyl position with C_{14} (Fig. 1). As indicated in Fig. 2, the excretion of radioactivity is rapidly increased in the urine for the first few hours after the onset of the infusion. In the seven subjects infused with the beta-C_{14}-*dl*-E-*d*-bitartrate, $91 \pm 3\%$ of the total radioactivity could be accounted for within 30 hours after the infusion. In the three subjects infused with methyl-C_{14}-*dl*-E, $34 \pm 3\%$ of the total radioactivity could be accounted for in the urine (Resnick and Elmadjian, 1958). The infusion of both types of isotopically labeled E resulted in the increase in the urinary excretion of nonmetabolized biologically active E. This increase was demonstrable

FIGURE 2.

The average cumulative hourly urinary excretion of total radioactivity. The top line (solid dots) represents the average values for seven infusions with β-labeled epinephrine. The bottom line (open circles) represents the average values for three infusions with methyl-labeled epinephrine. (Resnick and Elmadjian, 1958)

only during the first two hours after the onset of the infusion after which the urinary excretion of biologically active E returned to the control levels. The increase in biologically active E in these experiments ranged from approximately 1–2% of the infused E. It should be mentioned that the bioassays of the urine extracts measured biologically active E in the form of its laevo isomers. The radioactivity recovered in the urine, on the other hand, was due to the metabolites derived from dextro and laevo isomers of the isotopically labeled E and the nonmetabolized *dl*-E.

Chromatography studies of beta-labeled E indicated a major radioactive metabolite which was found to be a phenolic acid having the same Rf values as authentic 3-methoxy-4-hydroxy mandelic acid, generously supplied by M. D. Armstrong. Very little or no phenolic amines, such as methoxy-E, could be extracted from the urine of these subjects. When patients receiving iproniazid were infused with methyl labeled E, the counts excreted increased from 34% to 65% of the infused radioactivity. The urine of iproniazid-treated patients contained a major radioactive metabolite, which was found to be a phenolic amine having the same Rf values as those reported for methoxy-E by Axelrod (1957). These data clearly demonstrate O-methylation of E in man. Iproniazid treatment in man was observed to inhibit oxidative deamination of E, without influencing the process of O-methylation (Resnick *et al.*, 1958). Figure 3 shows pathways of E metabolism.

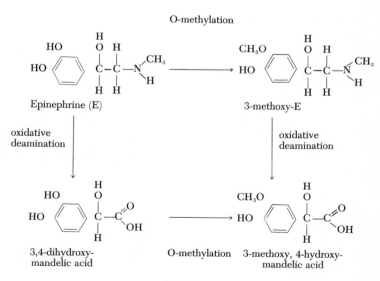

FIGURE 3.
Pathways of epinephrine metabolism.

TABLE 2
Pre-test norepinephrine (NE) and epinephrine (E) excretion of normal subjects.*

Normal subjects	Before insulin test		Before mecholyl test	
	NE (μg/hr)	E (μg/hr)	NE (μg/hr)	E (μg/hr)
Ba	3.4	0.35	1.7	0.13
El°°	3.2	0.16	4.9	0.17
El°°	4.1	0.17	—	—
Fo	0.9	0.02	—	—
Ma	1.2	0.10	2.8	0.18
Sp	1.5	0.05	1.0	0.20
Zi	1.9	0.15	3.2	0.51
Gi	3.7	0.22	7.7	0.17
Dm	—	—	8.9	0.07
Ms	4.2	0.52	3.2	0.80
Sm	9.0	1.82	3.5	0.96
Pa	—	—	3.2	0.07

° Elmadjian *et al.* (1956).
°° Same subject tested on different days.

Normal subjects in anticipatory states

Urine collections were made on eleven normal subjects before they underwent the usual insulin tolerance test and the Mecholyl test described by Funkenstein (Funkenstein *et al.*, 1950). The subjects consisted of laboratory personnel and students. There was a varying degree of knowledge and understanding as to the nature of these tests among the group. Note in Table 2 the variability of the excretion rates obtained (Elmadjian *et al.*, 1956). Those subjects who were familiar with the nature of the tests and the hospital setting were quiet and waited patiently. These subjects showed normal excretion rates of E and NE. On the other hand, the students and personnel unfamiliar with the tests and the setting were restless, asked many questions of the attending nurse and physician, and were quite anxious about the experiments. Subjects Gi and Da show very high NE excretions with normal E values, while Ms and Sm show high values for both amines in each instance.

Pursuitmeter operation

a. **Three-hour studies.** Table 3 shows the data on the four normal subjects who operated the Hoagland-Werthessen pursuitmeter (Pincus and Hoagland, 1943) (which simulates the operation of the controls of a plane) for three hours (Elmadjian, Lamson, and Neri, 1956). They had rest periods of 5 minutes at the end of the first and second hours. The pre-stress control sample represents urine collected approximately between 8:00 A.M. to 1:00 P.M.; the stress represents urine collected during the operation of the pursuitmeter, i.e., from 1:00 to 4:00 P.M.

Subject N.G. showed a marked response to stress in E excretion in each of the three experiments. On the other hand, S.K. showed little, if any, increase in E excretion, but fair increases in NE. T.H. and F.U. showed, in general, small increases in both NE and E excretion. Though precautions were taken to control the factor of motivation by awarding prize money for the best performer, it is possible that the results were influenced by the relative effort made by each subject in the psychomotor performance. It is of interest that subject N.G. was determined to be the best performer, and actually succeeded in being the highest scorer, whereas S.K. was indifferent and was the lowest scorer. The number of experiments was too small to serve as a basis for generalization; suffice it to state that consistent increases in E or NE were demonstrated in the four subjects tested with this procedure for inducing psychomotor stress.

TABLE 3

Epinephrine (E) and norepinephrine (NE) excretion in psychomotor stress without hypoxia (Hoagland-Werthessen pursuitmeter).

Subject	Date	E		NE
		(μg/hr)		(μg/hr)
N.G.	Jan. 26, '54	(C)°	0.17	4.2
		(S)°	1.13	7.6
	Feb. 2, '54	(C)	0.35	4.2
		(S)	0.93	6.6
	Feb. 9, '54	(C)	0.48	4.4
		(S)	2.00	3.8
S.K.	Jan. 27, '54	(C)	0.06	2.7
		(S)	0.07	5.9
	Feb. 3, '54	(C)	0.08	1.7
		(S)	0.10	2.7
	Feb. 8, '54	(C)	0.15	1.8
		(S)	0.14	3.4
F.U.	Feb. 15, '54	(C)	0.18	4.0
		(S)	0.23	—
	Feb. 23, '54	(C)	0.24	1.5
		(S)	0.24	1.7
	Mar. 2, '54	(C)	0.48	2.0
		(S)	0.68	2.5
T.H.	Feb. 26, '54	(C)	0.15	2.0
		(S)	0.37	2.6
	Mar. 5, '54	(C)	0.14	0.9
		(S)	0.16	1.5
	Mar. 12, '54	(C)	0.09	2.8
		(S)	—	—

° (C) = Control; (S) = Stress.

TABLE 4

Epinephrine (E) and norepinephrine (NE) excretion in pursuitmeter stress with hypoxia.

Subject	Age	Date	E (µg/hr)		NE (µg/hr)
P.P.	17	July 19, '54	(C)°	0.10	1.4
			(S)°	0.42	1.6
		Aug. 3, '54	(C)	0.03	3.2
			(S)	0.26	5.2
		Aug. 31, '54	(C)	0.04	2.0
			(S)	0.35	3.4
R.P.	17	July 15, '54	(C)	0.14	1.5
			(S)	0.16	1.5
		Aug. 6, '54	(C)	0.09	3.0
			(S)	0.05	1.6
		Aug. 27, '54	(C)	0.16	2.2
			(S)	0.17	1.5

° (C) = Control; (S) = Stress.

b. Two-hour studies. Six young men (aged 17 to 19) were each subjected to 3 or 4 psychomotor stress tests under hypoxic conditions (10% oxygen) for 2 hours (Elmadjian, Lamson, and Neri, 1956). The control urines were collected in the forenoon as in the 3-hour group. The experiments were conducted from 1:00 to 3:00 P.M. and the subjects did not have any rest during the stress period.

Under these conditions, considered as a group, there was a significant increase in the output of E during the stress period, compared with the control output, in 17 runs in which both stress and control output were determined. The mean values of the control NE excretions in 18 experiments was 2.3 µg per hour as compared with 2.7 µg per hour for the stress samples. The mean value of the control E excretions in 17 experiments was 0.08 µg per hour as compared with 0.18 µg per hour for the stress samples. The increase in the excretion of E during the stress was significant at 1% level. However, it was evident that there were individual differences. Subject P.P. showed a marked increase in E in each of his 3 runs, whereas subject R.P., his identical twin, showed no increase during the same procedure (Table 4). The individual difference could not be explained on the basis of the scores attained by the subject in this stress procedure.

Professional hockey players

This sport entails considerable aggressive activity in attack and defense. The game is fast and involves marked activity and man-to-man contact. Pre-game samples of urine were collected 10 to 30 minutes before the game and post-game samples were collected some three hours later. The latter samples included urine formed during the contest. Game time was 8:30 P.M. Table 5 lists the values for pre-game and post-game collections of defensemen and forwards who do the skating. The data are presented in terms of creatinine, because it was not always possible to obtain timed samples (Elmadjian *et al.*, 1957). For samples taken following the game, there was a sixfold increase in NE excretion. Two players were sampled before the game, but on physical examination by the trainer, they were not permitted to participate. In the same table are presented data on these players, indicating no post-game increase in NE, but appreciable increase in E. Both players sat on the bench and watched the game. Both were quite concerned about their injury.

In Table 5 are also the data on Player 16 who showed a ninefold increase in NE and a 20-fold increase in E. He skated his regular turn, but did not play an outstanding game. At the end of the second period, he got involved in a lively fist fight with an opposing player, and was ejected from the game.

The goal tender skates very little, but is in constant vigilance in front of the net, ready to defend the goal. The coach remains on the bench directing strategy. Data obtained on the goal tender in three games, and on the coach in six games are presented in Table 6. There was a marked increase in both E and NE excretion in the goal tender, but on the average there were no significant changes in the excretion of either amine in the coach. There were, however, individual games where the coach showed marked increases in E.

Amateur boxing

Six amateur boxers competing in the finals of the Amateur Athletic Union Boxing championship were studied (Elmadjian *et al.*, 1957). Added significance

TABLE 5

Excretion of norepinephrine (NE) and epinephrine (E) in members of a professional hockey team—defensemen and forwards versus nonparticipating players.[*]

Urine collection	Number of players sampled	NE (μg/100 mg creat.)	E (μg/100 mg creat.)
		Active hockey players (defensemen and forwards)[**]	
Pre-game	20	2.7 $\pm$ 0.43	0.36 $\pm$ 0.07
Post-game	20	15.3 $\pm$ 2.20	0.95 $\pm$ 0.21
		t = 5.66	t = 2.68
		p = <0.001	p = <0.05, >0.01
		Two players who did not participate in game[†]	
Pre-game	1 (No. 18)	2.2	0.23
Post-game		3.3	0.75
Pre-game	1 (No. 10)	5.6	0.78
Post-game		5.3	1.42
		Player involved in fist fight	
Pre-game	1 (No. 16)	3.5	0.18
Post-game		29.3	3.30

[*] Elmadjian *et al.*, (1957).

[**] The approximate hourly excretion is 10% less than the figure given in terms of 100 g creatinine when corrected by creatinine coefficient.

[†] Due to their physical condition.

TABLE 6

Excretion of norepinephrine (NE) and epinephrine (E) in goal tender and coach. [*]

Subject	No. of games	Urine collection	NE (μg/100 mg creat.)	E (μg/100 mg creat.)
Goal tender	3	Pre-game	3.3 ± 0.7	0.45 ± 0.20
		Post-game	9.2 ± 1.8	1.30 ± 0.81
Coach	6	Pre-game	1.8 ± 0.5	0.38 ± 0.09
		Post-game	3.7 ± 0.9	0.43 ± 0.21

[*] Elmadjian et al. (1957).

was placed on these finals because the fighters who were ultimately to win would also qualify for the final Olympic tryouts. Enthusiasm and a high state of expectancy characterized the attitudes of the fighters. This was reflected in the elevated E excretion rates observed in most of the pre-fight samples. Table 7 shows the data obtained on all fighters and the outcome of the fight.

The high NE pre-fight values were noted in fighters who engaged in shadow boxing before the contest. The highest pre-fight E excretions were found in the fighters who showed the greater degree of anticipation preceding the fight. Finally, increase in the post-fight samples over the pre-fight samples of E were observed in those fighters who had to fight for a decision in a close contest.

Basketball players

Basketball as a sport is characterized by skills related to timing and coordination of muscles, especially of the shoulders and arms. Unlike hockey, where ag-

TABLE 7

Excretion of norepinephrine (NE) and epinephrine (E) in amateur boxers. [*]

Boxer	Urine collection	NE[**] (μg)	E[**] (μg)	Outcome
Ch	Pre-fight	17.9	1.64	Winner by decision
	Post-fight	——	——	in the third round
Sm	Pre-fight	38.1	1.78	Winner by TKO in
	Post-fight	32.4	0.67	the third round
Pe	Pre-fight	6.7	0.22	Winner by decision
	Post-fight	2.8	0.41	in the third round
Br	Pre-fight	4.2	0.40	Winner by decision
	Post-fight	7.0	0.87	in the third round
Wh	Pre-fight	1.7	1.67	Winner by TKO in
	Post-fight	——	——	the second round
Bra	Pre-fight	——	——	Loser by decision
	Post-fight	15.9	1.70	in the third round

[*] Elmadjian et al. (1957).
[**] Micrograms per 100 mg creatinine.

gression is essential, in basketball aggressiveness may very well lose the game. Continuous vigilance with considerable self-control is a basic requirement. Five players of the Boston Celtics were sampled during the first play-off series with Philadelphia this year. Samples were obtained before and after the contest; the data are expressed in terms of gamma, of E, and NE/100 mgm creatinine in view of the difficulty in obtaining timed samples. In Table 8 are the data on the five players. Players 6, 17, and 19 showed marked increases in E during the contest. In none of the samples was there marked elevations in NE. Player 14 showed a very high level of E before the game, with a very marked elevation in NE as well. During the course of the game, his E titer dropped, but his NE excretion rate was further elevated. Player 14 is considered in basketball circles as being one of the most outstanding basketball players of our times and during this game he was observed to be very tense and preoccupied. His performance during this game was not up to the level expected from him. Player 15 showed a drop in both E and NE excretions. Though he did not play his usual game, this drop is unexplained.

The interesting feature about these data are the marked elevations in E excretions, with relatively normal NE excretions.

Baseball team

In general, baseball as a sport is characterized by periods of physical inactivity, interspersed with short periods of maximum effort and vigilance. Boston University baseball team was sampled May 17, 1958, during a crucial game with Holy Cross College. The game was won by Holy Cross 3–2, but Boston University had an opportunity to win the game several times in the late innings. Urine was collected during a 2½- to 3-hour period, consisting of a brief period before the game, where the team had batting and fielding practice, and during the actual period of the contest. Each sample consisted of the urine formed

TABLE 8
Celtics Basketball Team.

Player no.		E/100 mg creat.	NE/100 mg creat.
6	Pre	0.05	2.9
	Post	0.40	3.4
14	Pre	1.65	7.70
	Post	0.24	9.60
15	Pre	0.14	2.9
	Post	0.07	0.9
17	Pre	0.20	1.6
	Post	0.54	1.2
19	Pre	0.04	1.3
	Post	0.11	2.4

TABLE 9
Boston University Baseball Team
Played Holy Cross May 17, 1958.

Player	Position	E µg/100 mg creat.	NE µg/100 mg creat.
Can	ss	0.21	2.5
Leo	2b	0.12	3.7
Asa	3b	0.15	—
Mac	cf	0.21	4.8
Gaf	rf	1.11	1.4
Kop	1b	0.91	6.8
Gir	lf	0.10	4.7
Gur	c	0.33	2.4
Ped	p	0.45	5.0
Cle	Coach	0.80	13.3
Players not participating			
Dam	p	0.05	0.7
Pes	p	0.20	2.6
Kil	1b	0.37	1.3

during this 2½- to 3-hour period. In Table 9 are shown the E and NE of 9 players who participated in the game, the coach, and three players who sat on the bench. It may be noted that there is great variability in the data. Of particular interest are the elevations of E excretions of the right fielder, first baseman, catcher, and the pitcher, as well as the coach. The NE excretions of the center fielder, first baseman, pitcher, and the coach are quite elevated. The coach in this case was quite active throughout the game, giving orders and planning strategy, and the data showed marked elevations in E and NE. He was quite disappointed with the outcome of the game, which was shared especially by the pitcher who performed very well, though he was the losing pitcher.

These results were consistent with the general activity of the players during the game, except for the unexplained elevation of E for the right fielder.

Psychotic subjects in closed wards

In ten psychiatric patients a study was made of the relationship between results of Malamud-Sands rating scale and the excretions of E and NE (Elmadjian et al., 1957). In Fig. 4 is shown the relationship of the emotional state of the patient derived from the score of motor activity and hostility reactions to NE excretion; those with passive, self-effacing emotional display had normal levels of NE. In Fig. 4 when a line appears through the circles, it indicates that these subjects also had a high excretion of E. The subject indicated by an asterisk had normal NE excretion, but the excretion of E was 2.75 µg/hour, which is extremely high. This subject showed periodic bursts of excitement with expressions of fear and guilt.

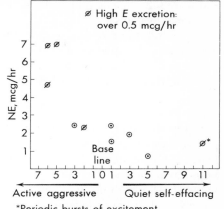

FIGURE 4.

The relation of norepinephrine excretion to emotional state of neuropsychiatric patients. The abscissa depicts the composite score for the functions of motor activity and hostility reactions from the Malamud-Sands rating scale, and the ordinate represents the excretion of norepinephrine in micrograms per hour during the observation period. (Elmadjian *et al.*, 1957)

Neuropsychiatric patients during staff interviews

The conditions of the interview were in marked contrast to those encountered by the athletes or patients in the psychiatirc wards. The patient sits across from the psychiatrist doing the interviewing in the presence of some 20 members of the hospital medical staff. All participants are seated and the exchange in this case is strictly verbal. The setting is serious and to the patient it is very important, because on the basis of his performance, decisions are made by the staff which affect his immediate future. Eleven subjects were studied, on eight of whom control samples were obtained (Elmadjian *et al.*, 1957). The interview took place on Thursday morning and the control sample was obtained at the same time on the next day—Friday. The results are listed in Table 10. There were no changes in NE excretion when the interview day was compared with the control. However, in every subject on whom a control was obtained, there was an elevated excretion of E during the interview. As might be expected, there were marked individual variations in this increase. The subjects in gen-

TABLE 10
Staff conference interview of neuropsychiatric patients.[°]

	No. of subjects	NE (μg/hr)	E (μg/hr)
Interview	11	2.6	0.50
		±0.4	±0.14
Control	8	2.3	0.27
		±0.2	±0.12
		NS	P = <0.001

[°] Elmadjian *et al.* (1957).

eral were self-effacing and on their best behavior, with no aggressive or active emotional displays.

In general, these results support the hypothesis that active, aggressive, hostile, emotional display is related to elevated NE excretion, with or without increase in E excretion, while in the passive, fearful, and self-effacing emotional reaction, there is elevation of E with normal rates of NE excretion.

ALDOSTERONE

In the course of a preliminary study on aldosterone excretion in psychiatric patients, we observed that aldosterone excretion was elevated in certain anxiety states (Lamson et al., 1956). Chronic schizophrenics who were passive and withdrawn showed low values, while markedly disturbed patients showed elevated aldosterone output. A number of nonpsychotic subjects in anxiety states were found to have elevated aldosterone excretion (Table 11). These results are consistent with the findings of Venning and her associates, who observed elevated aldosterone excretion in medical students during examinations, with or without concurrent increases in 17-hydroxy-corticoids (Venning et al., 1957).

We continued the study of nonpsychotic subjects in anxiety states where aldosterone, 17-ketosteroids (17-KS), and 17-hydroxycorticosteroids (17-OHCS) were determined in addition to E and NE.

Method

The 24-hour urine samples were continuously extracted for 24 hours with methylene dichloride at pH 1.0, followed either by a second 24-hour continuous extraction, or a hand extraction with a fresh portion of the organic solvent. Silica column chromatography described by Neher and Wettstein was performed (Neher and Wettstein, 1955), followed by ethylene glycol-toluene paper chromatography of Nowasczynski (1957). All final extracts were bioassayed for sodium retention on adrenalectomized rats (Cook and Elmadjian, 1953).

17-OHCS were determined after beta-glucuronidase hydrolysis after the method of Silber and Porter (Silber and Porter, 1954) and 17-KS were determined by the method described by Pincus (Pincus, 1945).

TABLE 11
Excretion of aldosterone in 24-hour samples.

	N	Aldosterone μg
Normals	8	2.4 (2.0–3.3)
Schizophrenics (chronic)	18	1.1 (0.0–5.4)
Schizophrenics (acute)	4	5.4 (2.9–7.9)
Nonpsychotic (anxiety states)	10	10.3 (8.0–12.2)

TABLE 12
Nonpsychotic subjects in anxiety states.[*]

Subject	Description	Aldosterone μg	17-OHCS mg	17-KS mg	NE μg	E μg
For	Doctorate examination	10.0	1.82	10.8	64.8	9.1
Thomp	Compensated malignant hypertension–anxiety state	10.0	8.64	2.88	31.2	2.9
O'G	Chronic–anxiety neurosis	12.2	12.96	6.48	48.0	—
Cock	Anxiety neurosis	9.3	15.6	16.10	21.6	1.9
Torn	Essential hypertension anxiety state	8.0	9.84	—	13.8	1.7
Lor	Chronic–anxiety neurosis	12.5	1.20	—	14.4	1.7
Ger	Anxiety neurosis	10.0	3.10	12.6	—	—
Cre	Suspected pheochromocytoma	8.0	9.36	—	40.8	3.6
Can	Suspected pheochromocytoma	10.0	.96	—	40.0	2.4

[*] Elmadjian, F., E. T. Lamson, and J. M. Hope. 1961. "Aldosterone Excretion in Anxiety States," Symposium on Performance Capacity, Dept. of Army, Research and Development Command, Quartermaster Food and Container Institute for the Armed Forces, pp. 217–225 (24-hour urine samples).

Results

In Table 12 are presented data on 17-KS, 17-OHCS, E, and NE, in addition to aldosterone excretion in 24-hour urine samples on the group of subjects in anxiety states (Elmadjian, in press). Note that, though all subjects showed elevated aldosterone excretion, the other indices of the adrenal gland seem to vary independently. The description of each subject is given in Table 12.

In Table 13 are the data obtained from six additional subjects with psychoneurosis from the Pratt Diagnostic Clinic of the New England Medical Center. We note that three of these subjects with anxiety neurosis had elevated aldosterone excretion, two had normal values, and one showed no measurable amounts of aldosterone.

There are two features of these data which seem of interest: (1) subjects with clinical symptoms, indicating subjective experiences of anxiety and objective signs of vasomotor activity showed normal excretion of E and NE, but with high values in aldosterone excretion; (2) the appearance of several subjects showing low 17-OHCS, normal 17-KS, but high aldosterone excretion. The results at first glance seem at variance with our previous findings, indicating variation in E and NE excretion in emotional states (Elmadjian et al., 1957). The subjects reported in this study showed emotional displays or had a vasomotor sign, indicating sympathico-adrenal activity, yet the catechol amine excretion was not elevated. Two possible explanations may be offered: (a) there may be in these cases increased rates of metabolism of the catechol amines secreted to biologically inactive derivatives appearing in the urine; or (b) the tissue response to normal amounts of catechol amine secreted is exaggerated so that

TABLE 13
Psychoneurotic subjects.[°]

Subject	Description	Aldosterone μg
Hel	Anxiety neurosis and depression	8.0
Pem	Anxiety neurosis	>10.0
Sw	Anxiety neurosis	>10.0
Res	Hysteria	0
Ci	Anxiety neurosis	2.4
Cha	Anxiety neurosis and depression	4.0

[°] 24-hour urine samples.

normal amounts of E and NE secretion result in greater than normal physiological response. A review of the data with respect to the latter possibility has been presented by Raab *et al.* (1956). The problem of the metabolism of E and NE is at present being pursued in our laboratories (Resnick and Elmadjian, 1958; Resnick *et al.*, 1958).

The findings related to the steroids excreted in these cases are in need of some explanation. We found several subjects who excreted very low amounts of 17-OHCS, normal amounts of 17-KS, but high rates of aldosterone. It is of interest that Albeaux-Fernet and his associates (1957), reported that, in chronic asthenia, they obtained low 17-OHCS excretion, with low 17-KS. They further observed that these subjects did not show increased 17-KS and 17-OHCS after ACTH injection. Data were presented indicating *increases in 17-desoxy-C21-steroids*. The inference was drawn that corticosterone was the major adrenal cortical steroid secreted in chronic asthenia. I wish to point out the similarity of these results and the inferences drawn to those of the Korean study which we reported on some years ago (Elmadjian, 1955).

The following hpyothesis relating to adrenal steroid biogenesis and metabolism is presented to possibly relate the various findings in adrenal steroid excretion to stress, and especially to explain, in part, the elevation of aldosterone in certain anxiety states. The adrenal cortex in the first stage of stress secreted 17-OHCS which are measurable by the Porter-Silber reaction (Silber and Porter, 1954) and some 17-KS which may be estimated by the Zimmerman reaction (Pincus, 1945). As the stress condition continues, either the adrenal cortex ceases to show an increment of 17-OHCS with an increase in 17-KS, or the 17-OHCS secreted are more rapidly metabolized to 17-KS (Elmadjian, 1955). As the stress is further sustained, both the excretion of 17-OHCS and 17-KS are low due primarily to inhibition of 17-hydroxylating mechanism in corticosteroid biogenesis (Albeaux-Fernet *et al.*, 1957). This inhibition of 17-hydroxylation would favor the biogenesis of corticosteroids of the 17-desoxy-C21 type.

The two principal candidates in this regard would be corticosterone (compound B) and aldosterone. At this stage, ACTH injection would not show an increase in 17-KS or 17-OHCS, but an increase in steroids of the 17-desoxy C21 compounds which would include corticosterone and/or aldosterone (Albeaux-Fernet *et al.*, 1957; Elmadjian, 1955).

The significant contributions of Bartter (1956) on the factors influencing the secretion of aldosterone, such as electrolyte and water balance, and the findings of Rauschkolb and Farrell (1956) showing possible diencephalic regulation of aldosterone secretion certainly make this area of study of great interest in the understanding of the physiology of stress as it relates to adrenal cortical function.

SUMMARY

The excretion of E and NE was determined in a series of stress studies on normal and psychiatric patients in experimental and life situations. The results support the hypothesis that active, aggressive, emotional displays are related to increased excretion of NE, whereas tense, anxious, but passive emotional displays are related to increased excretion of E.

The metabolism of C14-E indicates that oxidative deamination and O-methylation are the pathways of E metabolism.

Aldosterone was shown to be elevated in certain anxiety states without demonstrable increases in E and NE excretion.

The author wishes to thank Drs. Justin Hope, Harry Freeman, Oscar Resnick, and Mr. Edwin Lamson, who participated in the various studies reported in this paper.

REFERENCES

Albeaux-Fernet, M., P. Brugard, and J. D. Romani. 1957. J. Clin. Endocrinol. & Metab. *16:* 519.

Axelrod, J. 1957. Science *126:* 400.

Bartter, F. C. 1956. Metabolism *5:* 369.

Cook, M., and F. Elmadjian. 1953. J. Am. Pharm. Assoc. *42:* 329.

Elmadjian, F. 1955. Ciba Foundation Col. Endocrin., The Human Cortex, *VIII* 627.

Elmadjian, F., J. M. Hope, and E. T. Lamson. 1957. J. Clin. Endocrinol. & Metab. *17:* 608.

Elmadjian, F., J. M. Hope, and E. T. Lamson. 1958. Recent Progr. in Hormone Research *XIV* 513.

Elmadjian, F., E. T. Lamson, and J. M. Hope. 1961. "Aldosterone Excretion in Anxiety States," Symposium on Performance Capacity, Dept. of the Army, Research and Development Command, Quartermaster Food and Container Institute for the Armed Forces, pp. 217–252.

Elmadjian, F., E. T. Lamson, and R. Neri. 1956. J. Clin. Endocrinol. & Metab. *16:* 222.

Elmadjian, F., E. T. Lamson, H. Freeman, R. Neri, and L. Varjarbedian. 1956. J. Clin. Endocrinol. & Metab. *16:* 876.

Funkenstein, D. H., M. Greenblatt, and H. C. Solomon. 1950. Am. J. Psychiat. *106:* 889.

Gaddum, J. H., and F. Lembeck. 1949. Brit. J. Pharmacol. *4:* 401.

Gellhorn, E. 1943. *Autonomic Regulations,* Interscience, New York.

Lamson, E. T., F. Elmadjian, J. M. Hope, G. Pincus, and D. Jorjorian. 1956. J. Clin. Endocrinol. & Metab. *16:* 954.

Neher, R., and A. Wettstein. 1955. Acta. Endocrinol. *18:* 386.

Nowaczynski, W. J. 1957. J. Lab. & Clin. Med. *49:* 815.

Pincus, G. 1945. J. Clin. Endocrinol. *5:* 291.

Pincus, G. and H. Hoagland. 1943. J. Aviation Med. *14:* 173.

Raab, W., G. Schroeder, R. Wagner, and W. Gigee. 1956. J. Clin. Endocrinol. & Metab. *16:* 1196.

Rauschkolb, E. W. and G. L. Farrell. 1956. Endocrinology *59:* 526.

Resnick, O. and F. Elmadjian. 1958. J. Clin. Endocrinol. & Metab. *18:* 28.

Resnick, O., J. Wolfe, H. Freeman, and F. Elmadjian. 1958. Science *127:* 1116.

Selye, H. 1950. *Stress,* Acta Inc., Montreal.

Silber, R. H., and C. C. Porter. 1954. J. Biol. Chem. *210:* 923.

Venning, E. H., I. Dyrenfurth, and J. C. Beck. 1957. J. Clin. Endocrinol. & Metab. *17:* 1005.

von Euler, U. S., and S. Hellner. 1951. Acta Physiol. Scand. *22:* 161.

Carbon Dioxide and Certain Aspects of Adrenal Function

C. T. G. KING

Medical Research Laboratories, U. S. Naval Submarine Base, New London, Connecticut

Since the end of World War II, studies of the effects of increased amounts of carbon dioxide in inspired air have been intensified, especially by those interested in physiological processes in confined spaces where there is bound to be an increase of this gas unless adequate facilities for removal are available. Meduna (1950) and Kindwall (1949) have successfully used high concentrations of carbon dioxide in the treatment of psychoneurosis. These studies led to a discussion of the possible underlying mechanisms by Meduna (1950) and Gellhorn (1953). King *et al.* (1955) reported that, under prolonged exposure to 1.5% CO_2 for forty-two days, the blood sugar level of the normal, hypophysectomized rat and guinea pig did not vary, while the liver and muscle glycogen stores were significantly lowered; at the same time a lowering of the ascorbic acid and cholesterol content of the adrenal gland was observed. Schaefer, *et al.* (1949) exposed guinea pigs to carbon dioxide concentrations of 3% for periods of up to 17 days, and concluded that during these continuous exposures the reaction chain which includes adrenal medulla, pituitary gland, and adrenal cortex is first stimulated and later impaired or exhausted because of a decrease in adrenalin release by the adrenal medulla.

A general picture of the effects of carbon dioxide concentrations ranging from 10 to 30% in 21% oxygen has been given by Seevers (1944). He found that animals are depressed with concentrations of up to 30%, but are not narcotized until concentrations of 30% are inhaled.

Adrenal cortical stimulation in unanesthetized animals exposed to high concentrations of carbon dioxide has been determined by Fortier (1949) who found adrenal hyperplasia in rats after three days of exposure to 15% carbon dioxide in 19% oxygen, by Langley and Kilgore (1955) who reported adrenal cholesterol and ascorbic acid depletion in rats exposed for 4 hours to concentrations of 10 to 30% carbon dioxide. An increase in 17 hydrocorticosteroids in the adrenal venous vein of sodium pentobarbital anesthetized dogs exposed to concentrations of 10, 20, and 30% carbon dioxide in air has been demonstrated by Richards and Stein (1956). Schaefer *et al.* (1955) also confirmed adrenal cortical stimulation under conditions of carbon dioxide respiratory acidosis. However, a special or specific type of stimulation directly on the adrenal gland, and its relation to carbohydrate metabolism has been suggested by these authors. Furthermore, they reported a difference in response to 30% carbon dioxide in air and 30% carbon dioxide in oxygen. Under 30% carbon dioxide in air the added factor of anoxia was present. The large number of deaths, after one hour, which occurred with anoxia was not present under conditions of 30% carbon dioxide in oxygen in the rat. They also reported that the guinea pig was more susceptible than the rat to the lethal effects of 30% carbon dioxide in oxygen.

The present study is based on the findings of Schaefer *et al.* (1955), previously mentioned, and is an effort to elucidate further the role of the adrenal gland in regulating carbohydrate metabolism under these conditions of respiratory acidosis. For this purpose, blood sugar content, liver and muscle glycogen stores, and adrenal ascorbic acid and cholesterol studies were carried out.

MATERIAL AND METHODS

Schaefer *et al.* (1955) reported that the mortality of guinea pigs was 50% under 30% carbon dioxide in oxygen and that the rat was apparently more resistant to carbon dioxide. On the basis of this information it was decided to use this species to investigate further the effects of 30% carbon dioxide on normal, hypophysectomized, and adrenalectomized animals.

Mature male albino rats of the Wister-Hisaw strain weighing between 200 and 350 g were used. Adrenalectomy was performed under ether anesthesia by the dorsolumbar approach. Adrenalectomized rats were fed 1.9% NaCl, 0.045% $NaHCO_3$ in their drinking water and were allowed one week to recover before exposure to carbon dioxide. The hypophysectomized rats were obtained from the Hormone Assay Laboratories in Chicago, Illinois, and were fed a 5% glucose solution and one ounce of evaporated milk daily. All of the rats were allowed to eat Purina laboratory pellets ad libitum.

All of the animals were exposed to carbon dioxide in a plastic chamber that had a continuous circulation of 4 liters/minute of pre-mixed 30% carbon dioxide in oxygen.

Determinations were carried out at 1, 2, 3, 4 hours of exposure and in certain instances at 10 and 30 minutes. For each point, a minimum of 15 rats were used.

The animals were killed by a blow on the neck region and immediate exsanguination by cardiac puncture. The blood sugar content was determined by Nelson's technique (1944). At the time of autopsy a piece of liver and one of

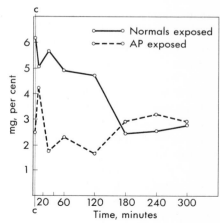

FIGURE 1.

Ascorbic acid of the adrenal cortex of the rat (30% CO_2 in O_2).

muscle were placed in 30% KOH for glycogen determination by the procedure of Good, Kramer, and Somogyi (1933). The adrenal ascorbic acid determinations were made according to the Roe and Kuether (1943) method and the cholesterol content of the adrenal cortex was evaluated by the Kingsley and Schaffert (1949) technique.

RESULTS

Ascorbic acid of the adrenal cortex (Fig. 1)

In the normal rat there is a severe drop in adrenal cortical ascorbic acid from 500 mg % to 380 and 280 mg % at 10 to 30 minutes of exposure, and at one hour values of 320 mg % are reached. From then until the fifth hour of exposure, the values remain significantly lower than the control. The hypophysectomized rat at first accumulates this metabolite to a small extent (from 270 to 300 mg % at 30 minutes) and then the content drops to 200 mg % at one and

FIGURE 2.

Adrenal cholesterol response of the rat (30% CO_2 in O_2).

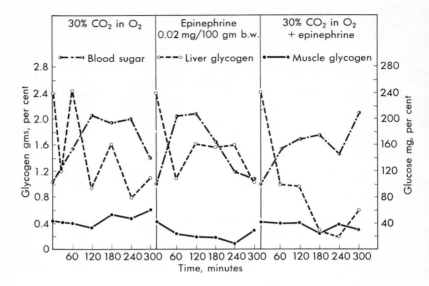

two hours of exposure with a further drop to 170 mg % at three hours, and remains below normal value throughout the exposure time.

The adrenal cholesterol response is depicted in Fig. 2. The response of the normal animal is parallel to the ascorbic acid response. At first, a lowering of cholesterol is demonstrated (from 6.2 to 5.0 mg. %), a transient increase to 5.6 mg % at thirty minutes, followed by a progressive decline from 4.9 mg % at one hour to a low of 2.5 mg % at three hours of exposure. At all times the cholesterol content of the adrenal gland is significantly lower under respiratory acidosis than the control value on air. The hypophysectomized rats increase the cholesterol content of their adrenal gland from 2.5 to 4.2 mg % at 10 minutes of exposure followed by a loss at 30 minutes to 1.8 mg %. The cholesterol remains below normal for the first two hours of exposure and on the third, fourth, and fifth hour it is slightly above normal. These results parallel fairly closely the ascorbic acid data.

Blood sugar response (Figs. 3, 4, and 5)

In the normal rat the blood sugar rose from 111 mg % control value to over 200 mg % at two hours. The concentration of glucose in the blood remained at this high level until after the fourth hour and then declined to 140 mg % (still above normal) during the fifth hour of the experiment. The hyperglycemia elicited in the hypophysectomized rat is not as severe, but the increase in the blood sugar is of about the same order of magnitude, from 80 mg % at the control level to 150 mg % at two hours of exposure. Again, as in the normal rat, the blood sugar tends to return to normal after the fourth hour, and by the fifth hour a value of 111 mg % was obtained (still 30 mg % above normal). The

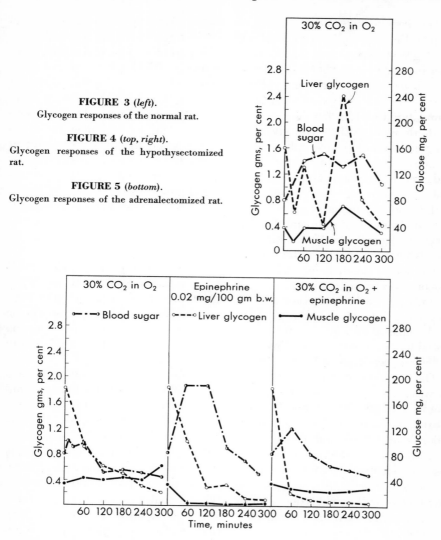

FIGURE 3 (*left*).
Glycogen responses of the normal rat.

FIGURE 4 (*top, right*).
Glycogen responses of the hypothysectomized rat.

FIGURE 5 (*bottom*).
Glycogen responses of the adrenalectomized rat.

hyperglycemia elicited in the adrenalectomized rat (Fig. 5) is slight, from 80 to 100 mg %, and transient in nature. It is followed by a continuous and severe hypoglycemia and by the fifth hour the blood sugar values were down to 40 mg %.

Liver and muscle glycogen response (Figs. 3, 4, and 5)

The normal, the hypothysectomized, and the adrenalectomized rat demonstrate a slight and continuous increase in muscle glycogen stores; however, this increase is not statistically significant.

The liver glycogen response is a completely different story. In the normal animal (Fig. 3) we observe a drop in glycogen stores from 2.4 g % while on air to 1.8 g % at thirty minutes of carbon dioxide, a return to normal at sixty minutes, followed by another and more severe drop to 0.914 g % at two hours. At three hours of exposure, the glycogen values are higher, 1.63 g %, and at four hours, we again observe a severe drop to 0.70 g % followed by a slight reaccumulation to 1.13 g % at five hours. We have tentatively named this response a "rhythmic or cyclic" liver glycogen response. The liver glycogen picture is not greatly altered by hypophysectomy (Fig. 4). Again, there is a severe drop at 30 minutes of exposure, from 1.6 g % in air to 0.6 g % under carbon dioxide, and a reaccumulation at one hour, 1.3 g %. The pattern continues, as in the normal, with even a greater accumulation at 180 minutes.

If the normal animal is adrenalectomized (Fig. 5) a different type of response is seen. As in the normal and the hypophysectomized rat, a depletion is observed at 10 and 30 minutes, but reaccumulation does not take place, and by the fifth hour of exposure the liver glycogen value was down to 0.25 g %.

The blood sugar, liver, and muscle glycogen response to a single subcutaneous injection of epinephrine hydrochloride at a dose level of 0.02 mg/100 g of body weight in the normal and adrenalectomized rat are depicted in Figs. 3a and 5a. Epinephrine alone gave the typical hyperglycemic response (Fig. 3a in the normal and Fig. 5a in the adrenalectomized rat). The hyperglycemia lasted for two hours followed by a return to normal in the unoperated rat and to hypoglycemic levels in the adrenalectomized one.

The much reported glycogenolytic effect of epinephrine in the liver and muscle was again observed, and the adrenalectomized rat was not able to reaccumulate its liver glycogen stores. The combined effects of exposure to 30% carbon dioxide in oxygen and a single subcutaneous injection of epinephrine hydrochloride at a dose level of 0.02 mg/100 g of body weight in the normal and adrenalectomized rats are represented in Figs. 3b and 5b. The hyperglycemic response elicited by either one of these substances in the normal animal is reduced when both are combined, but on the fifth hour of exposure a hyperglycemic peak (Fig. 3b) is demonstrated. The adrenalectomized rat under these same conditions exhibits a transient hyperglycemia at 60 minutes (Fig. 5b); however, this hyperglycemia is less severe than when epinephrine alone is administered and is also followed by hypoglycemia.

These two substances when administered simultaneously also drastically change the liver glycogen response of the normal animal (Fig. 3b) and reaccumulation of glycogen stores is inhibited for 4 hours at which time a mean value of 0.2 g % was obtained. The same effect was noted in the adrenalectomized rat where liver glycogenolysis (Fig. 5b) was also enhanced by this combination.

The response of the muscle glycogen stores was somewhat different in that the strong glycogenolytic effect (Figs. 3b, 5b) of epinephrine alone was partially inhibited when the rats were exposed to an atmosphere of 30% carbon dioxide in oxygen (Figs. 3b, 5b).

DISCUSSION

From the very rapid changes observed in the cholesterol content of the adrenal cortex of the hypophysectomized rat (first an increase followed by a decrease), we are led to believe that this material is transferred directly from the blood since there is no evidence that synthesis could occur in such a short period of time within the cortex itself. However, Rosenkrantz (1959) found that he could stimulate adrenal cortical secretion directly with serotonin and also found that this 5-hydroxytryptamine caused an increase in the cholesterol content of the gland and speculated that, since cholesterol is a precursor of corticoids and can undergo peroxidation, then inhibition of this latter process would afford higher concentrations of precursors for corticosteroid synthesis. It is evident that the decrease in the ascorbic acid content of the adrenal of the hypophysectomized rat is by no means as large or as significant as in the normal. The question then arises: is carbon dioxide, per se, like serotonin, able to alter the cholesterol and ascorbic acid content of the adrenal gland directly? Furthermore, are these changes, under these conditions, true indicators of adrenal cortical activity? Obviously other indices of adrenal cortical activity have to be determined before one can decide if there is a slight degree of autonomy in the adrenal gland of the hypophysectomized rat under these conditions of respiratory acidosis.

The hyperglycemia of the normal and the hypophysectomized rat can be, for the most part, the response to an increased adrenaline production under these experimental conditions. However, there is a transient hyperglycemia demonstrated by the adrenalectomized rat which need not be necessarily due to an increase titer of adrenaline and is more probably due to stimulation of the splanchnic nerve leading to the glycogenolysis observed in the liver of this animal.

The next observation not readily explained is the liver glycogen response of the hypophysectomized rat. The fall in liver glycogen could be explained on the basis of the effect of acidosis on the hepatic cells, a most probable epinephrine effect, plus the splanchnic nerve stimulation previously mentioned. But, what is the explanation or the mechanism for the rise in liver glycogen at one and three hours of exposure when the acidosis is still present? Could this be an epinephrine-insulin rebound effect? If this were so, one would expect a lower muscle glycogen at the time of the increase in liver glycogen since the lactate from the muscle would be necessary for the re-synthesis of liver glycogen. However, this is not the case, and muscle glycogen stores are slightly increased at the same time. However, this explanation does not eliminate the possibility that epinephrine might be the agent responsible for this rebound effect under these experimental conditions. Following this trend of thought, we then duplicated these experimental procedures on the normal and the adrenalectomized rats adding one more variable, and that was a single subcutaneous injection of 0.02 mg of epinephrine hydrochloride per 100 g of body weight just prior to the exposure to carbon dioxide (Figs. 3b and 5b). If epinephrine were the indirect agent for the "rebound" accumulation of liver glycogen, we might then expect to demonstrate at least one peak of the cycle observed in the normal and hypophysectomized animal under conditions of respiratory acidosis.

These results indicate very clearly that epinephrine, at a dose level of 0.02 mg/100 g of body weight, is not the agent responsible for the accumulation of liver glycogen of the rat under conditions of respiratory acidosis. The muscle glycogen stores are lowered with epinephrine in both the normal and the adrenalectomized animal under air or under 30% carbon dioxide, but the lactate that must have accompanied such a breakdown is not immediately demonstrated in the resynthesis of liver glycogen even though the animals are rendered hyperglycemic. The peaks of reaccumulation of liver glycogen cannot be explained readily in terms of an insulin effect in response to the hyperglycemia produced because a hyperglycemia was produced in the adrenalectomized rat and a secondary accumulation did not occur; it is well known that the adrenalectomized animals are unduly sensitive to the action of insulin. It is also doubtful that this reaccumulation is a direct effect of carbon dioxide on the liver parenchyma since it failed to act on the liver parenchyma of the adrenalectomized animal.

Richards and Stein (1956) demonstrated an increased seventeen-hydroxycorticosteroid output from the adrenal vein of dogs exposed to concentrations of 20% carbon dioxide. This increased concentration of corticoid output was eliminated by hypophysectomy. However, Lipsett and West (1957) in the same year reported traces of adrenal function after hypophysectomy in man and they pointed out that the possibility of continued secretion of small amounts of seventeen-hydroxycorticosteroids below the level of detection of present methods cannot be ignored. They also point out that totally hypophysectomized dogs, rats, and guinea pigs continue to secrete small amounts of corticotropin so that evidence for their hypothesis exists in different species.

From the results obtained in these studies, it is indicated that, under conditions of respiratory acidosis, epinephrine alone is *not* the agent responsible for the reaccumulation of liver glycogen. It could be possible that epinephrine might play a role in the presence of small amounts of corticoids associated with the processes of glycogen metabolism in both the normal and the hypophysectomized rat. Can the corticoids act upon glycogen metabolism in the absence of epinephrine under these conditions of respiratory acidosis? To answer this question one would have to administer glucosteroids to the adrenalectomized rat exposed to 30% carbon dioxide in oxygen. The other important point to consider is the dose relationship between these two hormones in any study of this kind.

SUMMARY

The adrenal cholesterol and ascorbic acid content of the normal rat are significantly lowered under respiratory acidosis produced by the inhalation of 30% carbon dioxide in oxygen. The animals are also rendered hyperglycemic during exposure. During this hyperglycemic period, they demonstrated a "cyclic or rhythmic" type of depletion and reaccumulation of liver glycogen stores while the muscle glycogen content increased slightly throughout exposure.

Hypophysectomy did not alter the "cyclic" reaccumulation of the liver glycogen stores or the hyperglycemic response. These animals also lost a small amount of cholesterol and ascorbic acid from the adrenal cortex.

Adrenalectomy eliminated the hyperglycemic response and the reaccumulation of liver glycogen. A single subcutaneous injection of epinephrine hydrochloride at a dose level of 0.02 mg/100 g of body weight just prior to exposure to 30% carbon dioxide in 70% oxygen did not cause a single peak or rebound accumulation of liver glycogen.

The results from these experiments indicate that in the hypophysectomized rat, under conditions of respiratory acidosis, there seems to be some residual adrenocortical activity associated with the processes of glycogen metabolism. Furthermore, it was demonstrated that under these experimental conditions exogenous epinephrine alone was not able to reaccumulate liver glycogen stores in the adrenalectomized rat.

REFERENCES

Fortier, C. L. 1949. Proc. Soc. Exptl. Biol. Med. 70: 76.
Gellhorn, E. 1953. University of Minnesota Press, Minneapolis.
Good, C. A., K. Kramer, and N. Somogyi. 1933. J. Biol. Chem. 100: 485.

Fortier, C. L. 1949. Proc. Soc. Exptl. Biol. Med. 70: 76.
Gellhorn, E. 1953. Physiological Foundations of Neurology and Psychiatry, University of Minnesota Press, Minneapolis.
Good, C. A., K. Kramer, and N. Somogyi. 1933. J. Biol. Chem. 100: 485.
Kindwall, J. A. 1949. Am. J. Psychiat. 105: 682.
King, C. T. G., E. E. Williams, J. L. Mego, and K. E. Schaefer. 1955. Am. J. Physiol. 182: 1, 46.
Kingsley, G. R., and R. R. Schaffert. 1949. J. Biol. Chem. 180: 315.
Langley, L. L., and W. G. Kilgore. 1955. Am. J. Physiol. 180: 277.
Lipsett, M. B., and C. D. West. 1957. J. Clin. Endocrinol. Metab. 173: 356.
Meduna, L. J. 1950. Carbon Dioxide Therapy, Charles C Thomas, Springfield, Illinois.

Nelson, N. 1944. J. Biol. Chem. 153: 375.
Richards, J. B., and S. N. Stein. 1956. Research Report Project, NMOO 081.22.12 Naval Medical Research Institute, National Naval Medical Center, Bethesda, Maryland.
Roe, J. H., and C. A. Kuether. 1943. J. Biol. Chem. 147: 399.
Rosenkrantz, H. 1959. Endocrinology 64: 33, 355–362.
Schaefer, K. E., C. T. G. King, J. L. Mego, and E. E. Williams. 1955. Am. J. Physiol. 183: 1, 53.
Schaefer, K. E., H. Klein, and K. H. Zinck. 1950. Klin. Woch. 28.
Schaefer, K. E., H. Storr, and K. Scheer. 1949. Pflüg. Arch. ges. Physiol. 251: 741.
Seevers, M. H. 1944. N. Y. State J. Med. 44: 597.

DISCUSSION

Dr. Franz Halberg: I would like to ask about the eosinophils. They show a decrease, but he said it was not significant. For a number of years CO_2 has been considered responsible for inhibiting a decrease in eosinophils, and actually it has been claimed that acute exposure to high doses of CO_2 brings about rising eosinophils. We have found this, the same as others did, and we would greatly appreciate your comments.

Dr. King: We have reported once before a rise of eosinophils in the guinea pig exposed to 30% CO_2. When you extend the exposure, you get first a very great increase in eosinophils, as you found, but this is followed by a decrease. This is not only in the eosinophils, but occurs in the total leucocytes within the first hour but after the first hour the total count is lowered.

Dr. Stein: Dr. King quoted the paper we wrote, but I want to make sure that it is understood that the responses to carbon dioxide were only one of a series of responses to "stresses" that we applied to these animals. There were other agents—heat, cold, etc.—that did produce similar if not exactly the same adrenal responses; and the 17-hydroxycorticoids and other adrenocortical measures did show very similar effects. I am not so sure that CO_2 in that sense is a specific stress.

Chairman Hoagland: I would like to make a comment on an aspect of Dr. Elmadjian's work which might be worth pointing out in passing. In a study that we made some three or four years ago of pursuitmeter stress as applied to twenty men consisting of four teams of five well-motivated men each, we found that for comparable stresses very young men tended to call less on their adrenal cortices to meet these stresses than did older men. One team was composed of five boys averaging 17 years of age and another team of five boys of 18 years of age. These were compared to two other teams averaging 26 years and 32 years respectively. We measured urinary adrenaline, noradrenaline, 17-steroids, and electrolytes before and after two-hour stresses on the pursuit-meter involving breathing air low in oxygen. We found that in general, while the eosinophils dropped in these very young men as markedly as they did in the older men, the drop seemed to be mediated primarily by the release of adrenalin, and not by the release of the corticoids, which were conspicuous by the absence of changes in their indices following stress in the younger men compared to those of the older men. A plot of the 17-ketosteroids excretion as a function of age produced by the stresses over control levels showed that the younger men do not call upon their adrenals as much as the older ones to meet these stresses. In our earlier studies of adrenal stress responses we used to speak among ourselves of "iron men." These were men who tended to perform very well under stressful conditions, but did not call upon their adrenals to anything like the degree of the less able performers. It is interesting that there seems to be this relationship with age and adrenocortical response to stress. This was not the case for the excretion of adrenaline and noradrenaline.

I think this work should be extended and more information obtained. Ours was a preliminary study, but it involved a number of repeated tests on the same individuals. A group, working with Thorne, studied the output of 17-hydroxy-corticoids and other measures of adrenocortical function of the Harvard crew during rowing practices and during the races. They found a rather small adrenal cortical response considering the magnitude of the stress. These undergraduates were, however, quite young men and may have responded less than would an older group in this regard.

Dr. King: I would like to mention that I purposely avoided the use of the word "stress," because if one goes by Selye's definition, we have to assume stress being nonspecific, and we could not possibly call CO_2 a typical nonspecific stressor agent, since it has also a specific action on the adrenal gland of the hypophysectomized rat.

Chairman Hoagland: Are there other questions or comments?

(There were none.)

If not, I would like to ask Dr. Elmadjian if he would like to comment about the nonappearance of adrenolutin and adrenochrome in the urine in the course of his investigations of the metabolites of adrenaline. These are substances which are produced by the oxidation of adrenaline *in vitro*, and there is controversy as to whether they occur *in vivo*. Were your methods adequate to detect their presence if they had been there, and did you find out anything about them?

Dr. Elmadjian: We looked for adrenochrome and adrenolutin. We used the methods that are at present available to us. We could not find any indoles, and no adrenolutin and no adrenochrome. Some years ago, Dr. Schayer, who was a pioneer in adrenaline metabolism, also tried but came up with negative answers. Dr. Resnick in our laboratory also tried to see if in the metabolites of infused C–14 epinephrine any indoles occurred, but he was unable to find any. Seventy-five per cent of the metabolites of epinephrine appear as 3-methoxy, 4-hydroxy mandelic acid, but 15% appear as 3-methoxy epinephrine, and 3 to 5% as 3,4-dihydroxy mandelic acid. This does not add up to 100%. It is still possible that under some conditions such metabolites may occur but we have not found any.

PART TWO

Effects of Acute and Chronic Environmental Changes on Metabolic Functions

Chairman

DR. BAIRD HASTINGS

Harvard Medical School
Boston, Massachusetts

Cell Metabolism, Electrolyte Exchange, and Peripheral Nervous System Excitability

H. LABORIT

Section de Recherches Physio-Biologiques de la Marine Française, Paris, France

The studies on neuromuscular excitability that we have been conducting for many years have enabled us to understand more clearly the importance in physiology and in pathology of intra- and extracellular ion exchanges and of the factors which regulate them. We have been able to observe both experimentally and clinically, certain variations of neuromuscular excitability in connection with simultaneous variations of ion concentration associated with various physio-pathological conditions (H. Laborit *et al.*, 1955; H. Laborit and G. Laborit, 1955; H. Laborit *et al.*, 1957).

Certain of our observations will be described and discussed, and in conclusion two hypotheses will be presented. The first is on "a concept of the functioning of the cell as an autoregulated system" and the second on "the meaning of excitability in a living entity."

METHOD AND RESULTS

Neuromuscular excitability was studied with a stimulator known as the electronic rheotome of Pluven and Guyot. It can generate square wave stimuli of known duration and intensity and thus permits the plotting of intensity-duration response curves.

A study of the muscle (generally the anterior tibialis) is carried out after the motor area of the homologous nerve has been located (lateral popliteal nerve) at the level of the neck of the fibula (Fig. 1).

The plotting of the curve is done in three segments (corresponding to short, average, and long or rheobasic excitation time segments) which seem to explore the three types of muscle fibers of Bourguignon: fast, average, and slow. The fibers studied with the long stimuli are sensitive to variations of potas-

131

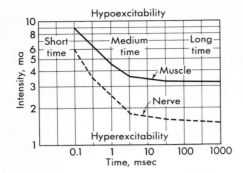

FIGURE 1.

Neuromuscular excitability-intensity duration curves of a normal subject. Differentiation in three segments: long, potassium; average, magnesium (?); short, calcium.

sium concentration; those studied with short stimuli to variations of calcium; and those studied with medium stimuli to variations of magnesium.

The quantitative determination of external ion balances (K, Na, Mg, and Ca) permit one to study with sufficient accuracy ion shifts between the intra- and extracellular compartments. A positive potassium, calcium, or magnesium balance brings each curve segment closer to the abscissa. A negative balance causes an inverse change. If variations of blood ion concentrations and urinary losses are compared, it becomes apparent that the curves seem to reflect intra- cellular ion concentrations. Variations of O_2 consumption (measured with the Durupt metabolimeter), alkaline reserve, pH, and blood ammonia, on the other hand, permit evaluation of the metabolic activity of the cell.

With this method, thousands of determinations have been made either by our group or by investigators who have followed the same approach (Hugue- nard and Fayot, 1955; du Cailar and Durand, 1956; Albeaux-Fernet and Bugard, 1957). Certain observations made under (1) physiological conditions, (2) negative potassium balance, and (3) positive potassium balance will be briefly reviewed and discussed.

(1) *Under physiological conditions,* the nerve excitability curve is below that of the homologous muscle. The nerve, therefore, seems more excitable than the muscle (Fig. 1). The greater the difference between nerve and muscle, the better the functional condition of the subject (Moynier *et al.*, 1956). The differ- ence observed in athletes is generally very marked.

(2) *A negative potassium balance* is first accompanied by an increase of ex- citability. As soon as this increase has become established it is followed by a continuous drop in excitability that can be observed first on the nerve (crossing over of the nerve-muscle curves), and then on the muscle. These variations are particularly noticeable on the segment corresponding to long stimuli. An increase of excitability is accompanied by an increase in oxidative metabolic processes, a rise in oxygen consumption, and, generally, by an acidosis (drop in alkaline reserve and pH).

Examples of these experiments are illustrated in Figs. 2–7 and Table 1.

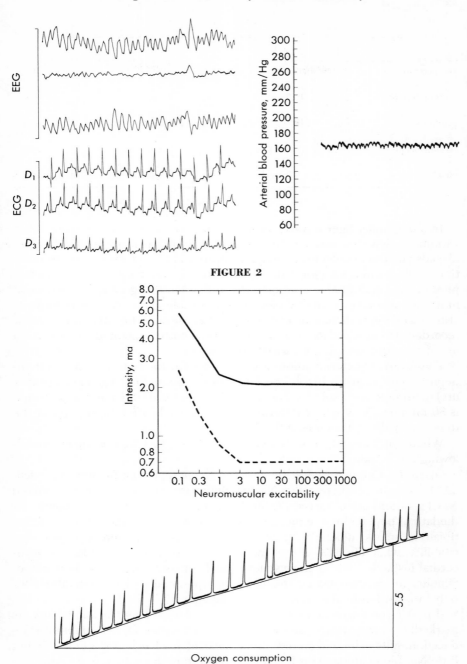

FIGURE 2

FIGURE 3

TABLE 1

	At T_1	At T_2	At T_3
Temperature	38.8°C	39°C	38.4°C
Serum potassium	16.0 mg %	22.0 mg %	————
Serum sodium	310 mg %	290 mg %	————
Serum calcium	6.8 mg %	10.5 mg %	————
Blood ammonia	0.3/ml %	0.4/ml %	0.7/ml %

In a dog under light intravenous pentothal anesthesia, the following observations are first recorded: electroencephalogram (3 leads); electrocardiogram (3 leads); neuromuscular excitability; intracarotid blood pressure; O_2 consumption (Figs. 2 and 3). An ion balance sheet for K, Na, and Ca (flame spectrophotometer) and a blood ammonia determination (Seligson's diffusion technique) are made on an arterial blood sample (Table 1). In many cases we have also studied the variations in arterial O_2 partial pressure. Rectal temperature is recorded. Urine is collected through a permanently implanted catheter, and urinary cation concentrations are determined.

These various determinations are performed at the time T_1, and a norepinephrine perfusion of variable concentrations (6 gamma and 8 gamma/kg/minute) in isotonic NaCl solution is started. The average duration of the perfusion is 80 minutes. New sets of determinations are made after 15 minutes at the time T_2 and after 80 minutes at the time T_3.

When comparing the results obtained at T_2 and T_3 with those at T_1, the following can be noted.

(a) At T_2, 15 minutes after the onset of the norepinephrine perfusion, definite hyperkaliemia, hypercalcemia, and hyponatremia (in spite of the injected NaCl solution) are observed (Table 1). At the same time, the excitability of the lateral popliteal nerve increases, whereas the excitability of the anterior tibialis muscle is influenced but little. The EEG shows an increase of brain excitability, while the ECG shows an increase of complex amplitudes and myocardial instability with extrasystoles. Finally, arterial hypertension is noted. Simultaneously, there is an increase in O_2 consumption and in temperature, but only by a few tenths of a degree (Figs. 4 and 5).

(b) At T_3, on the contrary, brain, cardiac, and neuromuscular excitability are markedly depressed. Arterial blood pressure collapses, O_2 consumption is reduced. In spite of limited diuresis, the urine contains a high proportion of K, but little Na. Blood ammonia is high and temperature drops by a few tenths of a degree (Figs. 6 and 7).

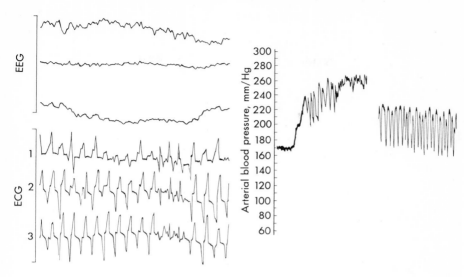

FIGURE 4

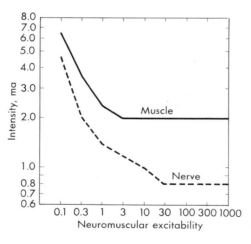

FIGURE 5

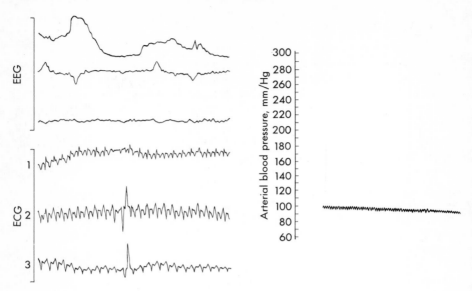

FIGURE 6

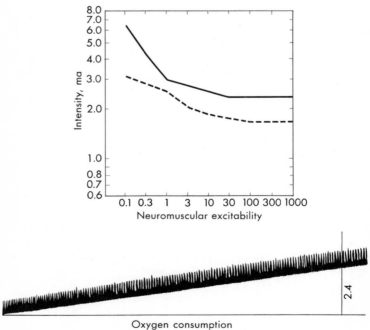

FIGURE 7

DISCUSSION OF RESULTS

We have chosen a norepinephrine perfusion as the stimulus since it produces autonomic responses similar to those caused by various other stimuli (emotion, trauma) and the hyperkaliemia that it creates is typical.

We had shown, along with Huguenard, as early as 1956 (Laborit and Huguenard, 1956), that the stress produced was not limited to a simultaneous hyperglycemia, and that the smooth muscle fibers of the vessels as well as the myocardial fibers contributed most likely to the hyperkaliemia by liberating a certain amount of their intracellular potassium. It would also seem that the cells of many organs and tissues react similarly. Consequently, the ratios of potassium concentrations $\frac{K_i}{K_e}$ (K_i = intracellular K) and (K_e = extracellular K) are lowered. Membrane polarization (mP), which depends upon this ratio, is also lowered. *Cell excitability* increases during the first phase (T_2). This depolarization favors the combination of actin and of myosin and causes hypertension at the level of the cardiovascular system.

Depolarization increases muscle cell permeability and exchanges are intensified. Oxidative metabolism increases as evidenced by the rise in oxygen consumption and temperature. The latter is also likely to be elevated by peripheral vasoconstriction which decreases heat loss.

Although we have not investigated variations of the extracellular volume, many observations lead us to believe that the hyponatremia observed is the result of the passage of the Na into the cell to compensate for the loss of K.

Thus, in T_2, the mechanism of norepinephrine action can be briefly described as a membrane depolarization, a compensatory intensification of oxidative metabolic processes and an increase in cell excitability.

In T_3, on the contrary, since the perfusion is maintained, the oxidative processes are unable to restore membrane potential by reintroducing K ions into the cell and by ejecting Na ions. A stable depolarization and shock result. A central neuromuscular and cardiac hyperexcitability can be observed, as well as a decrease in the intensity of oxidative metabolism. Exhausted cardiovascular fibers lose their tone and collapse ensues. Hepatic anoxia alters ammonia metabolism and is responsible for the hyperammoniemia. Thus in T_3 the prolonged action of norepinephrine has led to a condition of cell exhaustion, characterized by stable depolarization, a decrease of oxidative metabolic processes and in general a considerable decrease in cell excitability.

An identical development can be observed with any intense and prolonged organic stimulation or irritation.

(a) *During fatigue:* the study of neuromuscular excitability and ion shifts show similar variations (Figs. 8 and 9). There is an increase of excitability in light fatigue, and a decrease in severe fatigue (Figs. 10 and 11).

(b) *During general anesthesia:* the excitation phase corresponds to a depolari-

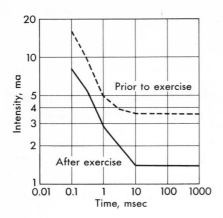

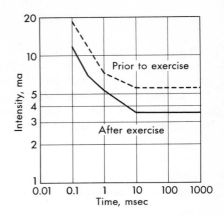

FIGURE 8 (*left*).

9 a.m.; subject at rest. 11 a.m.: work performed on the bycycle, 15,000 kg/m/sec. Observe the nerve hyperexcitability after work and light fatigue.

FIGURE 9 (*right*).

9 a.m.: subject at rest. 11 a.m.: work performed on the bycycle, 15,000 kg/m/sec. Observe the muscle hyperexcitability after work and light fatigue.

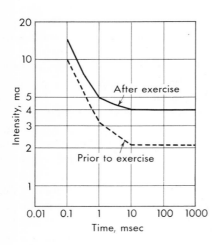

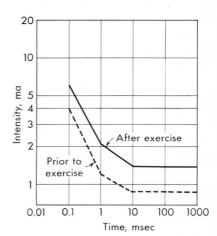

FIGURE 10 (*left*).

9 a.m.: subject at rest. Total work performed in two periods on the bycycle, 25,000 kg/m/sec; 11:30 a.m., 15,000 kg/m/sec; 2 p.m., 10,000 kg/m/sec. Observe the nerve hypoexcitability after intense work and marked fatigue.

FIGURE 11 (*right*).

9 a.m.: subject at rest. Total work performed in two periods on the bycycle, 25,000 kg/m/sec; 11:30 a.m., 15,000 kg/m/sec; 2 p.m., 10,000 kg/m/sec. Observe the muscle hypoexcitability after marked fatigue.

zation phenomenon with compensatory metabolic reactions, and the so-called surgical plane corresponds to a stable depolarization due to disturbances in oxidative processes.

(c) The stimulation of a muscle with an *electric current* of subliminal intensity, unable to cause a motor response, is nevertheless capable of causing a certain loss of muscle K^+, and of initiating depolarization in such a manner that, after the passage of this type of current, the use of a weaker current is capable of inducing muscular contraction. The first stimulus, therefore, has increased excitability by causing a slight depolarization.

(d) *Anoxia* acts similarly. We have been able to study its effect on the heart muscle in experimental cardiac surgery during the past eight years. It increases myocardial excitability in the first stage by facilitating membrane depolarization, and if it continues, it is finally responsible for inexcitability due to metabolic exhaustion.

(e) *Injected* K^+ in the circulation in doses small enough not to cause cardiac fibrillation will result in hypertension as will any cardiovascular fiber depolarizing agent. In fact, the increase of K_e facilitates a decrease of membrane potential and the combination of actin and myosin, thereby producing an increase in vascular tone. It is known (Kimura and Niwa, 1953), that an increase of K concentration in the extracellular fluid of tissue slices will increase their oxygen consumption. In the intact animal a true membrane phenomenon occurs since we were able to observe it even after clamping the aorta above the diaphragm. This technique prevents epinephrine liberation by the adrenal medulla under the action of K^+ (Fig. 12).

(3) Conversely, *a positive potassium balance,* i.e., an increase in intracellular K^+, also may end in inexcitability but it would occur in this case through an ion overload.

It is known that the injection of a K salt into the coronary circulation will produce cardiac arrest in diastole and myocardial atonia. Similarly, an isolated heart perfused with a solution rich in K^+ will become atonic. But repeated successive electric stimulations of equal intensity, with no response at first, will

FIGURE 12.
Injection of KCl does not produce fibrillation. Increase of cardiovascular tonus through decrease in ratio of Ki (intracellular potassium).

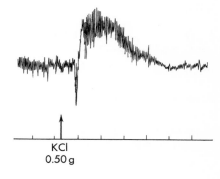

KCl
0.50 g

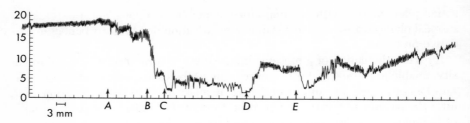

FIGURE 13.

Carotis pressure 20 kg dog. (*A*) Open chest preparation; respiration controlled O_2. Potassium level 4.5 mgr%. (*B*) I.V. injection of 25 mg/kg of KCl in 30 sec. fibrillation. Potassium level 15 mgr%. (*C*) I.V. injection of gm glucose (30%) cardiac massage. (*D*) Potassium level 3.5 mgr%. Electric shock. From D-E automatism. (*E*) I.V. injection of 25 mgr% of KCl in 30 seconds. No fibrillation. Return of the blood pressure to control values.

progressively cause a decrease of K excess in the myocardial fiber, and contractions of increasing force will then appear in response to stimulation, yielding a staircase-shaped curve (Bowditch's phenomenon) as membrane polarization approaches a normal level because of the return toward normal of the $\dfrac{K_i}{K_e}$ ratio. A similar phenomenon is found in certain types of familial periodic paralysis that we have recently studied (Laborit *et al.*, 1957). The following experiment gives some insight in the mechanism of such phenomena in the myocardium.

A 20 kg dog is anesthetized with intravenous pentothal, thoracotomized and put under controlled breathing of pure oxygen. The carotid blood pressure is recorded. The following changes can then be observed (Fig. 13).

At A, (K_e) = 4.5 mEq.

At B, a KCl solution (500 mg) is injected intravenously in 30 seconds.

At C, ventricular filbrillation, (K_e) = 14.5 mEq. Decrease of $\dfrac{K_i}{K_e}$.

From C to D, heart massage. Intravenous injection of 60 ml of 30% hypertonic glucose and 10 units of insulin. Atonia by overpolarization = increase of the $\dfrac{K_i}{K_e}$ ratio since:

At D, (K_e) = 3.5 mEq. Electric shock. Resumption of automatism. The carotid blood pressure is lower than in A because the cardiovascular tone is lowered by the continuous increase of the $\dfrac{K_i}{K_e}$ ratio. A certain amount of the injected K^+ must have penetrated into the intracellular space since (K_e) in D is smaller than (K_e) in A.

At E, an identical injection of 500 mg of KCl in 30 seconds no longer produces fibrillation, but rather a return to the initial blood pressure.

Before a functional inhibition and an inexcitability or atonia by overpolarization can be achieved, the loading of K^+ requires an intensification of metabolic processes. Such an intensification can be caused by the action of hypertonic glucose and insulin, or by a moderate rise in temperature. These conditions permit a temporary nerve and muscle excitability increase until overpolarization appears, which is then responsible for a decrease or a temporary absence of excitability.

Discussion of results (Fig. 14)

(1) Stimuli (or depolarizations) of low intensity such as light fatigue, the first stages of general anesthesia, the injection of small quantities of epinephrine, or the first stages of anoxia, cause a central and peripheral *hyperexcitability* and an increase of metabolic processes, although they are accompanied by a shift of the intracellular K toward the extracellular space.

Hypoexcitability and inexcitability appear only after an intense or prolonged stimulus—or else in an organism in which the metabolic processes are already disturbed—and are accompanied by a decrease of oxidative processes and by a stable depolarization. In these cases potassium balance is strongly negative.

(2) The intracellular penetration of the K^+ requires active metabolic processes and during the first stage is accompanied by an increase in excitability and O_2 consumption. During the second stage, if overpolarization is attained (insulin + glucose, cardiac arrest caused by K salts, certain types of periodic familial paralysis) a decrease of excitability and even an inexcitability are observed, accompanied by atonia and a decrease in O_2 consumption.

The observed phenomena support the following hypothesis.

An ideal average excitability reflects a physiological intra- and extracellular ion equilibrium under the control of normal metabolic processes.

Any variation of the ratio between the intra- and extracellular ion concentration, and consequently any membrane polarization and metabolic activity variation, is *first* responsible for an increase of nerve and muscle excitability (and probably of all cells in general).

It is only when these variations go beyond a certain limit that hypoexcitability and then inexcitability appear (Fig. 14).

CELLULAR MECHANISM — AN AUTOREGULATED SYSTEM (FIG. 15)

The observations which have been presented lead to the concept that in its physiological state, the living cell functions as an autoregulated system. Actually, membrane permeability regulates exchanges between the intra- and extracellular compartments. It therefore controls the intensity of metabolism. Metabolism, in turn, regulates polarization and thus membrane permeability,

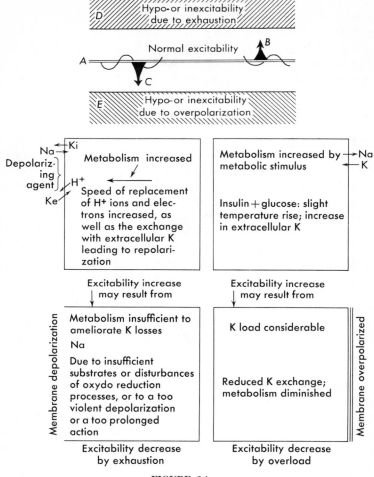

FIGURE 14.

A. Ideal normal excitability: average membrane permeability and polarization; physiological intra- and extracellular K loads and Ki Ke ratio; normal *metabolic processes.* The autoregulated functioning of the cell makes these values vary slightly above and below the ideal equilibrium level. (For example, physiological alternating vasoconstriction and vasodilation of arterioles.)

B. Depolarization; slight potassium loss by the cell; increased permeability. Consequently, *increase of metabolic processes* and autoregulation; *increase of excitability.*

C. Increase of metabolic processes (insulin and glucose); polarization increases; permeability decreases; intracellular K load increases; *excitability increases.*

D. Hypo- or inexcitability: very high and stable permeability; depolarization of the membrane; very low intracellular potassium concentration. Metabolic processes are temporarily or permanently insufficient or disturbed, and not able to restore average ion and membrane characteristics.

E. Hypo- or inexcitability: very low and stable permeability; overpolarized membrane; very high intracellular potassium concentration. Consequently, indirectly depressed *metabolic processes.* Can return to average values (staircase, for example).

In summary, excitability is determined by the intensity of metabolism. It increases directly in *C,* and indirectly in *B* after the starting of autoregulation; tends toward zero in *D* and in *E* on account of the overly or insufficiently permeable membrane.

since it maintains the specific inequality of extra- and intracellular ion concentrations through Na^+ ejection and K^+ reabsorption.

Provided it remains within physiological limits, any depolarization will make the membrane more permeable and will intensify exchanges and metabolic processes. This increase of metabolic intensity will guarantee a return to the original polarization and ion equilibrium until the further augmentation of polarization will finally decrease exchanges and diminish the intensity of metabolic processes. Conversely, any decrease of membrane permeability that diminishes exchanges—therefore metabolism—will facilitate depolarization with a tendency toward augmenting permeability and exchanges, and so on.

As far as we are concerned, physiopathology begins where the homeostatic functioning of this autoregulated system ends; in other words, when stable disturbances appear, either in the physical processes of ion exchanges or in the regulatory metabolic processes. In our opinion the automatic functioning of certain organs, such as the heart and respiratory centers, resides in such a mechanism.

THE MEANING OF EXCITABILITY IN A LIVING ENTITY

If a nerve or muscle cell, too rich or too poor in potassium, over- or underpolarized, cannot be excited, it is due to the fact that in both of these cases the intensity of its metabolism is either reduced or its oxidative mechanism disturbed.

On the contrary, a rise in metabolic activity augments excitability. This will happen with an increase of polarization since it can be achieved—except by a direct action on the physical structure of the cell—only by a temporary rise in metabolic activity (action of insulin + glucose). But this is also the case with

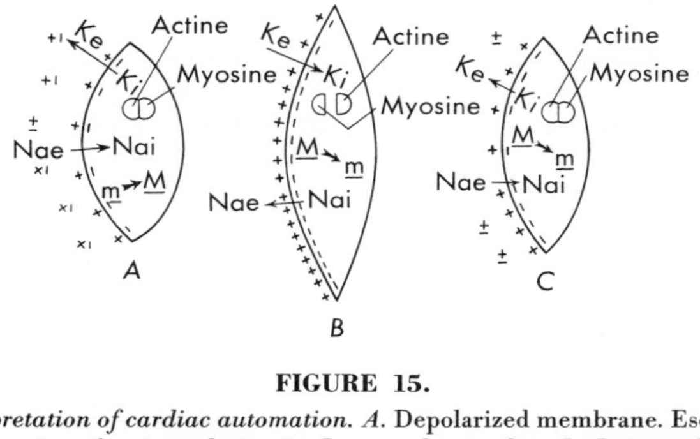

FIGURE 15.

Hypothetical interpretation of cardiac automation. A. Depolarized membrane. Escape of Ki, penetration of Nae. Combination of actin and myosin. Increased tone. *Systole.* Increased membrane permeability. Metabolism increases: m → M. *B.* The increase of metabolism has shifted Ke into Ki and ejected Nae, and has caused membrane repolarization and dissociation of actin and myosin. *Diastole.* Repolarization → decrease of exchanges → *decrease of metabolism:* m → M. *C.* The decrease of metabolism permits depolarization: K escapes. Na goes in, and the cycle starts again.

a light depolarization of the membrane which augments exchanges and forces metabolic processes to increase. In either instance, as soon as a certain membrane state is reached, the inverse phenomenon takes place, that is to say a decrease of excitability.

The excitability of a living entity appears, therefore, to be regulated by the metabolic rate. In other words, by the rate at which the electron flux and the transfer of H^+ can take place along the biocatalytic chain.

In our opinion, this notion is as valid in the case of oscillating physiological variations of excitability as in the case of stable pathological variations. In many instances it is helpful in orienting diagnosis and therapy.

SUMMARY

The author has shown experimentally and clinically the synergistic variations of neuromuscular excitability, of ion exchanges through membranes, and of cell metabolism. Observed facts lead him to regard cell functioning as autoregulated. Cell excitability appears to him as the physiological expression of the rate at which the electro-ionic flow moves along the biocatalytic chain. This interpretation seems to explain observations on physiological and physiopathological variations.

REFERENCES

Albeaux-Fernet, and Bugard. 1957. La Presse Médicale 4: 61–64.
Conferences d'Agressologie. 1958. S.P.E. édit., 1 vol., Paris.
du Cailar, J., and M. Durand. 1956. Anesthésie et Analgésie 14: (3), 486–495.
Huguenard, P., and G. Fayot. 1955. Anesthésie et Analgésie 12: (3), 557–591.
Kimura, Y., and T. Niwa. 1953. Nature 171: 881.
Laborit, H., R. Favre, R. Guittard, and G. Laborit. 1955. La Presse Médicale 12: 223–227.
Laborit, H., and G. Laborit. 1955. Excitabilité neuro-musculaire et equilibre ionique, 1 vol., Masson & Cie, Paris.
Laborit, H., R. Coirault, and G. Guiot. 1957. La Presse Médicale 25: 571–575.
Laborit, H., and P. Huguenard. 1956. J. Physiol. (Paris) 48: 871–879.
Moynier, R., J. L. Bastard, Gros, and G. Guiot. 1956. Société de Medécine Militaire Française, In: Bulletin No. 2.

Exchange of Electrolytes under Carbon Dioxide*

G. NICHOLS, JR.† and K. E. SCHAEFER

*Departments of Medicine and Biochemistry, Harvard Medical School, and
Naval Medical Research Laboratory, U. S. Submarine Base,
New London, Connecticut*

Maintaining life in a sealed cabin requires supplying adequate amounts of oxygen and removing from the confined atmosphere the CO_2 excreted by the individuals living inside. Mechanically the maintenance of an adequate oxygen supply is far simpler than CO_2 removal. In fact, the maintenance of CO_2 concentrations as low as those of the ambient air is often impractical. Thus it is of great importance to know how the human body responds to excess CO_2 in the atmosphere, what the tolerance limits are, and what the pattern of adaptation to such an atmosphere may be.

Since CO_2 dissolved in water becomes hydrated to form the weakly dissociated acid H_2CO_3, an increase of the CO_2 tension in the inspired air increases the CO_2 tension in the body fluids and produces an acidosis of the respiratory type. This paper is a review of the changes found in the electrolyte composition of the blood, urine and tissues as a result of respiratory acidosis and how long those changes take to develop—in other words, what the adaptive responses of the organism to this stress seem to be. For the sake of clarity we have arbitrarily divided this discussion into a consideration of the changes in the blood, in the urine, and in the several tissues so far studied. It is obvious that all these changes are interdependent and occur simultaneously. Therefore, we shall try to present the changes in each area in terms of duration of exposure to CO_2 so that the various phenomena may be tied together into a unified whole. Data are drawn largely from our own experiments with animals and to some extent with man. Where we do not have adequate illustrative

* Supported in part by grants from the National Institute of Arthritis and Metabolic Diseases, U. S. Public Health Service.
† Markle Scholar in Medical Science.

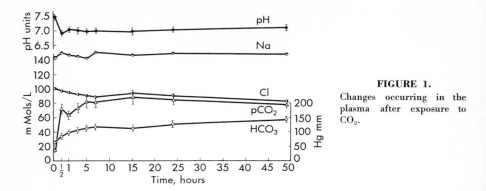

FIGURE 1.

Changes occurring in the plasma after exposure to CO_2.

material, we shall borrow from the published data of the many others who have studied various aspects of these phenomena.

The changes which occur in the plasma after various periods of exposure to CO_2 are illustrated in Fig. 1. These data are taken from some experiments with rats exposed to 24% CO_2 in air for various periods of time, ranging from 30 minutes to 48 hours (Nichols, 1958). They serve to illustrate several points of importance.

In the first place it is evident that equilibration of the body fluids with the CO_2 tension in the inspired air is largely complete in a very brief period of time. In the first half-hour the pCO_2 of the plasma rose from a control value of 38 mm of Hg to 175 mm. Since the concentration of carbonic acid is directly proportional to the pCO_2 of the body fluids, this indicated that the concentration of this acid had increased in the blood almost fivefold. It was not surprising therefore to find that the pH of the plasma fell from 7.47 to 6.92, despite an increase of plasma bicarbonate ion concentration. Thus the development of acidosis upon exposure to atmospheres containing high CO_2 tensions occurs extremely rapidly in contrast to the slower development of acidosis following the ingestion of an acid load by mouth (Shock and Hastings, 1935). Similar results have been obtained by many other workers (Miller, 1940; Consolazio *et al.*, 1947; Elkinton *et al.*, 1955; Platts and Greaves, 1957; Brodie and Woodbury, 1958).

Some years ago Shock and Hastings (1935) pointed out that, if no changes occurred in the concentrations of the other anions and cations of the plasma, the disturbance of acid-base balance with CO_2 excess followed the CO_2 dissociation curve of the blood. The changes in pH which occurred in these animals in the first half-hour approximated but were slightly less than would have been predicted by such a curve. Thus something else must have changed in the plasma even in this very brief period in order to compensate to some degree for the acidosis. From this figure it can be seen that both the fixed cation sodium and the anion chloride had begun to change—the sodium increased 6 mEq and the chloride decreased 3 mEq per liter. Thus even in the very early phases of respiratory acidosis, changes had begun in the concentrations of the other electrolytes.

As the duration of exposure to the high CO_2 atmosphere increased further changes developed. The pCO_2 increased slightly and then stabilized at a level slightly higher than that of the atmosphere. The plasma bicarbonate, however, continued to rise fairly rapidly until the seventh hour and then more slowly for the rest of the 48 hours studied. At the same time the pH of the plasma rose slightly so that by 48 hours it had increased to 7.10. It is apparent that further changes in the direction of metabolic alkalosis (or an increase in buffer-base (Singer and Hastings, 1948)) had occurred in the fixed electrolytes as the time of exposure increased. Turning to the curves for sodium and chloride, we find that in this particular series of animals almost all of this change was due to a slow but steady decrease in plasma chloride, while the sodium concentration increased only very slightly. The potassium concentration in the plasma —not shown in this figure—seemed to increase, but the change was small and not present in all animals. Similar changes in serum potassium have been found by others. Although the extent of the increase reported has varied considerably, in general the higher levels of plasma potassium have been seen in animals with the most severe and acute acidosis (Elkinton *et al.*, 1955; Singer and Hastings, 1948; Scribner *et al.*, 1955; Giebisch and Pitts, 1955; Cooke *et al.*, 1952; Foulds *et al.*, 1958; Schaefer, 1949, 1955; Levitin *et al.*, 1958).

From these curves, then, we can summarize the changes found in plasma. An acute phase of respiratory acidosis is followed by a phase of adaptation in which compensatory changes occur in the fixed electrolytes in the direction of metabolic alkalosis. As a result plasma pH returns toward normal and plasma bicarbonate increases. At the same time plasma pCO_2 stabilizes at a level slightly above that of the inspired air. As we have seen, these adaptive changes begin almost immediately. The total duration of this phase and the completeness of the adaptation vary with the duration of exposure and the concentration of CO_2 inspired (Schaefer, 1951, 1961).

Since the composition of the plasma is merely a reflection of the excretory pattern of the kidneys and the exchanges between extracellular fluid and the cells of the tissues, we must turn our attention to the urine and the tissues in order to explain the changes in plasma composition.

In contrast to the plasma response which is fairly well agreed upon by all, the renal response is far less clear and the studies so far published have dealt almost entirely with very short periods of exposure. However, several recent studies are pertinent.

It seems well established by both Relman, Etsten, and Schwartz (1953) and

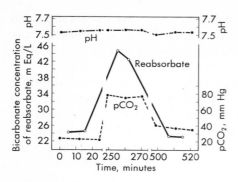

FIGURE 2.
Renal response to respiratory acidosis.

Dorman, Sullivan, and Pitts (1954) that the rate of reabsorption of bicarbonate by the renal tubule is increased by increases in the pCO_2 of the plasma. This fact is well illustrated by Fig. 2 taken from Relman and Schwartz's report. It can be seen that increasing the plasma pCO_2 in the dogs studied resulted in a marked increase in the amount of bicarbonate reabsorbed. This was independent of pH change, since in these experiments pH was kept constant by bicarbonate infusion. This finding serves to explain the increase in plasma bicarbonate seen during the adaptive period and the fall below control values in urine bicarbonate seen in man by one of us (K. E. Schaefer, 1949) during the early phases of exposure to 3% CO_2. The later rise in urine HCO_3^- excretion in this latter experiment, which appeared after the adaptive phase was complete, presumably was due to an increase in the filtered load of bicarbonate which exceeded the new rate of HCO_3 resorption.

Two other observations are noteworthy in this regard. Sullivan and Dorman (1955) have indicated by renal clearance studies that prolonged exposure to elevated CO_2 tensions further increases the ability of the renal tubule to reabsorb bicarbonate. In addition, one of us (K. E. Schaefer) (Killian and Schaefer, 1954) has demonstrated enhanced carbonic anhydrase activity in homogenates of renal tissue taken from guinea pigs exposed to 30% CO_2 for several hours. Thus it would appear that in addition to the immediate effects of increasing pCO_2 on the bicarbonate reabsorbing system in the renal tubule, adaptation, perhaps of this enzyme, further potentiates this effect in time.

Although less definitive information concerning changes in other urinary electrolytes is available, Fig. 3, adapted from a recent article by Barker, Singer, Elkinton, and Clark (1957), illustrates the immediate response of the kidney to CO_2 inhalation very well. These studies in man describe the effects of a 30-minute period of inhalation of 7% CO_2. Urinary pH fell while titratable acidity and H ion excretion increased. These findings are in keeping with the need of the body to rid itself of excess H ion. Among the anions, besides the fall in bicarbonate excretion already discussed, it can be seen that phosphate and chloride are cleared in increased amounts. Potassium excretion falls—perhaps contributing to the rise described in plasma potassium concentration—and NH_4^+ ion increases a small but significant amount. Sodium excretion surprisingly seemed to increase. All these changes, with the exception of the sodium excretion, are in substantial agreement with the results of a group of experiments in respiratory acidosis performed by medical students in their studies of acid-base balance at Harvard Medical School under the guidance of Dr. Hastings. Furthermore, they are in the direction which would be predicted in order to bring about the changes in plasma composition already described. Unfortunately, these changes have not always been found by other workers (Barbour *et al.*, 1953). In the few experiments of longer duration reported, the results are difficult to interpret. Denton (Denton *et al.*, 1952) found low plasma Cl/Na ratios but no consistent change in the Cl/Na ratio of the urine collected over a 72-hour period of exposure to high CO_2 tensions. There was only a suggestion from his data that this ratio in the urine might have been increased. Furthermore, in an abstract published in 1958, Carter, Seldin, and Teng (1958) reported finding elevated chloride, titratable acidity, and ammonia in the urine

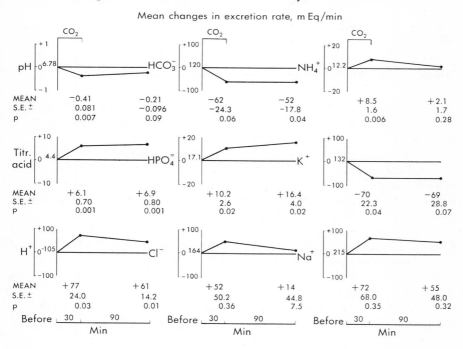

FIGURE 3.
Renal response to respiratory acidosis. (Adapted from Barker, Singer, Elkinton, and Clark. 1957. J. Clin. Invest. *36*: 515.)

TABLE 1
Red cell electrolytes in chronic respiratory acidosis.

		Na	K	Cl	HCO$_3$	Blood pH
				mEq/L of red cell water		
Control	Mean	23.1	146	83.5	22.8	7.38
	S.D.	3.0	10	6	3.5	.05
	N	25	30	31	30	25
15% CO$_2$	Mean	64.9°	101.8°	80.9	28.7°	7.21°
1 day	S.D.	7.0	9	5.0	4.1	.08
	N	24	23	10	26	38
15% CO$_2$	Mean	45.3°	143	89.0	39.0	7.29°
2–3 days	S.D.	6.1	8	6.0	3.8	.03
	N	21	22	12	21	25
15% CO$_2$	Mean	50.3°	136.6	108.3°	40.3°	7.35
4–7 days	S.D.	6.0	11	9	3.2	.06
	N	25	25	21	30	34
15% CO$_2$	Mean	11.1°	129.3°	97.1°	36.3°	7.34
20–73 days	S.D.	3.3	13	8.0	3.5	.08
	N	10	14	14	12	12

° Differences from controls statistically significant at the 5% level and better.

of rats exposed to 10% CO$_2$ for the first 24 hours only. In their animals they found potassium excretion increases up to 14 days of exposure which is in sharp contrast to Barbour's data (Barbour *et al.*, 1953).

To summarize the urinary changes, then, bicarbonate reabsorption by the renal tubule increases throughout the exposure to high CO$_2$; the net excretion of bicarbonate is low in the adaptive phase, but increases during prolonged exposure. In the acute and early adaptive phase, evidence is available that the kidney acts to produce a metabolic alkalosis or an increase in "buffer base" to compensate for the respiratory acidosis. However, the long-term effects of CO$_2$ on the renal excretory pattern, and the changes in total body balance of electrolyte under these conditions have not yet been worked out.

What is known of the renal excretion of electrolytes under CO$_2$ indicates that the kidney plays an important role in the phenomenon of adaptation. However, the changes in excretion observed are inadequate to explain fully the changes which are seen in the plasma and extracellular fluids. It is apparent, therefore, that exchanges between the extracellular and cellular compartments must occur. This brings us to a consideration of changes in the concentrations and total amounts of the various tissue electrolytes during the respiratory acidosis produced by the inhalation of CO$_2$.

The importance of various body tissues in the buffering of loads of carbonic acids has been known for many years (Shaw, 1926–1927; Brocklehurst and Henderson, 1927). Yet, except for the red cell (Van Slyke *et al.*, 1923), the manner in which this buffering is accomplished, and the total buffer capacity of each tissue remain undecided questions. Equally obscure at present are the chronic effects of such an acidosis on many aspects of cellular metabolism and intracellular ionic composition. The following tables and graphs illustrate some of our findings in recent experiments (Nichols, 1958; Schaefer and Barton, 1956). These are presented here not because they answer these questions but because they illustrate the type of results obtained and the great difficulty which remains in interpreting them.

It can be seen in Table 1 that the rise in cell bicarbonate during the uncompensated phase of respiratory acidosis (one day of exposure) is associated with a cation exchange. Intracellular sodium increased while intracellular potassium decreased at a nearly equivalent amount. No significant change in red cell chloride was observed at this period. However, preliminary experiments with a shorter exposure of one hour demonstrated that the chloride shift is clearly expressed during more acute exposure. This suggests that the cation exchange is a later process associated with the bicarbonate influx into the cell. During the compensated phase of respiratory acidosis, beginning after 2–3 days of exposure, the bicarbonate level in the red cells reached a plateau and potassium concentration returned to practically normal levels, while intracellular sodium remained elevated.

With extended exposure to 15% CO_2, a state of exhaustion developed, during which cation and bicarbonate concentrations decreased. However, the chloride concentration was significantly elevated during this period. It is obvious that until measurements of other components in these cells are made and knowledge of the effects of CO_2 on the factors which control electrolyte exchange across the cell membrane is available, no clear interpretation of these data is possible.

Figure 4 illustrates the rate and extent to which CO_2 accumulates in 3 other

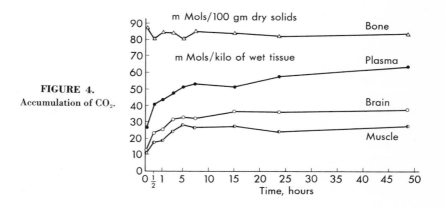

FIGURE 4.
Accumulation of CO_2.

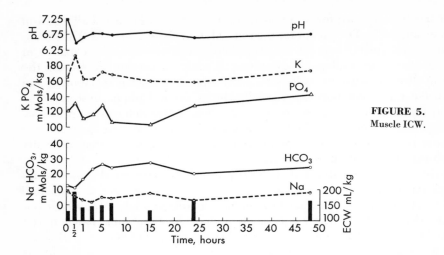

FIGURE 5.
Muscle ICW.

tissues and the plasma of rats exposed to 24% CO_2. Two points are evident. First, muscle and brain take up CO_2 in a similar fashion although muscle contains slightly less than brain. Bone, on the other hand, although it contains large amounts of CO_2 as CO_3^- ion, if anything, loses CO_2. It is only after very long exposure that bone CO_2 rises, as was shown by Freeman and Fenn (1953). It is also important to note that, while plasma CO_2 content continued to increase slowly, brain and muscle CO_2 stores rapidly reached a plateau and did not increase further. From these data it appears that both brain and muscle buffer much of the CO_2 retained at least up to 48 hours of exposure. However, their ability to accumulate this material in the intracellular compartment reaches a limit quite rapidly. Thus it would appear that in the acute and early adaptive phases of exposure to CO_2 changes in soft-tissue CO_2 stores play a major role in the buffering of this acid.

The final two figures present the changes in the intracellular composition which we found in these tissues. These data were calculated using two assumptions: first, that the pCO_2 was the same in all body water, and second, that the chloride space was equal to the extracellular phase.

The first of these, Fig. 5, concerns muscle. It is evident that a profound intracellular acidosis developed in this tissue within 30 minutes of the start of exposure. Simultaneously there was a sharp rise in intracellular potassium and a fall in sodium. While phosphate appeared to rise slightly, the bicarbonate ion concentration did not change in this period. At the same time the fraction of the total water which was extracellular rose sharply. (Total muscle water did not change except at 48 hours, when it was decreased 2%.) Within the next two and one-half hours, as bicarbonate accumulated, the ECF volume and intracellular potassium returned to normal. The return of the potassium to normal in these animals, while supported by some reports (Elkinton *et al.*, 1955; Cooke *et al.*, 1952), is different from the results obtained by two groups of workers who have recently found decreased intracellular potassium after CO_2 exposure (Levitin *et al.*, 1958; Carter *et al.*, 1958). The only persistent changes seen in the rest of the experiment were the low pH, low sodium, and increased bicarbonate. In the period of adaptive change between 5 and 24 hours the phosphate level appeared low. This suggests that in this tissue reduction in this anion was the means by which compensation for the accumulation of bicarbonate occurred. Unfortunately for such an hypothesis, by 48 hours the phosphate concentration was significantly higher than the controls! Once again, in this tissue, while the changes in pH and bicarbonate are in accord with concepts previously described, we are unable to interpret the changes in sodium, potassium, or phosphate. Why these differences should exist is unknown, but they serve to emphasize the difficulties inherent in interpreting the results of tissue analysis in abnormal states and our ignorance of the mechanisms by which these changes are mediated.

The final diagram, Fig. 6, illustrates the electrolyte composition of whole brain-cell water. The only similarities to the changes seen in muscle were the fall in pH and the rise in bicarbonate. Even these were different in the half-hour exposure period where brain bicarbonate can be seen to have risen rapidly, in contrast to muscle where it did not change at all. This rapid rise of bicarbonate apparently protected this tissue from the extensive fall in pH seen in muscle at this time. The pattern of adaptation in other respects was quite different. Cell sodium content changed little if at all, while potassium, after a brief increase in the first half-hour, appeared to be lower than in control animals. The phosphate of these cells, while it varied widely, showed no consistent change which might indicate that it participated in the adjustment of acid-base balance of the tissue. Finally, in this tissue the extracellular volume ap-

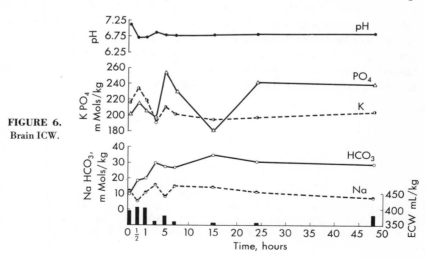

FIGURE 6.
Brain ICW.

peared decreased, especially after several hours under CO_2, while in the muscle it appeared increased. In this tissue total water did not change at all.

Although we have data on two other tissues—liver and bone—neither showed great change in composition and therefore do not add significantly to the conclusions which can be drawn at present. As you have seen only three conclusions can be arrived at from this work with tissues: First, the several soft tissues act as a repository for CO_2 stored in the body during exposure to CO_2 and participate in the buffering of the carbonic acid so produced. Second, the mechanisms by which this buffering is accomplished and the changes in composition which result vary widely from tissue to tissue. Finally, although there are suggestions that the changes in the tissues are different after various periods of exposure and adaptation, it is not yet possible to correlate these changes with either the plasma or the urinary changes seen at corresponding times.

It is obvious that in this very brief review it was necessary to skip a number of important areas and the results of many excellent experiments were not mentioned. Nothing has been said of the important matter of readaptation to atmospheric air and the changes that occur during this process; changes in the metabolism of such ions as Mg and calcium have been omitted; nor has mention been made of the tolerance limits of man to CO_2. Indeed, the entire subject of change in function in relation to change in composition has not even been hinted at.

Rather, it was tried to outline the changes that occur in the plasma with progressive hours of exposure to CO_2 indicating that reasonable agreement exists as to their nature. In dealing with the urinary changes, it was attempted to show that here not only does less agreement exist between workers but that these changes alone are insufficient to account for the plasma pattern. Finally, in a brief survey, were discussed some of our findings in the composition of various tissues. If you have been left with a feeling of confusion concerning the interpretation of these latter findings, we can assure you it is shared by ourselves and many others who have explored this field! At the same time we hope that we have shown you that our present knowledge in several areas is far too limited to interpret what we find in the tissues and that extensive work is needed to answer even a few of the questions which they raise.

REFERENCES

Barbour, A., G. M. Bull, B. M. Evans, N. C. Hughes-Jones, and J. Logothetopoulos. 1953. "The effect of breathing 5–7% CO_2 on urine flow and mineral excretion," Clin. Sci. *12:* 1.
Barker, E. S., R. B. Singer, J. R. Elkinton, and J. K. Clark. 1957. "The renal response in man to acute experimental respiratory alkalosis and acidosis," J. Clin. Invest. *36:* 515.

Brocklehurst, J. R., and Y. Henderson. 1927. "The buffering of the tissues as indicated by the CO_2 capacity of the body," J. Biol. Chem. 72: 665.

Brodie, D. A., and D. M. Woodbury. 1958. "Acid-base changes in brain and blood of rats exposed to high concentrations of carbon dioxide," Am. J. Physiol. 192: 91.

Carter, N. W., D. W. Seldin, and H. C. Teng. 1958. "Renal and cellular responses to acute and chronic respiratory acidosis," J. Clin. Invest. 37: 883.

Consolazio, W. V., M. B. Fisher, N. Pace, L. J. Pecora, G. C. Pitts, and A. R. Behnke. 1947. "Effects on man of high concentration of CO_2 in relation to various oxygen pressures during exposures as long as 72 hours," Am. J. Physiol. 151: 479.

Cooke, R. E., F. R. Coughlin, Jr., and W. E. Segar. 1952. "Muscle composition in respiratory acidosis," J. Clin. Invest. 31: 1006.

Denton, D. A., M. Maxwell, I. R. McDonald, J. Munro, and W. Williams. 1952. "Renal regulation of the extracellular fluid in acute respiratory acidemia," Australian J. Exptl. Biol. and Med. Sci. 30: 489.

Dorman, P. J., W. J. Sullivan, and R. F. Pitts. 1954. "The renal response to acute respiratory acidosis," J. Clin. Invest. 33: 82.

Elkinton, J. R., R. B. Singer, E. S. Barker, and J. K. Clark. 1955. "Effects in man of acute experimental respiratory alkalosis and acidosis on ionic transfers in the total body fluids," J. Clin. Invest. 34: 1671.

Foulds, H. P. S., D. Mendel, and R. R. de Mowbray. 1958. "Changes in serum potassium levels and in pH of arterial blood in respiratory acidosis," Lancet. 1: (1707), 405.

Freeman, F. H., and W. O. Fenn. 1953. "Changes in carbon dioxide stores of rats due to atmospheres low in oxygen or high in carbon dioxide," Am. J. Physiol. 174: 422.

Giebisch, G., and R. F. Pitts. 1955. "The extrarenal response to acute acid-base disturbances of respiratory origin," J. Clin. Invest. 34: 231.

Killian, P. J., and K. E. Schaefer. 1954. "Effects of exposure to 30% CO_2 in air and in O_2 on carbonic anhydrase activity in blood and kidney," Fed. Proc. 13: 259.

Levitin, H., C. R. Jockers, and F. H. Epstein. 1958. "The response of tissue electrolytes to respiratory acidosis," Clin. Res. 6: 259.

Miller, A. T., Jr. 1940. "Acclimatization to CO_2: A study of chemical and cellular changes in the blood," Am. J. Physiol. 129: 524.

Nichols, G., Jr. 1958. "Serial changes in tissue carbon dioxide content during respiratory acidosis," J. Clin. Invest. 37: 1111.

Platts, M. M., and M. S. Greaves. 1957. "The composition of the blood in respiratory acidosis," Clin. Sci. 16: 695.

Relman, A. J., B. Etsten, and W. B. Schwartz. 1953. "The regulation of renal bicarbonate reabsorption by plasma carbon dioxide tension," J. Clin. Invest. 32: 972.

Schaefer, K. E. 1949. "Respiration and acid-base balance during prolonged exposure to 3% CO_2," Pflueg. Arch. 251: 689.

Schaefer, K. E. 1951. "Studies of carbon dioxide toxicity. I. Chronic CO_2 toxicity in submarine medicine," U. S. Nav. Med. Res. Lab. Report No. 181 10: 156.

Schaefer, K. E., and B. Barton. 1956. "Phases in blood and tissue electrolyte shifts in chronic respiratory acidosis," XXth Internation. Physiol. Congress. Communications, p. 797.

Schaefer, K. E., C. T. G. King, J. L. Mego, and E. E. Williams. 1955. "Effect of a narcotic level of CO_2 on adrenal conical activity and carbohydrate metabolism," Am. J. Phys. 183: 53.

Schaefer, K. E. 1961. "A concept of triple tolerance limits based on chronic carbon dioxide toxicity," Aerospace Medicine 32: 197.

Scribner, B. H., K. Fremont-Smith, and J. M. Burnell. 1955. "The effect of acute respiratory acidosis on the internal equilibrium of potassium," J. Clin. Invest. 34: 1276.

Shaw, L. A. 1926–27. "The comparative capacity of blood and of the tissues to absorb carbonic acid," Am. J. Physiol. 79: 91.

Shock, N. W., and A. B. Hastings. 1935. "Studies of the acid-base balance of the blood. IV. Characterization and interpretation of displacement of the acid-base balance," J. Biol. Chem. *112:* 239.

Singer, R. B., and A. B. Hastings. 1948. "An improved clinical method for the estimation of disturbances of the acid-base balance of human blood," Medicine *27:* 223.

Sullivan, W. J., and P. J. Dorman. 1955. "The renal response to chronic respiratory acidosis," J. Clin. Invest. *34:* 268.

Van Slyke, D. D., H. Wu, and F. C. McLean. 1923. "Studies of gas and electrolyte equilibria in the blood. V. Factors controlling the electrolyte and water distribution in the blood," J. Biol. Chem. *56:* 765.

The Effect of Prolonged Exposure to Carbon Dioxide on Calcification

W. R. STANMEYER, C. T. G. KING, H. SCOFIELD and
R. COLBY

U. S. Naval Medical Research Laboratory, New London, Connecticut

It has long been suspected that carbon dioxide exerts some effect on the process of calcification. In the German Submarine Medical Service (Schaefer) during World War II, deviations from normal calcification patterns in persons subjected to increased CO_2 content of atmospheric air were first clinically observed. After repeated prolonged submergence, during which time atmospheric conditions of CO_2 rose within the boats, it was observed that pitting, ridging, splitting, and areas of hypercalcification occurred in the finger nails of the crew. Schaefer, Nichols, and Carey (1957) found that in subjects exposed for long periods of time to low concentrations of CO_2 there appeared to be an increase in the calcium content of red cells and a decrease in phosphorous content of these same cells. Studies in guinea pigs (Schaefer, 1961) exposed to 15% CO_2 up to 7 days, with recovery periods of two weeks, have indicated a significant decrease in inorganic phosphorus of whole blood and plasma and an increase in calcium in the serum. Nichols (1958) attempted to determine the affinity of certain tissues for CO_2 and reported that rats showed a decline in total bone CO_2 under experimental conditions. This was explained by the demonstration that CO_2 exists in bone as the carbonate ($CO_3^=$) rather than the bicarbonate (HCO_3^-) ion. Further search of the literature has revealed no additional references to the problem of CO_2 and calcification.

This study was undertaken to determine what effect continuous exposure to 15% CO_2, in air enriched to 21% O_2, had on the calcification of normally calcifying tissues as expressed by changes in the calcium-phosphorus serum values and changes in calcification of the dentin of the rat incisor.

157

ANIMAL OF CHOICE

The incisor of the rat is a tooth of continuous eruption in which the rate of attrition equals the rate of growth. The rate of dentin matrix deposition has been measured at 16 μ daily (Schour and Steadman, 1935). Hoffman and Schour (1938) state that the rate of dentin growth is independent of the animal's weight and general condition. As the layers of dentin are formed, they move forward, recording not only the rate of growth but changes in calcium metabolism similar to the rings of a tree recording climatic variations (Farris and Griffith, 1942). The incisor teeth reflect with a high degree of accuracy and sensitivity the fluctuations of calcium and phosphorus metabolism (Schour et al., 1937). Karshan and Rosebury (1933) believe that the histologic analysis of the rat incisor is most sensitive to slight alterations of the blood serum content of these electrolytes. Schour (1938) has expressed the opinion that in experiments involving modifications in calcium-phosphorus ratios the calcifying dental tissues will show clean-cut responses that may not be recognizable in other tissues. The withdrawal of calcium from these tissues is thought to be impossible (Farris and Griffith, 1942; Thoma, 1950; Schour, 1953); consequently, the changes recorded are permanent within a period of 40–42 days, which is the length of time required for the rat incisor to replace itself.

CALCIFICATION MECHANISMS IN THE DENTIN OF THE RAT INCISOR

A comprehensive review of the calcification of dentin can be found in the literature (Farris and Griffith, 1942; Schour, 1953; Maximow and Bloom, 1953); a brief review follows. One of the structural elements of the dental pulp is the odontoblast. These are highly specialized columnar connective tissue cells forming a layer of the pulp adjacent to the dentin and having protoplasmic fibrils extending into the dentin. Histochemical studies have illustrated the presence of calcium, phosphorus, and potassium not only in the odontoblasts but in their fibrils. In addition, the cytoplasm contains alkaline phosphatase and glycoprotein indicating the role of the odontoblast in the calcification of the dentin.

As these odontoblasts form new dentin matrix, the matrix previously laid down is being calcified in an incremental ring fashion. The precipitation of calcium salts in a protein matrix is probably a physico-chemical process. It occurs in typical Liesegang ring formation with calcium being precipitated in the predentin as crystals of tricalcium phosphate. These crystals occur as clusters and are termed calcospherites. These calcospherites coalesce when their size increases, resulting in the formation of a regular layer of calcified dentin.

METHOD

Sexually mature male rats of the Wistar-Hisaw strain weighing between 200–300 grams were exposed to 15% carbon dioxide in air for 1, 2, 3, 4, 5, 6, 7, and 15 days, plus 7 days with 7 days recovery and 14 days with 14 days recovery. To prevent the effects of blood and tissue changes due to an anoxia, the gas mixture was enriched to contain 21% oxygen.

Rigid controls were maintained prior to, and during the experiment. Animals were first removed from the animal rooms and placed in the experimental chambers under experimental conditions with the exception that the air furnished them was room air. They were maintained under these conditions until they were acclimated to their new surroundings as indicated by a resumption of weight gain. After three days of continuous weight gain, the gaseous content of air furnished them was changed to 15% CO_2 in air enriched to 21% O_2. During the entire period of acclimatization and experimentation, temperature was maintained at 78°F ± 2, humidity 65%, night-day light cycles of 12 hours of light and 12 hours of darkness with standard Rockland Rat Diet and tap water ad libitum. Animal waste products fell through the wire mesh floor of the chamber into large trays of Kitty Litter which were removed frequently.

Upon the termination of experimental conditions the animals were weighed prior to killing. Since calcification may be defined in terms of the concentration of calcium and phosphate in the blood (Maximow and Bloom, 1953), blood was carefully procured through heart punctures after the animal was stunned by a blow at the base of the skull.

Blood serum calcium was determined by the method of Munson et al. (Munson et al., 1955) and serum inorganic phosphorus by the method of Fiske and Subbarow with modifications of Roe and Whitmore (Roe and Whitmore, 1938).

The mandibles and maxillae were resected and prepared for histologic viewing, imbedding some specimens in celloidin and others in paraffin. Sections were stained using both hematoxylin-eosin stains and silver impregnation techniques.

RESULTS

Body weights

Figure 1 illustrates the differences between body weights of control and experimental animals. The weight curve of the control group was upward with a mean daily weight gain of 4 grams. The general trend of the experimental group's weight curve was downward with a mean daily weight loss of 2.2 grams. In the groups of animals exposed to CO_2 for 7 days and allowed to recover for 7 days and in that group exposed for 14 days and allowed to recover for

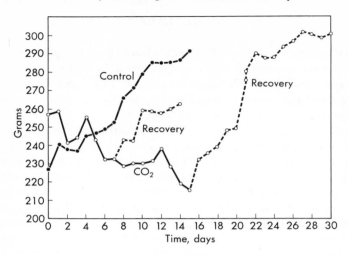

Comparison of weight changes of control rats with group exposed to 15% CO_2 in air enriched to 21% O_2.

14 days, the recovery phase in both instances was accompanied by a daily weight gain of 4 grams paralleling that of the control group.

HISTOLOGIC FINDINGS

When staining with hematoxylin-eosin, tissues that are well calcified stain dark with hematoxylin and those tissues less well calcified stain with eosin. In the tooth sections of animals killed at 15 days and cut at 7 μ from paraffin and 15 μ from celloidin there appeared accentuated pairs of light and dark lines first noticeable in an area which varied between 220 and 250 μ from the pulp. The rate of dentin formation being approximately 16 μ per day, 240 μ should be the region in which dentin was forming 15 days prior to sacrifice.

Figure 2a clearly illustrates the demarcation between normally calcifying dentin and the accentuation of this pattern following the introduction of CO_2. This accentuation of the incremental calcification pattern appeared in all animals, but was more evident in some than others. In most animals there were light and dark lines alternately all the way to the uncalcified predentin as illustrated in Fig. 2b.

In silver preparations the bands that stained eosinophilic stained darker than the rest of the dentin. This would suggest that in these areas the dentin matrix forms normally but fails to calcify.

Vascular inclusions were noted in over half of the specimens studied. Some of these vascular inclusions were deep, extending through the entire area of dentin formed during the experimental period, while others were quite shallow. It is of interest to note that these inclusions occur more frequently at a point exending from the pulp toward a point where the enamel meets the root (cemento-enamel junction).

The width of the predentin did not appear to increase beyond its normal 10–20 μ, but the border of the dentin where calcification is first beginning is moderately wavy.

SERUM CALCIUM VALUES

The average serum calcium level for the strain of rat used was found to be 10.02 mg %. After the first day of exposure the blood calcium values rose to 10.35 mg % continuing to rise through the second day to 11.06 mg %. The values fell on the third day to 9.84 and remained at this level during the fourth day. The fifth day of exposure to CO_2 saw the serum calcium values rise to 11.20 mg % and continue rising to 11.55 mg % on the sixth day. The seventh day values began decreasing. There were no intermediate points between the seventh and fifteenth day when blood calcium values were measured at 10.30 mg %. The serum calcium values after seven days exposure to CO_2, followed by a seven-day recovery period, and those following a fourteen-day exposure and fourteen-day recovery gave values of 9.65 and 9.98 mg %, respectively. The rapidity with which these values are reached following a return to a room air environment is not known.

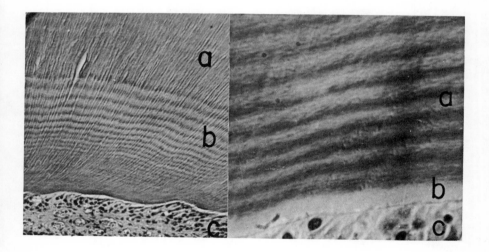

FIGURE 2.
Left: (a) Normal dentin calcified before CO_2; (b) start of CO_2; (c) odontoblasts (x 100). *Right:* (a) Accentuation of incremental pattern; (b) predentin; (c) odontoblasts (x 440).

SERUM INORGANIC PHOSPHORUS VALUES

The serum inorganic phosphates in control animals were measured at 9.85 mg %. During days one and two of exposure, phosphate values dropped to 9.3 and 5.5 mg %, respectively. The inorganic phosphorus values rose on the third day to 8.9 mg % only to drop on the fourth and fifth day to 8.1 and 8.0 mg %. The drop became precipitous on the sixth day, falling to 6.4 and continuing into the seventh day to 5.1 mg %.

A value was determined on the fifteenth day of 8.1 mg %, but any intermediate fluctuations have not been studied. In like manner, values were established after seven days exposure with seven days recovery and fifteen days exposure with fifteen days recovery at 9.8 and 9.6 mg %, respectively. As in the calcium recovery determinations, it is not known how soon after return to room air these points are reached. Figure 3 illustrates the relationship of the changes in serum calcium to the serum phosphorus levels.

DISCUSSION AND COMMENTS

Histologic changes in the calcification pattern of the dentin of the rat incisor may be indicative of such things as the effects of inorganic salts, endocrine function, vitamin utilization, or direct cellular reaction to a toxic or traumatic

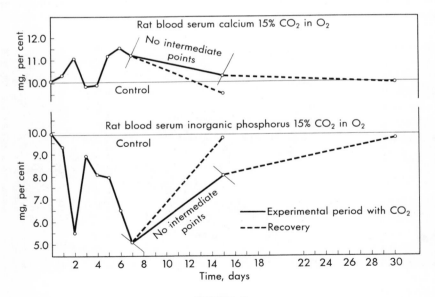

FIGURE 3.

A comparison of blood serum calcium and phosphorus levels during exposure to 15% CO_2 in air enriched to 21% O_2 for from 1 to 15 days, with periods of recovery following the 7th and 15th days.

substance on the animal. Frequently the changes in patterns are so distinctive that the basic reasons for the changes are readily discernible. In other instances, changes may be seen that strengthen one's conclusions based on other methods of diagnosis.

In studying the effects of CO_2 on calcification, it became readily apparent in examining the dentin that calcification was being affected. This was apparent from the accentuation of the incremental deposition of dentin and the rhythmic and marked increase in hypercalcified and hypocalcified lines. The finding of vascular inclusions and the moderately wavy border of the dentin just beginning to calcify were all indicative of changes in normal calcification.

The effects of inorganic salts or a state of hyper- or hypo-vitaminosis being the causative factors of these calcification changes seem unlikely since the food offered was a balanced standard laboratory diet given ad libitum. Experimental animals did lose weight amounting to a mean of two grams a day over a fifteen-day period. Closer analysis of the weight curves, however, discloses that during the first 24–48 hours there is actually a weight gain. Previous investigators (Schaefer, Storr and Scheer, 1949) have shown that the general behavior of animals under CO_2 can be divided into two phases. The first stage is one of increased excitation during which time there is noted an increase in mobility and in the amount of food consumed. The increase in mobility was not observed in this experiment but the increase in food consumption is evidenced by the increase in weight. The second stage is one of depression during which time the animal's mobility is decreased and they "now ate a smaller although still sufficient amount of food." It was evident during this second phase that our experimental animals commenced losing weight.

Talmage et al. (1953) have shown that the calcium levels in blood serum are maintained for at least 42 hours of starvation even though there is a considerable drop in the serum phosphate levels after 36 hours.

Animals under CO_2 continued to eat so starvation never became a problem influencing serum electrolyte levels. In addition, the histologic changes appear to start immediately upon introducing the animal to a CO_2 environment and these changes continued until killing.

The use of silver preparations indicated that the eosinophilic staining dentin matrix formed normally but failed to calcify. This would indicate that CO_2 does not have a direct effect on the dentin-forming cellular elements.

It can be concluded, then, that the changes observed in calcification are not due to the effects of inorganic salts or vitamins in the diet and, since the dentin matrix forms normally, are not a result of toxic action of the CO_2 on the cell itself. The changes occurring, therefore, must be a reflection of changes in the calcium-phosphorus metabolism.

Collip et al. (1925) first discovered the influence of the parathyroids on calcium-phosphorus metabolism. It has since become well established that with the removal of the parathyroids the serum calcium level falls rapidly, and that in intact animals an injection of parathyroid extract causes a rise in the serum calcium levels. In like manner, the serum inorganic phosphorus levels rise when the calcium levels fall, and fall when the calcium levels rise.

Variations in the blood serum calcium from one day through seven days of exposure to CO_2 suggest that there is a stimulation of the parathyroids during the first two days evidenced by a rise in blood calcium values. During the third and fourth days serum calciums return to normal. On the fifth and sixth days the calcium values rise to heights above the peak of the second day. A drop begins on the seventh day.

It will be noted (Fig. 3) that when the suggested parathyroid stimulation occurs calcium values rise and phosphorus values decline with a depression of values far surpassing those rising values of calcium.

Further work between the seventh and fifteenth days must be done. If the present trend continues, we would expect a third and fourth peak of calcium values surpassing those occurring during the first six days.

It has previously been pointed out that neither calcium nor phosphorus can be removed from the teeth. The incremental lines of hyper- and hypocalcification seen histologically must be the result of changes in calcium-phosphorus levels of the blood. Schour and Ham (1934) have shown that during an episode of hypercalcemia dentin was poorly calcified and a well-calcified stripe was formed when the serum calcium values fell after the hypercalcemia. The increase in blood calcium values found in parathyroid stimulation must come from the bone. This was demonstrated in 1942 by Schour and Massler, who stated that in hyperparathyroidism there is an abnormal increase in osteoclastic action and fibrous changes occurring in the bone marrow.

It appears then that CO_2 acts as a stimulus to the parathyroid glands. The stimulus does not produce a constant hypercalcemia since calcium values intermittently fell to normal only to rise to a higher peak. In recovery studies done first at 14 days and then at 7 days, calcium values approach normal but the shape of the recovery curves is not known at this time. The areas of hypo- and hypercalcification of the dentin must reflect changes in blood serum calcium and phosphorus values, the dentin hypocalcifying during hypercalcemia, and hypercalcifying when serum calcium levels approach control values.

SUMMARY

Rats of the Wistar-Hisaw strain were exposed to 15% CO_2 in air enriched to 21% O_2 to determine the effect of CO_2 on the process of calcification. Histologic analysis of the dentin of the incisor tooth showed an accentuation of the incremental calcification pattern and vascular inclusions. The dentin matrix was formed at the rate observed in control animals.

Calcium and phosphorus blood serum levels were studied and variations occurred suggesting a parathyroid stimulation during which two peaks were reached at the second and sixth days. Serum calcium values returned to control values between these peaks. Phosphorus levels declined as calcium levels rose.

REFERENCES

Collip, J. B., E. P. Clark, and J. W. Scott. 1925. Biol. Chem. *66:* 439.

J. Q. Griffith, and E. J. Farris. 1942. *The Rat in Laboratory Investigation*, J. B. Lippincott Co., Chap. 6, p. 151.

J. Q. Griffith, and E. J. Farris. 1942. *The Rat in Laboratory Investigation*, J. B. Lippincott Co., Chap. 6, p. 114.

Hoffman, M. M., and I. Schour. 1938. "Rate and Gradients of Growth in Rat Molars As Demonstrated by Injections of Alizarin Red S," J. Dent. Research *17:* 307–308.

Karshan, M., and T. Rosebury. 1933. "Correlation of Chemical and Pathological Changes in Teeth and Bones on Rachitic and Non-Rachitic Rats," J, Dent. Research *13:* 305.

Maximow, A. A., and W. Bloom. 1953. *A Textbook of Histology*, 6th ed., Philadelphia, Chap. 22, p. 347.

Ibid., p. 137.

Munson, P. L., O. Iseri, A. Kenny, U. Cohn, and M. Sheps. 1955. "A Rapid and Precise Semimicro Method for the Analysis of Calcium," J. Dent. Research *34:* 714.

Nichols, George, Jr. 1958. "Serial Changes in Tissue CO_2 during Respiratory Acidosis," J. Clin. Invest. *37:* 1111.

Roe, J. H., and Whitmore, E. R. 1938. "Clinico-pathologic application of serum phosphate determination with special reference to lesions of the bones," Am. J. Clin. Path. *8:* 233.

Schaefer, K. E. Personal communication. U. S. Naval Medical Research Laboratory, New London, Connecticut.

Schaefer, K. E., G. Nichols, and C. Carey. 1957. "The Effect of Prolonged Exposure to Low CO_2 Concentrations on Acid Base Balance and Electrolytes in Blood and Urine," U. S. Naval Med. Res. Lab. Report No. 292.

Schaefer, K. E., M. Hasson, and H. Niemeoller. 1961. "The effect of prolonged exposure to 15% CO_2 on calcium and phosphorus metabolism," Proc. Soc. E.B.M., in press.

(*a*) Schaefer, K. E., H. Storr, and K. Scheer. 1949. Pflüg. Arch. *251:* 741.

(*b*) Schaefer, K. E. 1951. Am. J. Physiol. *167:* (3).

Schour, I., and A. W. Ham. 1934. "Action of Vitamin D and of the Parathyroid Hormone on the Calcium Metabolism," Arch. Pathol. *17:* 22–39.

Schour, I., and S. Steadman. 1935. "The Growth Pattern and Daily Rhythm of the Incisor of the Rat," Anat. Rec. *63:* 325–333.

Schour, I., S. Chandler, and W. Tweedy. 1937. "Changes in the Teeth Following Parathyroidectomy," Am. J. Pathol. *13:* 945–970.

Schour, I. 1938. "Calcium Metabolism and Teeth," J. Am. Med. Assoc. *110:* 870–877.

Schour, I. 1953. *Noyes' Oral Histology and Embryology*, 7th ed., Philadelphia, Ch. 6, p. 89; Ch. 7, p. 128.

Schour, I. 1953. *Noyes' Oral Histology and Embryology*, 7th ed., Philadelphia, Ch. 7, p. 123.

Talmage, Roy V., F. W. Kraintz, R. C. Frost, and L. Kraintz. 1953. "Evidence for a Dual Action of Parathyroid Extract in Maintaining Serum Calcium and Phosphorus Levels," Endocrinology *52:* 318–323.

Thoma, Kurt H. 1950. *Oral Pathology*, 3rd ed., St. Louis, Ch. 3, p. 76.

Tissue Metabolism Under Low and High Oxygen Tension

D. E. BEISCHER

U. S. N. School of Aviation Medicine, Pensacola, Florida

Hypoxia and hyperoxia are central problems in a discussion of the ecology of closed biological systems. Although the limitations of higher life in an atmosphere deficient in oxygen are well recognized, it is not always realized that pure oxygen at atmospheric or higher pressure is sooner or later lethal to all living matter. A search for the final causes of hypoxia and hyperoxia on the cellular level was first suggested by Paul Bert. Recent progress made in cell morphology by the use of the electron microscope combined with advances in the biochemistry of cellular metabolism promises new insight into the physiological disturbances caused by the lack or surplus of oxygen.

Mitrochondria are widely accepted as the main seat of enzyme activity in cellular respiration. Electron microscopy demonstrates an organized intramitochondrial structure. The enzymes involved in cellular respiration are likely to be arranged in an orderly manner in the "cristae" of the inner structure of a mitochondrion. This array of the single enzymes in the insoluble matrix of mitochondria is assumed to facilitate the transport of matter and energy in the multienzyme system (Green, 1956–1957).

The sequence of components in the respiratory chain as proposed in the work of Keilin and Hartrees (1939), Slater (1938), and Chance (1954), is outlined in Fig. 1. Approximately thirty substrate specific dehydrogenases start the chain at the reducing end near the substrate. They are followed by flavoproteins and cytochromes. All respiratory enzymes consist of a "prosthetic group" attached to a protein. Neither the protein nor the prosthetic group by itself is enzymatically active. The enzyme molecules are embedded in a framework of lipoproteins and polysaccharides. The terminal oxidase transmits electrons to oxygen. The resulting oxygen ion reacts with hydrogen ions and forms water (Table 1).

166

The energy set free in the oxidation of the substrate is siphoned from the enzyme chain at three places marked in Fig. 1. It is used to transfer adenosine diphosphate to adenosine triphosphate. The precise mechanism of oxidation phosphorylation is still unknown.

This general outline of cellular oxidation may serve as a guide in tracing irregularities which occur in hyperoxia and hypoxia. In man, many of the temporary beneficial effects of an increase in oxygen concentration in the inhaled gas mixture may be traced to the fact that some cells remote to arterioles, as in the brain, live normally at the brink of anoxia.

The long-term *adverse* effects of high oxygen concentrations in the tissue of all living material must be connected with fundamental disturbances of the normal processes of cellular oxidation. The most widely accepted explanation of these disturbances stresses that the enzymes may fall prey to *irreversible* oxidation. Enzymes with -SH groups appear to be very susceptible to this kind of oxidation (Dickens, 1949). Mainly dehydrogenases are described as being irreversibly oxidized at the -SH groups of their apoprotein. Because all enzymes of the respiratory chain are protein-linked, other members of the chain that carry -SH groups in the apoprotein may also be affected by irreversible oxidation. The prosthetic groups of the respiratory enzymes seem to be more resistant to irreversible oxidation. The effect of activators and metal ions on the irreversible oxidation of respiratory enzymes cannot be described in detail here.

In addition, higher concentrations of oxygen in the tissue may favor other pathways of oxidation (Table 1). Although the role of oxygen as electron acceptor is predominant, other functions of this molecule have to be considered.

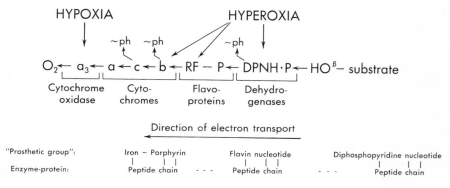

FIGURE 1.

Inhibition of respiratory enzyme chain by hypoxia and hyperoxia.

TABLE 1

Functions of oxygen in cellular metabolism

1. *Electron acceptor* under the influence of electron transfer oxidases with formation of one molecule of hydrogen peroxide or two molecules of water:

$$O_2 + 2e \rightarrow O_2^{--} + 2H^+ \rightarrow H_2O_2$$
$$O_2 + 4e \rightarrow 2O^{--} + 4H^+ \rightarrow 2H_2O$$

2. *Addition* of one or both atoms of oxygen to the substrate under the influence of oxidases:

$$AH + O_2 + 2e \rightarrow AOH + O^{--}$$

or oxygen transferases:

$$A + O_2 \rightarrow AO_2$$

3. *Perturbation* of the movement of electrons in neighboring molecules of the enzyme by the paramagnetic properties of oxygen.

The addition of one or both atoms of oxygen to a substrate under the influence of oxidase or oxygen transferase might possibly inactivate enzymes of the respiratory chain.

A further property of oxygen which may affect cellular respiration was recently stressed by Szent-Györgyi (1957). The paramagnetic properties of oxygen are likely to exert an influence on the movement of electrons in adjoining parts of the respiratory chain. An excess or lack of oxygen may well influence the movement of electrons and may jeopardize the normal function of the multienzyme system. Measurements of the magnetic resonance of electrons in biological systems at different oxygen pressures would be valuable in a further study of this effect.

The orderly array of the multienzyme system in the matrix of the mitochondrion may afford a steric protection for single members of the respiratory chain. With a single enzyme, cytochrome c, Theorell (1956) demonstrated that the surrounding peptide spirals enclose the hemin plate from all sides so completely that the molecular oxygen has no access to the iron atom of the hemin. Reduced cytochrome c cannot be oxidized by oxygen gas. However, electrons can pass the screening enclosure.

The effect of *low* oxygen concentrations on tissue metabolism was investigated frequently (Knox *et al.*, 1956). No general adaptation of cellular metabolism to hypoxia was found. A number of specific adaptive changes in the respiratory enzyme system are described (Knox *et al.*, 1956) such as an increase of up to 300% in the concentration of cytochrome c in the skeletal muscle of guinea pigs adapted to low oxygen tension (Delachaux and Tissiers, 1946). However, the beneficial use of doses of cytochrome c in oxygen deficiency is still uncertain (Editorial, 1956).

More pronounced effects were observed at very low oxygen concentrations near the zero value (Chance, 1957). The rate of tissue respiration for yeast and tissue homogenates is constant until the oxygen concentration reaches a value of approximately 1 μM. At a further decrease of the oxygen concentration the rate of oxydation falls abruptly. Chance (1957) could demonstrate by kinetic observation of the single members of the respiratory chain that the terminal oxidase, cytochrome oxidase, is especially sensitive to oxygen lack. Under normal conditions an over-abundance of oxidase in the mammalian respiratory chain affords a protective or cushioning effect which allows considerable changes in the tissue respiratory rate. In severe hypoxia, which approaches the anaerobic state, the reduction of oxidase determines the decrease of respiration rate. At zero oxygen concentration all members of the respiratory chain, including cytochrome oxidase, are completely reduced. This state can be reversed by renewed access of the respiratory chain to oxygen. The permanent damage of anoxia to tissue is probably caused by the lack of energy normally produced by the oxidation process.

At a drastic reduction of oxygen tension and during total absence of oxygen the cell may procure part or all of its energy demand temporarily or permanently by fermentation. However, fermentation which produces energy by changes in the arrangement of the atoms in the metabolites cannot support a high order of specialization in cells. Warburg (1956), in particular, stressed the degeneration of cells which were temporarily exposed to a restricted oxygen supply. Degenerated cells which use fermentation as an energy source lose their respiratory abilities permanently and may develop malformation and finally become cancerous. The observations of Goldblatt and Cameron (1953) made with *in vitro* cultures of fibroblasts exposed to intermittent oxygen deficiency for long periods of time support this hypothesis. Tumor cells appeared under these conditions; no tumor was observed in control cultures. Oxygen seems to be vitally important for the development and sustenance of organized cell functions. It is possible that cell organization depends not only on the great amount of energy available from aerobic metabolism but also on the paramagnetic properties of oxygen mentioned above.

Summarizing, one can say that hypoxia and hyperoxia influence primarily the opposite ends of the respiratory chain. *Hyperoxia,* by irreversible oxidation of some parts of the respiratory chain, ultimately brings tissue respiration to a complete standstill. The cells may survive *hypoxia* and even *anoxia* by conversion from respiration to fermentation with loss of higher structural identity of the cell.

REFERENCES

Chance, B. 1954. *In:* McElroy and Glass, editors, *The Mechanism of Enzyme Action,* Johns Hopkins, Baltimore.
Chance, B. 1957. Fed. Proc. *16:* 671.
Delachaux, A., and A. Tissiers. 1946. Helv. Med. Acta *13:* 333.
Dickens, F. 1949. Biochem. J. *40:* 171.

Editorial article. 1956. Deut. Med. Wsch. *81:* 248.
Goldblatt, H., and G. Cameron. 1953. J. Exptl. Med. *97:* 525.
Green, D. E. 1956–57. The Harvey Lectures *52:* 177.
Keilin, D., and E. F. Hartrees. 1939. Proc. Roy. Soc. Med. London *B127:* 167.
Knox, W. E., V. H. Auerbach, and E. C. C. Lin. 1956. Physiol. Rev. *36:* 164.
Slater, E. G. 1938. Biochem. Z. *295:* 262.
Szent-Györgyi, A. 1957. *Bioenergetics,* Academic Press, New York.
Theorell, H. 1956. Science *124:* 467.
Warburg, O. 1956. Science *123:* 309.

The Biological Effects of Increased Oxygen Tension*

REBECA GERSCHMAN

Department of Physiology, University of Rochester School of Medicine and Dentistry, Rochester, New York

Reports describing deleterious effects of oxygen have been accumulating in the literature since the classical experiments of P. Bert (Bert, transl. 1943). He showed in 1878 that exposure to unphysiologically high oxygen tensions causes irreversible damage to living matter. The problem of oxygen toxicity has become increasingly important in clinical medicine and in submarine and space medicine.

Its electronic configuration confers on the oxygen molecule special properties. Paramagnetism is one of them (Pauling, 1945). Figure 1 shows the electronic configuration of the oxygen molecule. The axes of the p orbitals (x, y, and z) are represented by the straight lines. Notice the two unpaired electrons (p_y and p_z electrons). Actually these electrons form two three-electron bonds, but give the property of paramagnetism to the oxygen molecule. Oxygen has a very high oxidizing potential which makes it a good potential energy source used by living matter. However, this high potential carries with it a threat to tissue integrity and life itself.

According to Oparin (1957), oxygen in the atmosphere was derived from living matter by the process of photosynthesis. Although oxygen is also produced by the photochemical dissociation of water vapor in the upper atmosphere, the rate of this production is very small in comparison to the rate of oxygen production from photosyntheses (Mason, 1958). Photosynthesis in green plants might be considered a process of transforming solar energy into the potential energies stored in the form of carbohydrate in the cell and oxygen in

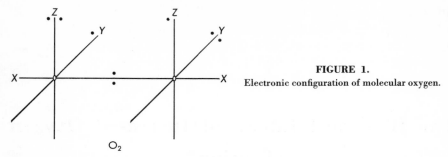

FIGURE 1.
Electronic configuration of molecular oxygen.

the atmosphere which can be utilized by the living cell through controlled enzyme systems by a reverse process (respiration). The fact that oxygen is a sluggish oxidizing agent actually permits its use as a potential energy source. If it were a rapid oxidizing agent, it would react too quickly to permit the storage of any energy. Gorin (1940) has postulated that due to sluggishness of oxygen as an oxidizing agent it first has to be activated to the free radical state. According to the theory of Michaelis (1949) the reduction of oxygen proceeds by univalent steps which would imply intermediate free radical states.

Free radicals in biological systems have been recently demonstrated by electron spin resonance spectroscopy measurements (Commoner *et al.*, 1957; Sogo and Tolbert, 1957). Oxygen in the presence of hydrogen would pass through the free radical states $HO_2^{\cdot}$ or O_2 and $OH^{\cdot}$ (Fig. 2). Notice the unpaired electrons of these free radicals which are a characteristic of free radical states. The Pauli exclusion principle requires that the two electrons in the same or-

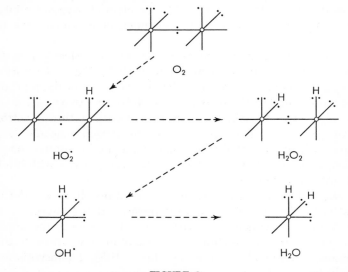

FIGURE 2.
Hydrogen-oxygen species.

bital have opposite spins; thus the magnetic moment of each electron is neutralized. However, when an orbital contains an unpaired electron, the magnetic moment is not neutralized and gives rise to paramagnetism. Figure 3 shows the free energy changes [calculated from data given in Latimer (1952)] in the reduction of oxygen by hydrogen, assuming a univalent transfer of electrons. It can be seen that the free radical states act as energy barriers to oxidation. However, once the free radicals are formed, they react very easily, releasing energy. Thus once the oxygen is in the free radical state it reacts rapidly. Since oxygen possesses such a high oxidizing potential it has the capability to react with many substances. Enzymes and other cell constituents are no exception. Many of these reactions will proceed extremely slowly since a considerable amount of energy is necessary to activate the oxygen to the free radical form. However, once the oxidizing free radicals of oxygen are formed in sufficient amounts, possible chain reactions and other destructive reactions can be started. "Sufficient amounts" does not necessarily imply a large quantity; in fact it could even be extremely small.

To protect against the destructive ability of oxygen the living cells had to build up antioxidant defenses. The convenience of storing potential energy brought with it the necessity for all living matter to produce defenses against uncontrolled oxidations. Although the cell may "buffer" against the destructive

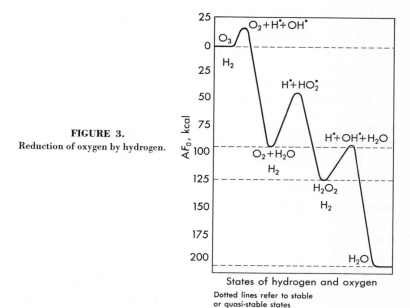

FIGURE 3.
Reduction of oxygen by hydrogen.

* This work was supported by funds provided under contract with the U.S. Air Force School of Aviation Medicine, Randolph Field, Texas.

Oxidizing free radicals may be originated by:

A. Ionizing Radiation

1) $H_2O \xrightarrow{\hspace{0.3cm}\sim\!\sim\!\sim\hspace{0.3cm}} H_2O^+ + E^-$

2) $H_2O^+ + H_2O \longrightarrow H_3O^+ + OH°$

3) $E^- + H_2O \longrightarrow OH^- + H°$

B. Reduction of O_2 (Michaelis)

$O_2 \longrightarrow HO_2° \longrightarrow H_2O_2 \longrightarrow OH° + H_2O \longrightarrow 2H_2O$

C. Reduction of O_2 by $R°$

1) $R°$ Is Formed in Normal Metabolism

2) $R° + O_2 \longrightarrow RO_2°$

FIGURE 4

tendency of oxygen, it seems unlikely that the antioxidant defense will be complete. In an analogous way we can think of acid-base buffers which can resist but not completely prevent the change of pH caused by acids or bases. What is considered a normal concentration of oxygen (air) is what we are prepared for with our antioxidant defenses. It is plausible that a continuous small "slipping" in the defense could be a factor contributing to aging and death and in this sense one might consider that there is no threshold tension necessary for the appearance of the toxic effects of oxygen.

As photosynthetic processes increased during the evolution of green plants, probably the oxygen content of the atmosphere likewise increased, and one can picture a slow development of compensatory increments in the antioxidant defense. In the absence of adequate antioxidant defense the toxicity of oxygen becomes apparent. The presence of oxygen has been known to inactivate enzymes (Stadie *et al.*, 1944; Bean, 1945; Barron, 1936; Fisher *et al.*, 1954; Hellerman *et al.*, 1933).

The importance of oxygen toxicity in relation to bacterial growth has been known for many years. In fact bacteria have been classified according to the observable effects of oxygen. The bacteria which are known to be inhibited by the presence of oxygen in air are called anaerobic. Evidence that anaerobic bacteria contain little antioxidant defense is given by the observations that these bacteria contain no catalase (Porter, 1946), and that in the presence of oxygen hydrogen peroxide is formed (Annear and Dorman, 1952; Gordon *et al.*, 1953; Holman, 1955). Under appropriate conditions high oxygen pressures have been shown to depolymerize DNA (Gilbert *et al.*, 1957). Thus it was not surprising to find that mutation rates can be increased by high oxygen pressures (Fenn *et al.*, 1957).

If there is a lack of antioxidant defense, then the toxic effects of oxygen may become evident. We like to think that some of the symptoms of vitamin E deficient animals may be due to the toxic effect of oxygen at 0.2 atmosphere (air). Vitamin E deficient animals are also more sensitive to high oxygen pressures (Gerschman *et al.*, 1955; Taylor, 1956).

We have postulated that the basic mechanism of oxygen poisoning has simi-

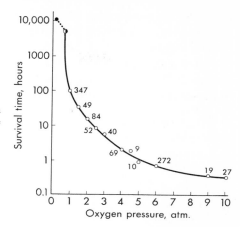

FIGURE 5.

Survival time of female mice at high oxygen pressures. The numbers next to the points on the curve indicate the number of animals exposed.

larities with the initial biological effects of x-irradiation (Gerschman *et al.*, 1954a). The whole problem of x-irradiation, oxygen poisoning, and anoxia, has brought prominently to our minds the thought of biological oxidations in general. One can choose to think that in some aspects of biological oxidations it would be irrelevant whether oxygen is activated by ionizing radiations or by enzymes or other catalysts so long as its sluggishness is overcome. It could be argued that observed differences in these processes might be mainly quantitative and distributional. Antioxidant mechanisms can curtail chain reactions and inhibit auto-oxidations. Figure 4 illustrates some ways in which oxidizing free radicals may be originated. For example, the primary process of ionizing radiation on water is to "bump off" an electron from a water molecule. Both the positively charged water molecules and the electrons can become hydrated to form the free radicals H· and OH· (Hart, 1957). According to the Michaelis theory of univalent oxidation, as mentioned earlier, free radical intermediates will be formed. Thus, the reduction of oxygen by hydrogens would lead to the formation of the free radicals, $HO·_2$ and $OH·$, and H_2O_2. In normal metabolism free radicals have been demonstrated and can react with oxygen to form the free radical $RO·_2$.

However, it could be expected that above a certain oxygen tension chain reactions would be significant and the toxic effects of oxygen would suddenly become more apparent. If so, in our experiments reported below it would appear that this critical oxygen tension for mice lies between 0.1 and 1 atmosphere in the inspired air as judged by the abrupt decrease in their survival time (Fig. 5). It is also of interest to note that a critical dose of x-rays result in a sudden decrease in the survival time of mice (Brues and Sacher, 1952).

To modify the toxic effects of oxygen, various chemical agents have been used (Gerschman *et al.*, 1954a; Gerschman, Gilbert and Caccamise, 1958; Gerschman, Gilbert, and Frost, 1958), and it has become evident that the effects of the same chemical can act in an apparently different manner, dependent upon the oxygen tension. The fact that antioxidants can act as prooxidants has been known for many years (Moureu and Dufraisse, 1926; Mattill, 1947). Thus a substance like glutathione protected mice against 6 atmospheres of oxygen but not against 1 atmosphere of oxygen (Gerschman, Gilbert, and Caccamise, 1958). Part of the explanation of how a given substance can act either as a pro-oxidant or an antioxidant is illustrated in Fig. 6. It can be seen that glutathione can aid in initiation of chain reactions by forming free radicals (pro-oxidant effect). The greater the concentration of free radicals, the more rapidly the propagating reactions will take place. However, glutathione can also act as an antioxidant by removing free radicals and terminating the chain reaction. Depending upon the system studied, it would be expected that glutathione can either have an over-all pro-oxidant or antioxidant action.

CHAIN REACTION

Initiating Reactions (Free Radical Formation)

Pro-oxidant Effect

$$GSH + O_2 \longrightarrow HO_2^\circ + GS^\circ$$
$$HO_2^\circ + RH \longrightarrow R^\circ + H_2O_2$$

Propagating Reactions

Free Radicals Act as Chain Centers

$$R^\circ + O_2 \longrightarrow RO_2^\circ$$
$$RO_2^\circ + RH \longrightarrow R^\circ + RO_2H$$

Terminating Reactions (Free Radical Removal)

Antioxidant Effect

$$RO_2^\circ + GSH \longrightarrow GS^\circ + RO_2H$$
$$R^\circ + R^\circ \longrightarrow RR$$
$$R^\circ + RO_2^\circ \longrightarrow RO_2R$$

FIGURE 6

Of special interest are the substances that might protect animals against moderately increased oxygen tensions. It seems that cobalt may hold a promise in this direction. Cobalt has been shown to destroy hydrogen peroxide (Gilbert et al., 1958) and to protect mice against 1 atmosphere of oxygen (Gerschman, Gilbert, and Caccamise, 1958). It also appears to reverse some of the effects in vitamin E deficiency (as evidenced by changes in the testes[1]).

Another important point is the role of stress. Stimulation of the adrenal glands during oxygen stress has a deleterious effect against oxygen poisoning (Gerschman et al., 1954b). This aspect should be kept in mind for submarine and space travelers.

Also of interest is the observation that prolonged fasting can increase the survival time of mice exposed to 6 atmosphere of oxygen (Gilbert et al., 1955).

Other deleterious effects of oxygen are retrolental fibroplasia (Ashton et al., 1953; Patz et al., 1953; Gerschman et al., 1954c), decreased division rates of Protozoa exposed to oxygen (Fig. 7), and decreased growth rate of mice (Fig. 8).

Since the time Priestley, the discoverer of oxygen (Priestley, 1894), made philosophical remarks on this "pure air" almost every one of the investigators in this field has referred to the toxicity of oxygen as *puzzling, baffling, per-*

[1] In a few experiments performed at our request by Dr. S. I. Mauer of the Dept. of Anatomy, University of Rochester.

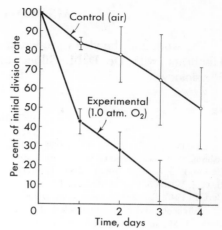

FIGURE 7.

Effect of 1.0 atmosphere oxygen on the division rate of daily isolation cultures of paramecium caudatum.

plexing, etc. The discovery by electron spin resonance spectroscopy of free radicals in living material has substantiated Michaelis' theory and strengthened our views on the mechanism of oxygen toxicity. By doing so we feel that it has greatly decreased the perplexing aspect of the problem and has left a line to follow in the still enormous research waiting to be accomplished in the field.

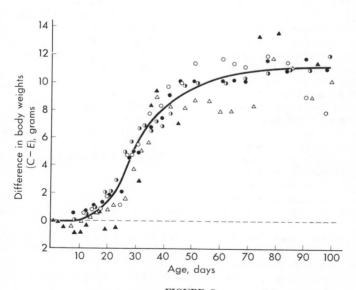

FIGURE 8.

Effect of 0.7 atmosphere of oxygen on body weight of mice.

ACKNOWLEDGMENT

The work and the views presented here are in great part the result of collaboration with Dr. D. L. Gilbert and with others in the Department of Physiology.

REFERENCES

Annear, D. I., and D. C. Dorman. 1952. Australian J. Exptl. Biol. Med. Sci. *30:* 191.

Ashton, N., B. Ward, and G. Serpell. 1953. Brit. J. Ophthalmol. *37:* 513, 1953.

Barron, E. S. G. 1936. J. Biol. Chem. *113:* 695.

Bean, J. W. 1945. Physiol. Rev. *25:* 1.

Bert, P. 1943. *Barometric pressure researches in experimental physiology* 1878. Translated by M. A. Hitchcock and F. A. Hitchcock, College Book Co., Columbus, Ohio.

Brues, A. M., and C. A. Sacher, *In:* J. J. Nickson. 1952. *Symposium on radiobiology. The basic aspects of radiation effects on living systems,* John Wiley & Sons, Inc., New York, p. 441.

Commoner, B., J. J. Heise, B. B. Lippincott, R. E. Norberg, J. V. Passonneau, and J. Townsend. 1957. Science *126:* 57.

Fenn, W. O., R. Gerschman, D. L. Gilbert, and D. E. Terwilliger. 1957. Proc. Natl. Acad. Sci. (U.S.) *43:* 1027.

Fisher, H. F., A. J. Krasna, and D. Rittenburg. 1954. J. Biol. Chem. *209:* 569.

Gerschman, R., D. L. Gilbert, S. W. Nye, and W. O. Fenn. 1955. Fed. Proc. *14:* 56.

Gerschman, R., D. L. Gilbert, S. W. Nye, P. Dwyer, and W. O. Fenn. 1954a. Science *119:* 623.

Gerschman, R., D. L. Gilbert, S. W. Nye, P. Nadig, and W. O. Fenn. 1954b. Am. J. Physiol. *178:* 364.

Gerschman, R., D. L. Gilbert, and J. Frost. 1958. Am. J. Physiol. *192:* 572.

Gerschman, R., D. L. Gilbert, and D. Caccamise. 1958. Am. J. Physiol. *192:* 563.

Gerschman, R., P. W. Nadig, A. C. Snell, Jr., and S. W. Nye. 1954c. Am. J. Physiol. *179:* 113.

Gilbert, D. L., R. Gerschman, and W. O. Fenn. 1955. Am. J. Physiol. *181:* 272.

Gilbert, D. L., R. Gerschman, J. Cohen, and W. Sherwood. 1957. J. Am. Chem. Soc. *79:* 5677.

Gilbert, D. L., R. Gerschman, B. K. Ruhm, and W. E. Price. 1958. J. Gen. Physiol. *41:* 989.

Gordon, J., R. A. Holman, and J. W. McLeod. 1953. J. Pathol. Bact. *66:* 527.

Gorin, M. H. 1940. Ann. N.Y. Acad. Sci. *40:* 123.

Hart, J. E. 1957. J. Chem. Educ. *34:* 586.

Hellerman, L., M. E. Perkins, and W. M. Clark. 1933. Proc. Natl. Acad. Sci. (U. S.) *19:* 855.

Holman, R. A. 1955. J. Pathol. Bact. *70:* 195.

Latimer, W. M. 1952. *The oxidation states of the elements and their potentials in aqueous solutions,* second edition, Prentice-Hall, New York.

Mason, B. 1958. *Principles of geochemistry,* second edition, John Wiley & Sons, Inc., New York.

Mattill, H. A. 1947. Ann. Rev. Biochem. *16:* 177.

Michaelis, L. 1949. Adv. Enzym. *9:* 1 and Biol. Bull. *96:* 293.

Moureu, C., and C. Dufraisse. 1926. Chem. Revs. *3:* 113.

Oparin, A. I. 1957. *The origin of life on the earth.* Translated by Ann Synge, Academic Press, New York.

Patz, A., A. Eastham, D. J. Higginbotham, and T. Kleh. 1953. Am. J. Ophthalmol. *36:* 1511.

Pauling, L. 1945. *The nature of the chemical bond,* Cornell University Press, Ithaca, New York.

Porter, J. R. 1946. *Bacterial chemistry and physiology,* John Wiley & Sons, Inc., New York.

Priestley, J. 1775. *The Discovery of oxygen, Part I, 1894.* Alembic Club Reprints, No. 7, Simpkin, Marshall, Hamilton, Kent, and Co., Ltd., London.

Sogo, P. B., and B. M. Tolbert. 1957. Adv. Biol. Med. Phys. 5: 1.
Stadie, W. C., B. C. Riggs, and N. Haugaard. 1944. Am. J. Med. Sci. 207: 84.
Taylor, D. W. 1956. J. Physiol. 131: 200.

DISCUSSION

Dr. Tappan (University of Maine): I think my comments will have no direct bearing on the paper that Dr. Beischer gave concerning his experiments and his review of the subject of low and high oxygen pressures on metabolic activity. However, I might mention briefly our work at the Andean Institute of Biology at Lima, Peru, which concerned the effect of the adaptation of animals to low oxygen tensions.

The observation has been made that man can work for longer periods at 15,000 feet and accumulate less lactic acid if acclimatized. It has been suggested that some oxidative mechanism was stimulated in acclimatized man. We therefore made some investigations of the oxidative enzymes in a subject from this altitude that we could utilize for tissue studies. For our subjects we chose guinea pigs which were native to high altitudes. We assured ourselves they were native by obtaining these animals from isolated villages and, similarly, guinea pigs from sea level colonies in isolated situations. Of course, guinea pigs were readily available because these animals are used as an item of food among the Andean Indians.

The relatively normal situation of our animals was very different, I think, from what Dr. Beischer was referring to. Our findings indicated that succinoxidase levels were very significantly increased in the high-altitude animals. We found, as have others, that red tissues which have increased some of their pigments—notably myoglobin—were higher in oxidase activities than were white tissues. As has also been observed by others, increases in myoglobin content occurred in animals taken from low levels to high levels. In addition, high-altitude animals had an increased ratio of red tissue to white muscle tissue. Thus the high-altitude animals had a twofold advantage: They had higher succinoxidase levels and more of the pigmented tissue containing greater amounts of oxidative enzymes. Such things as enlargement of the heart—a tissue very rich in these oxidative systems—also augmented the supply of succinoxidase.

We noted that not all the enzyme systems were increased to the same degree. There was some tendency toward increased activity of glycolytic systems in the high-altitude guinea pigs. We also found increased ability in the high-altitude animals not only to synthesize but also to store high-energy phosphates. I do not think this is contradictory to the toxic effects of low oxygen tension; it's a much more normal circumstance and very different from Dr. Beischer's studies.

Dr. J. R. Pappenheimer: I would like to ask whether detectable effects on oxidative metabolism have been noted in magnetic fields.

Dr. Gerschman: I am not aware of any evidence on the subject, but I have been looking into the possibilities.

Dr. Forster (University of Pennsylvania): I would like to ask either Dr. Nichols, Dr. Schaefer, Dr. Stanmeyer, or perhaps Dr. Hastings, whether we are to conclude that breathing high concentrations of CO_2 does or does not increase the calcification of bones. It seems to me that Dr. Nichols' work would suggest it does not, while Dr. Stanmeyer's that it does. Have I interpreted that correctly?

Dr. Nichols: I would rather not get too deeply into it, because I don't think we know. The data we have on bone composition after 48 hours of exposure would suggest that there is no significant change in the calcium, phosphate, or sodium content of these bones. On the other hand, we have no studies on bones of animals after chronic exposure.

Dr. Stanmeyer: I am sure that I cannot add to what Dr. Nichols has said. I said in my presentation, this particular calcifying tissue was a depository, not a repository. In other words, calcium had been deposited within the dental tissues, but it could not be taken out. I do not know of any work which has been done on bones over a long period of time in which the actual calcium content of bones has been studied.

Chairman Hastings: Did I get the impression that the period when you returned the animals to low CO_2 tension was when the tooth wasn't being calcified?

Dr. Stanmeyer: Yes. We appear to get greater calcification of the dentin under CO_2. This would indicate to us that when we do serum studies we probably will find hypercalcemia at that particular time.

Chairman Hastings: How do you account for those alternate light and dark lines? Do those correspond to days?

Dr. Stanmeyer: Yes, that is right. We would normally get one light and one dark line deposited every day due to the diurnal cycle that occurs normally in the rat calcification mechanism. The dark lines were areas that stained more densely with hematoxylin, and the light lines less densely. In the CO_2 animals we showed that there was an accentuation of the dense staining line followed by a decrease in the calcification pattern and less dense staining. This alternated over the entire period of time, rather than on one particular day.

Chairman Hastings: I suppose everyone knows that we found a diurnal variation in arterial CO_2 tension about 20 years ago. It is not very much—about 5 mm—which goes up when you sleep. I wonder if we go through the same diurnal calcification ourselves.

Dr. Stanmeyer: This is very interesting to us, Dr. Hastings, and something that we would like to go into much further.

Dr. Schaefer: I do not understand the difference between bone and teeth. In the teeth apparently, from what I learn from Dr. Stanmeyer, the calcium and phosphorus is deposited and cannot be moved out, but it is relatively easy to move calcium and phosphorus out of the bones. Could you comment on this, Dr. Hastings?

Chairman Hastings: It makes a great difference where that calcium and phosphorus are in the bone. It is pretty hard to get at in some areas. You can move calcium and phosphorus around in the teeth, as I understand it, except in the enamel.

Dr. Stanmeyer: Yes, that is right.

Chairman Hastings: I do not think we have any information, actually, Dr. Forster, on whether more or less bone is deposited under these conditions. It is awfully hard to measure.

Dr. Nichols: This matter of calcification is even more complicated than I, for one, realized. We have been doing some experiments recently with adrenal steroids and their effects on bone composition. It would appear that these steroids have a considerable effect on the amount of calcium that we find in the bone. The reasons for these changes are not particularly germane to this argument, except that you have seen evidence of change in adrenal activity under CO_2. This change may influence bone metabolism as well as other parameters.

Chairman Hastings: You see, you cannot get anybody to measure total calcium, phosphorus, CO_2, citrate, sodium, collagen, and mucopolysaccharides, all under controlled conditions in a single bone. That is what it will take to understand these matters.

Dr. Stein: I would like to ask Dr. Stanmeyer whether any other factors, such as cold, cause a similar pattern in the deposition of calcium in the bone, or is this an isolated finding?

Dr. Stanmeyer: The only work that I know of was done by Dr. Schour (Illinois) during World War II, when it was shown that taking rats up to about 30,000 feet under anoxic conditions gave much the same histologic pattern that we found under CO_2. In other words, this accentuation of the calcification pattern was seen. I do not know of any work that is being done with heat and cold specifically.

Chairman Hastings: Do you remember the work of Dr. Schour on parathyroid hormone?

Dr. Stanmeyer: Certainly. He has worked on parathyroid hormone and hypophysectomized animals. In fact, he has written an excellent chapter in a book on the effects of the parathyroid hormone on the various endocrine systems and the use of the rat to study them.[1] He states in this book that there are many times when merely looking at the calcification pattern allows one to pinpoint what is happening physiologically to the animal.

Chairman Hastings: I am reminded that you can lay down calcium-45 in

[1] *The Rat in Laboratory Investigation* by E. J. Farris and J. Q. Griffith, 2d ed., 1949, J. P. Lippincott Co., Philadelphia.

the bone and under certain conditions study rates at which the isotope will be released. It has been done with steroids. There is no reason why it could not be done with CO_2.

Dr. Stanmeyer: I might say one more thing. In the latest textbook on histology by Maxwell Glick there is a statement made that with the use of radioactive phosphorus some interchange of calcium and phosphorus occurs between enamel and dentin, and between the dentin and the blood supply. In the teeth, for example, that do not have a blood supply, the interchange takes place between the dentin and the surrounding tissues. He does not give a reference for this work, and I have been unable to find it in the literature.

On the other hand, in 1925 Fischer put some dogs on a rachitic diet for many weeks. He extracted a dog's tooth and determined its calcium content prior to this diet. He then extracted another tooth at the end of the experiment, and even though the bones were so soft that they could be cut with a knife, there was no measurable difference between the calcium and phosphorus content of the teeth before and after the experiment.

Dr. Stein: Still, you do not know whether or not there is a variation in pattern. He did not do histologic sections.

Captain A. R. Behnke: In all space ships it is apparent that CO_2 may accumulate in the cabin. Of course, from diving mammals, we know that protoplasm does adapt or compensate to high concentrations of carbon dioxide. However, to me it is amazing that there should be such a gap in our knowledge of the chronic effects of CO_2. I would like to know if experiments have been carried out in which small animals have been exposed to CO_2 of 3 or 5% (since smaller animals tolerate the effects of CO_2 better) from the time they were weaned until they died. I am not talking about intermittent but, rather, continuous exposure. How do we know that individuals cannot adapt to increased concentrations of CO_2, provided that these concentrations are maintained for longer periods of time?

Chairman Hastings: I do not think there have been many such studies, but I remember one that was done by Buchanan and others at the Argonne National Laboratory right after the war, in which they kept mice for months and months with $C^{14}O_2$. They had radioactive CO_2 in the atmosphere, and the objective was to get it all equilibrated, if they could, to see what would be the steady state of specific activity of the carbons in the different body fluids and tissues. The results have been published. Someone here may even remember what the CO_2 tension was.

Dr. Schaefer: As you know, we had men exposed to a low CO_2 concentration of 1.5% for 42 days during Operation Hideout. Most of the physiological parameters were measured during this study. It was found that it took about three weeks for the men to adapt and compensate for the slight respiratory acidosis which existed at first. De-acclimatization was not completed within 28 days of recovery on air, as indicated in an altered calcium phosphorus metabolism, increased red-cell CO_2 content, and reduced cardio-vascular capacity. This suggests possible development of pathophysiological states on greatly prolonged exposure to 1.5% CO_2. Supporting evidence for this notion is given in histopathological findings in guinea pigs, which showed increasing evidence of kidney calcification when exposure to 1.5% CO_2 was prolonged from 40 to 93 days.

On the basis of animal experiments with high and low CO_2 tensions, work with 3% CO_2, and the results of Operation Hideout, we can plot a time-concentration curve for CO_2. We get an asymptote, and when one follows it out, a concentration is reached at which no acidosis occurs, with its accompanying adaptative changes.

The point is that the human organism is able to tolerate a CO_2 concentration only within his normal regulatory capacity. If the concentration is high enough to induce respiratory acidosis and produce compensatory changes, you get into trouble.

Dr. Bartlett: One of the things that Dr. Buchanan measured in his long-term CO_2 exposures was the distribution of radioactive CO_2 in the tissues of the animal, and more specifically in biochemical compounds. He found $C^{14}O_2$ in all the members of the tricarboxylic acid cycle right up to glycogen. This must reflect a temporary or regional reversal of the metabolic cycle in the animal. It must also be an endothermic reaction, since ordinarily these reactions are exothermic. It might even reflect a temporary or regional adaptation on the part of the tissues.

Chairman Hastings: You are quite right. Buchanan's work showed that the CO_2 is important not just because it makes carbonic acid, producing the consequences of increased acidity, but because every protein is bound to have some NH_2 groups that are uncharged at certain pH's, and uncharged NH_2 groups can take on CO_2 and become carbamic acid. This is a function of the CO_2 pressure, not of the carbonic acid. I'm speculating, of course, but it is possible that CO_2, *per se*, influences the activity of some enzymes (since they are all proteins) because of this property. If such an NH_2 group is the key part of the enzymatic action of the particular enzyme, changing it to a carbamic acid group would render the enzyme no longer suitable for, let us say, combination with the substrate.

Besides, as you pointed out, CO_2 combines with pyruvate to make oxal-acetate. That is one way CO_2 fixation takes place, and that in turn would be proportionate to the CO_2 pressure. So there are at least two ways in which CO_2 could be effective metabolically, simply by virtue of the pressure of the CO_2 in the system.

Dr. Lambertsen (University of Pennsylvania): Since we are discussing the fixation of CO_2, I would like to find out how much is fixed in the various tissues. As you pointed out, this was part of Buchanan's results. However, there is a simpler reaction that we have omitted here so far which I will have the privilege of including in my paper later on. That is, the reaction between CO_2 and ammonia (not ammonium ion) in a manner similar to that which occurs between CO_2 and water to form carbonic acid. The carbonate is then transformed enzymatically into carbamyl phosphate. Thus it enters the metabolic system in a very simple reversible way.

Chairman Hastings: I think this all points up the fact that CO_2 is not something inert.

Dr. Marshall Reed: I was just wondering about the possibility that Dr. Hastings pointed out. I think that while this is a possibility, it is not a very probable one, because CO_2 combines only with an NH_2 group. We do not have many NH_2 groups in the molecules of proteins, because they exist largely as NH_3^+ groups at physiological pH. Now, CO_2 only combines with a NH_2, which normally is not dissociated, except at a very alkaline range of pH. Therefore, most proteins do not bind appreciable amounts of CO_2. Only very basic proteins will bind CO_2 in a carbamino form.

Chairman Hastings: You are right. Most of the NH_2 groups are there as NH_3^+, but there are some proteins normally which have some free NH_2 groups, including hemoglobin. It all depends on what the pK of that NH_2 group is. There are not many such free groups, but there are some.

Dr. Fenn: I should not like the session to close without someone asking whether the effects of CO_2 that have been discussed are really effects of CO_2 or of the change which is produced by a CO_2 group.

Dr. Lambertsen: I will answer the question concerning nerve tissue. Although each tissue has a different form of reaction, as far as nervous tissue is concerned, pH change is not the factor involved. One cannot reproduce the effect of CO_2 by change of pH alone, so that actually CO_2 has its own unique effect.

Dr. Stein: To answer Dr. Behnke, we are in the process of writing up a report on cats—adult cats—exposed to 3% and 4.5% CO_2 for 90 days, and rats exposed from the moment of weaning till death to 10% CO_2. I hope that study will answer some of your questions.

Captain Behnke: It certainly will. What did you find? A shortened life span?

Dr. Stein: Not at these concentrations.

Captain Behnke: Has there been a single experiment to indicate that the life span is shortened as a result of continuous exposure to elevated CO_2 tensions?

Dr. Stein: I believe the tensions must be elevated above those we have used to give an indication of shortening of the life span, at least in rats. It seems in general, that there is not a great deal wrong with these animals at these concentrations. They do compensate quite well and, for a short period, very well.

Dr. H. Laborit: I would like to stress again the role of CO_2 in the formation of urea, with ornithine in the urea cycle. Recently we placed a dog in a CO_2 enriched atmosphere of 10%, and, as we have seen this morning, when the ventilation is controlled and alkaline reserve is stabilized, CO_2 excretion is also found to be constant. Then we injected a mixture of potassium and magnesium aspartate. We observed a decrease of total CO_2 in plasma, a decrease in excreted CO_2, and a slight increase in urea concentration, which leads one to believe that the increase in aspartic acid concentration permitted excretion of CO_2 through another route than the lung.

Chairman Hastings: I have great faith in the adaptability of our cells. They have already found out how to lead a submarine existence with the fish and how to fly with the birds, by developing such anions to control the composition of their extracellular fluid environment. This environment has to have a volume nearly a million to one for just one cell trying to get along in the sea. Thanks to the lungs, kidneys, and gastrointestinal tract, however, we need only a relative volume of one to five.

Dr. Gerschman: May I say that we do not believe that there is adaptation to increased oxygen tension unless we supply a chemical or unless the cells can fabricate more of the antioxidant.

Chairman Hastings: Dr. Gerschman, didn't you say that the oxygen in the atmosphere is the result of life on earth?

Dr. Gerschman: Yes.

Chairman Hastings: Perhaps then we can regard the 20% oxygen in the atmosphere as an adaptation of the atmosphere.

Dr. Gerschman: In a sense, yes.

Dr. Dean Burke: I would like to make a comment on the last two papers, but before that I would like to say, with regard to CO_2 fixation, that I have yet to have anybody show me any data in the literature of net CO_2 fixation by animal tissues, animal cells, or animal homogenates.

Regarding the last two papers, I believe we are forgetting somewhat the role of hydrogen peroxide. The question arises in both, particularly in considering the combined action of x-rays and oxygen. I would like to call attention to the recent experiments of Farber in which he has been able to measure the hydrogen peroxide formed by x-rays. By giving an equivalent quantity of hydrogen peroxide, he gets the same effect. Therefore, I believe that much of the discussion of free radicals in connection with these mechanisms can still be referred to hydrogen peroxide. I would like to have Dr. Gerschman's comments on this idea.

Dr. Gerschman: Yes, hydrogen peroxide is always there, since it is known as a product of most biological oxidations. Probably free radicals are formed by the decomposition of hydrogen peroxide. When you do not find it, it is probably because the rate of its decomposition is faster than the rate of its formation.

Dr. Angrist: Isn't there a limit to the anti-oxidant possibility? We do know that some of the effects of ionizing radiation may be produced by hydrogen peroxide reacting with protein. This work has been done on isolated spindles, but it can also attack cells, and the mycotic effect may represent either selective protolysation or exhaustion of the SH radicals. I wonder whether there is not a limit to the protective action of SH beyond which we probably get into trouble. We may in fact have to rely on the selective action of oxygen to explain the mycotic effects of radiation.

Dr. Gerschman: We have recently published four papers discussing these subjects. I have put a lot of emphasis on the fact that an anti-oxidant can also be a pro-oxidant depending on the system, for example, in *in vitro* studies we used sulfyhydryl compounds, which exhibited pro-oxidative effects and peroxide formation. However, under other circumstances we have also shown that they are efficient anti-oxidants.

PART THREE

Effects of Various Acute and Chronic Environmental Changes on Circulation

Chairman

DR. OTTO GAUER

William G. Kerckhoff Institut
der Max-Planck-Gesellschaft
Bad Nauheim, Germany

Environmental Factors Affecting Capillary Exchange

J. R. PAPPENHEIMER

Career Investigator, American Heart Association, and Department of Physiology, Harvard Medical School, Boston, Massachusetts

Two principal aspects of capillary exchange can be distinguished—first, the movement of fluid between blood and extravascular compartments, and second, the exchanges which occur by diffusion and do not necessarily involve volumetric fluid shifts. The first process, namely fluid movement, is specially important for homeostasis of blood volume and is relevant to this symposium because of fluid shifts which occur as a result of accelerative forces, pressure breathing, long-term starvation, and changes of local temperature in the extremities. The second process, namely diffusion, is the principal means for metabolic exchange and its relevance to the present symposium is chiefly in connection with gas exchange.

Environmental factors affect capillary exchange by acting indirectly on one or more primary variables controlling fluid movement or diffusion. For purposes of exposition I have listed these primary variables in Fig. 1 which provides a schema for qualitative discussion. Subsequently, we can choose numerical examples to indicate the magnitude of normal capillary exchange and changes which have been found or which are anticipated as a result of altered environment.

Whether we consider transcapillary movement of whole fluid or diffusion of solutes without fluid movement, in each case we have to consider force and permeability. Rates of transfer are proportional to force × permeability, i.e., pressure × area × permeability. The driving forces for metabolic exchange, i.e., for diffusion processes, are not the same as those for fluid movement, although the two processes often occur together, in the same or in opposite directions, to produce complex molecular sieving. The driving forces

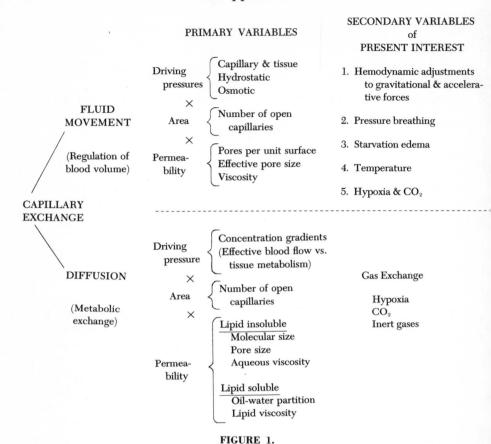

FIGURE 1.

for fluid flow through capillary walls are capillary pressure, tissue pressure, and osmotic pressure. Normally, the effective osmotic force is derived from plasma proteins but in severe exercise or hypoxia we have also to consider osmotic transients from release of lactic acid, which tends to draw fluid from plasma into the interstitial compartment. In the normal steady state, however, the classical Starling hypothesis in which fluid movement is proportional to transcapillary differential between hydrostatic and protein osmotic pressures has been shown to operate with almost mathematical precision by Landis (1927), working with individual frog mesenteric capillaries and by Pappenheimer and Soto-Rivera (1948), working with mammalian muscle capillaries.

The driving force for diffusion, on the other hand, is concentration difference which can be expressed as a pressure difference through van't Hoff's law. Concentration gradients are established by tissue uptake or output and, except for large lipid-insoluble molecules, are essentially independent of capillary hydrostatic pressure. They may, however, be limited by effective capillary flow. For example, the concentration gradients of substances which penetrate rapidly into intracellular water may be limited by the rate at which they are brought to or from the tissues by the blood. Such substances include D_2O, K, Rb, antipyrine, and various gases; these are useful indicators of effective tissue blood flow. Let me emphasize the word *effective*. In skin, muscle, intestine, and possibly in other organs, there are functional circulatory shunts so that blood flow supplying the nutritive circulation may be very much less than that supplying the tissue as a whole. For example, a three- or fourfold increase in total blood flow through skeletal muscle, elicited by the recently discovered sympathetic vasodilator pathway, has very little effect on nutritive blood flow as measured by clearance of radioactive tracers (Uvnäs and Hyman; Walder, 1953). In the kidney, and possibly in other organs, we have to consider effective red cell flow separately from effective plasma flow as we shall see subsequently. In this case, as in muscle or skin, the supply of oxygen to the metabolizing tissue may be very much less than that estimated from total measured flow.

Some of the permeability factors determining rate of transcapillary fluid movement differ from those governing transport by diffusion, although both processes share the important factor, the number of open capillaries. The permeability factor for fluid movement is determined primarily by hydrodynamic law—that is, it varies with the 4th power of effective capillary pore size. Whereas, transcapillary diffusion of lipid-insoluble molecules is primarily determined by the 2nd power of pore size and the ratio of pore size to molecular size (Pappenheimer, 1953; 1954). In the case of lipid soluble molecules, including the respiratory gases, permeability is determined by lipid solubility— presumably endothelial cell membrane lipids—rather than by dimensions of aqueous channels (Renkin, 1952). Lipid solubility is a major determinant of capillary permeability in all tissues but especially in brain tissue where exchange of ionic constituents is limited by the blood-brain barrier, but lipid soluble molecules such as O_2, CO_2, free NH_3, or anesthetics penetrate with great rapidity. Winterstein (1955) has emphasized the dependence of central control of respiration upon this mechanism.

Finally, we have to consider viscosity as a factor in permeability. Rates of fluid movement in the extremities are altered by changes in temperature, partly as a result of the temperature coefficient of viscosity of water. The effects of changes in viscosity of membrane lipids has not yet been adequately studied although it is known that the temperature coefficient of transcapillary diffusion of antipyrine and related substances is far greater than can be accounted for by changes in viscosity of water (Renkin, 1953).

I turn now to a more quantitative description of the capillary exchange, beginning with fluid movement. The filtration coefficient, i.e., the permeability coefficient for net fluid movement through the capillary wall, is about 0.01

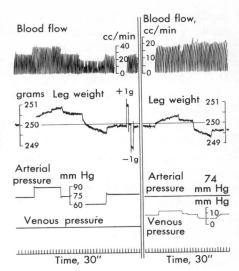

FIGURE 2.
Effects of arterial pressure and venous pressure
on net fluid movement through capillary walls of
perfused cat limb. (Renkin and Pappenheimer,
1957)

ml/min/cm H_2O pressure in the capillaries of 100 grams of dog or cat
muscle. It is slightly less than this in the forearms or legs of man (Landis and
Hortenstine, 1950). 0.01 ml/min/cm H_2O sounds like a low order of permeability and, indeed, it is sufficiently low to protect the circulation against
crippling loss of fluid during brief exposure to high accelerative forces. It is
also sufficiently low that the extravascular circulation, i.e., normal ultrafiltra-
tion and absorption in the capillary bed, is negligble from the point of view
of metabolic exchange. In man we estimate that the extracapillary circulation
is something less than 2% of the plasma flow (Pappenheimer, 1953; Renkin
and Pappenheimer, 1957). But from the point of view of long-continued environmental stress, the capillary filtration coefficient must be looked upon as
quite large. Even a moderate change of capillary pressure such as that caused
by pressure breathing, release from gravitational force, slow continued acceleration, or sustained abnormal posture would cause really serious changes of
blood volume were it not for the operation of efficient homeostatic mechanisms. For example, a rise of only 10 cm H_2O in venous pressure would
cause loss of half the entire plasma volume within an hour if there were no
opposing mechanisms. Figure 2 shows the rate of filtration or absorption of
fluid when mean capillary pressure is altered experimentally in a perfused
limb that has no efficient homeostatic mechanisms. In this case, filtration or
absorption represented by gain or loss of weight is caused by relatively small
changes of arterial pressure at constant venous pressure—or changes of
venous pressure at constant arterial pressure. Fluid loss through the capillaries
will go on for hours in this preparation unless the mean capillary pressure is
adjusted to equal effective protein osmotic pressure.

In the intact animal, three major homeostatic mechanisms oppose fluid loss. One of these derives from the osmotic pressure-concentration curve of serum albumin shown in Fig. 3. The physiological significance of the disproportionate increase of osmotic pressure with concentration is often not appreciated. An increase of 25% in protein concentration caused by prolonged filtration under stress causes a 70% increase in the restoring force. Conversely, 1 or 2% protein in interstitial fluid exerts relatively little force for fluid loss because in this range of concentration the osmotic effect per gram protein is small.

Although protein concentration is important, especially under conditions of fluid loss, we have to look elsewhere for the principal mechanism responsible for homeostasis of blood volume. A dramatic example of this has recently been provided by Dr. Bennhold of Tübingen, Germany (Bennhold *et al.*, 1954). Dr. Bennhold has found two people, brother and sister, who have no albumin at all in their plasma. The total protein osmotic pressure in these remarkable people is only about 10 mm Hg, yet, from a clinical point of view they "are doing just fine." I think we have to look to nervous and chemical or endocrinological control of capillary pressure for the chief regulatory mechanism. As shown in Fig. 4, mean capillary pressure is primarily determined by arterial pressure, venous pressure, and the ratio of post-capillary to pre-capillary resistance to flow. Mean capillary pressure is independent of the flow itself except insofar as flow determines arterial and venous pressures. This formulation suggests that the ratio of venular to arteriolar vascular tone is a critical determinant of mean capillary pressure. We know a great deal of arteriolar reactions, but we have a lot to learn about reactions of the small veins which must play an important role in the regulation of capillary pressure, and hence of blood volume. In the gravity-free state the hydrostatic component repre-

FIGURE 3.
Osmotic pressure-concentration curves of plasma proteins.

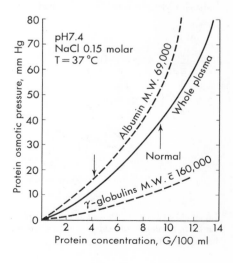

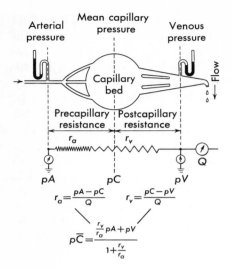

FIGURE 4.
Determinants of mean capillary pressure.

sented by pV is zero and in this case the sole determinant of capillary pressure is the hemodynamic component represented by rv/ra. A relatively small increase in this ratio, brought about by reflex adjustment of arteriolar or venular tone, or both, would compensate for loss of normal venous pressure. From what little we do know about the physiological range of control of this ratio, there should be no special difficulty in making this adaptation by means of normal vascular reflexes.

I turn now to a brief consideration of the effects of anoxia on capillary exchange. This should, I think, be brief because it has been fairly well established (McMichael and Morris, 1936; Landis, 1928; Henry *et al.*, 1947;

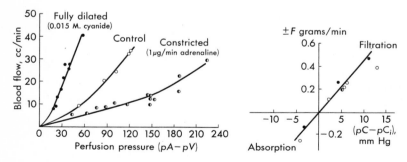

FIGURE 5.

Effect of NaCN (0.015 M) on blood flow (*left*) and on transcapillary fluid movement (*right*) in perfused cat limb. Inhibition of oxidative metabolism has little effect on filtration coefficient, even after several hours of perfusion.

Pasquale and Schiller, 1951). Severe hypoxia is required to produce demonstrable changes in capillary permeability, whether detected by fluid movement or by protein loss. McMichael (1936) failed to find changes even when arterial oxygen saturation was reduced to 65%. Henry *et al.* (1947) failed to find appreciable protein loss from human forearms until venous saturation fell to about 20%, and even at this low saturation the results did not reveal clear-cut permeability changes. Actually, we have evidence that under suitable conditions some capillaries can withstand complete anoxia for several hours. On several occasions we have perfused hind limbs with blood containing 10 mM NaCN without detectable loss of effective protein osmotic pressure or change of filtration coefficient (Fig. 5). The essential trick in these experiments is to keep the perfusion volume large compared to tissue volume, a circumstance which implicates products of anaerobic metabolism rather than oxygen lack *per se* as an essential factor causing increased capillary permeability in extreme hypoxia or circulatory arrest. R. B. Reeves, in our laboratory, is currently studying the anaerobic metabolism of the turtle heart; his preparations, which have adequate coronary perfusion, perform at normal rates of useful work for many hours at less than 1 mm Hg O_2 pressure with no sign of edema as judged by ratio of wet to dry weight.

There is relatively little to report concerning the effects of CO_2 on properties of capillaries. However, we can say that pH of the blood can be varied over a wide range without detectable effects on capillary permeability as measured by Landis in the frog's mesentery (Landis, 1928) or by our group using the perfused hind limbs of cats.

The effects of temperature deserve brief consideration. In the perfused limb

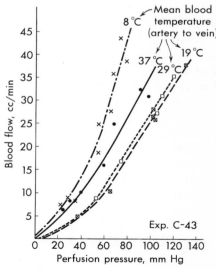

FIGURE 6.
From unpublished data of H. Badeer, C. Rapela, and J. R. Pappenheimer.

TABLE 1

Effect of temperature on resistance to hydrodynamic flow and molecular diffusion through muscle capillaries

	$36 \pm 2°C$	$10 \pm 2°C$	Ratio
Filtration coefficient, K_f (Av. of 15 experiments) ml/min/mm Hg/ 100 g muscle	0.0146	0.0083	$K_f^{36°}/K_f^{10°} = 1.76$
Average diffusion ½ time across capillaries, minutes	NaCl 5.3	9.7	$½T_{10}°/½T_{36}° \begin{cases} = 1.8 \\ = 1.6 \end{cases}$
	Sucrose 7.3	12	
Viscosity of water centipoises	0.7085	1.308	$\dfrac{\eta 10°}{\eta 36°} = 1.85$

the deep tissue temperature can be varied from 5-42° C without detectable damage to the capillaries. Typical vascular reactions are shown in Fig. 6. With moderate cold, there is vasoconstriction, especially in the AVA of the paw. At tissue temperatures below about 18° C, however, there is marked vasodilatation of the blood vessels in muscle. Despite these rather large vascular reactions, the capillary exchange of fluid and lipid-insoluble molecules, measured quantitatively in terms of transfer rate per unit force, is affected only by the temperature coefficient of viscosity. Thus in changing from 36° C to 10° C the filtration coefficient, or the diffusion half-times for NaCl or sucrose, decrease almost exactly in inverse proportion to the viscosity of water (Table 1). In the intact human forearm it is not possible to make such exact measurements; nevertheless, over a limited but appropriate range the filtration coefficient expressed in terms of filtration rate per unit rise in venous pressure also varies inversely with aqueous viscosity (Fig. 7). Above 36° C the filtration coefficient increases more than predicted by viscosity, perhaps owing to increased number of open capillaries. Below 20° C the filtration coefficient is also greater than predicted from viscosity, perhaps owing to capillary damage in superficial areas exposed to greatest cold.

So much for fluid exchange. In a recent symposium on tissue oxygen tension, Kety (1957) reviewed the major determinants of blood-tissue gas exchange. Using a simple model of capillary-tissue geometry Kety worked out the theoretical relations between capillary blood flow and tissue oxygen tension. It will, I think, be obvious that for any given intercapillary distance and O_2 consumption the capillary flow must exceed a critical value to keep tissue oxygen tension greater than zero everywhere in the tissue. In the hind limbs of cats this critical flow turns out to be surprisingly high—of the order of 2-4 ml/min per 100 grams of muscle at normal temperatures (Fig. 8). The average

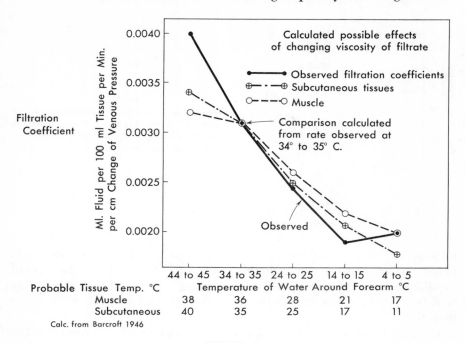

FIGURE 7.
Effects of temperature on transcapillary fluid movement in human forearm. (Courtesy of Dr. E. M. Landis)

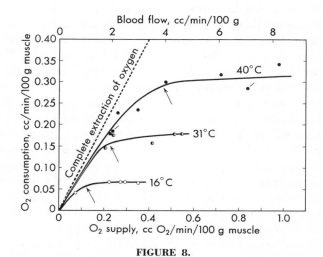

FIGURE 8.
Limiting blood flows to supply oxygen demand of perfused cat hind-limb muscles at various temperatures. (From unpublished data of H. Badeer, C. Rapela, and J. R. Pappenheimer.)

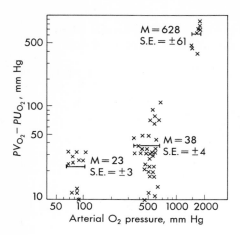

FIGURE 9.

Oxygen pressure difference between renal venous blood and urine. Anesthetized dogs breathing oxygen tension up to 2.5 atmospheres. (Rennie, Reeves, and Pappenheimer, 1958)

intercapillary distance calculated from the critical flow at each temperature is about 150 microns—or about double that assumed by Kety on the basis of capillary counts. We are, however, measuring total blood flow and it may well be that the effective capillary flow through metabolizing areas is less than this.

We have found a special case of tissue gas exchange which operates in the kidney. Kidneys have a very high rate of total blood flow relative to their metabolism and the O_2 tension in renal venous blood is exceptionally high. The high extraction ratio of PAH or Diodrast indicates that most of the plasma entering the kidney passes the proximal tubules. This is not necessarily true of the red blood corpuscles, however. W. B. Kinter and I (1956) have advanced reasons for believing that red cells are partly separated from plasma within the kidney, and that a cell-rich component of the intrarenal flow traverses a short circulation, bypassing the metabolizing tubules entirely. The dynamic hematocrit of blood within the renal cortex is less than two-thirds that in systemic blood and in the renal medulla there are only one third the number of red cells relative to plasma as in blood entering the kidney. Given these facts one may predict that the oxygen tension surrounding the tubules and in tubular urine will be far lower than in the renal vein. This turns out to be the case (Rennie *et al.*, 1958). Urine collected from the renal pelvis of anesthetized dogs during rapid diuresis contains oxygen at a tension of only 27 mm Hg as compared with more than 50 mm in renal venous blood. The difference between renal venous blood and urine does not represent a diffusion gradient across tubule cells. This is shown clearly by the fact that when inspired oxygen is increased to 2.5 atmospheres the difference between renal venous blood and urine increases 30-fold to the extraordinary value of 600 mm Hg as shown in Fig. 9. As arterial oxygen is increased above the point where renal venous hemoglobin is fully saturated the venous oxygen tension increases rapidly. But the urine tension remains low, presumably because the hemoglobin capacity of cell-poor blood supplying the metabolizing tissue remains unsaturated. The observed urine tensions at all pressures are approximately those expected if the urine were equilibrated with blood containing half the arterial red cell concentration. I think, therefore, that we must add the kidney to the growing list of organs in which the nutritive blood supply has been found to be distinct from the total blood flow through the organ.

In this brief review we have covered a number of different aspects of the capillary exchange. I think we can say that the capillaries are more resistant than most organ systems to environmental stresses of the type we are anticipating. It is up to the neurophysiologists and neurochemists to provide us with a central nervous system which is equally resistant.

REFERENCES

Bennhold, H., H. Peters, and E. Roth. 1954. Deutsch. Ges. inn. Med. *60:* 630.

Henry, J., J. Goodman, and J. Meehan. 1947. J. Clin. Invest. *26:* 1119.

Kety, S. S. 1957. "Tissue oxygen symposium," Fed. Proc. *16:* 666.

Landis, E. M. 1927. Am. J. Physiol. *82:* 217.

Landis, E. M., and J. C. Hortenstine. 1950. Physiol. Rev. *30:* 1.

Landis, E. M. 1928. Am. J. Physiol. *83:* 528.

McMichael, J., and K. M. Morris. 1936. J. Physiol. *87:* 74P.

Pappenheimer, J. R. 1953. Physiol. Rev. *33:* 387.

Pappenheimer, J. R. 1954. Annual Lecture of National Heart Institute, Bethesda.

Pappenheimer, J. R., and W. B. Kinter. 1956. Am. J. Physiol. *185:* 377.

Pappenheimer, J. R., and A. Soto-Rivera. 1948. Am. J. Physiol. *152:* 471.

Pasquale, E. L., and A. A. Schiller. 1951. Proc. Soc. Exptl. Biol. & Med. *78:* 567.

Renkin, E. M., and J. R. Pappenheimer. 1957. Ergeb. Physiol. *49:* 102.

Renkin, E. M. 1953. Am. J. Physiol. *173:* 125.

Renkin, E. M. 1952. Am. J. Physiol. *168:* 538.

Rennie, D. W., R. B. Reeves, and J. R. Pappenheimer. 1958. Am. J. Physiol. *195:* 120.

Uvnäs, B., and C. Hyman. Personal communication.

Walder, D. N. 1953. Clin. Sci. *12:* 153.

Winterstein, H. 1955. Ergeb. Physiol. *48:* 328.

Homeostasis of the Extra-Arterial Circulation

OTTO H. GAUER

William G. Kerckhoff Institut der Max-Planck-Gesellschaft, Bad Nauheim, Germany

The title of this paper implies that in some way the pulmonary circulation and the veins of the greater circulation, which together constitute the extra-arterial circulation, form a functional unit. If we adopt this concept, we may be further encouraged to search for some well-defined physiological parameters, which may be just as important for the homeostasis of this "low-pressure system" as blood pressure is for the homeostasis of the arterial circulation. The breach with the tradition of dividing the circulation according to anatomical principles, into the pulmonary circulation and the systemic circulation, was suggested by the observation of the circulatory effects of gravity, immersion in water, breathing against a constant pressure, blood loss and transfusion. One factor that all of these stresses have in common is that they affect the circulation as a whole and that they are always accompanied by gross changes of the volume of the blood and/or its distribution. It should be mentioned that we usually find a concurrent change in the excretory function of the kidney, which cannot be readily explained on the basis of renal hemodynamics or the osmotic conditions of the plasma.

THE LOW-PRESSURE SYSTEM (PULMONARY CIRCULATION PLUS VENOUS SYSTEM) AS A FUNCTIONAL UNIT

Figure 1 indicates schematically the distribution of the blood volume and the relative distensibility of the various compartments of the circulation. There are few dependable data available (Bazett, 1949), but the order of magnitude given here and the various relationships are very probably correct. The pulmonary and the venous circulations occupy approximately 80% of the total blood volume, while the arterial system holds 20%. The relative volumes given in Fig. 1 are in agreement with measurements which estimate the intra-

200

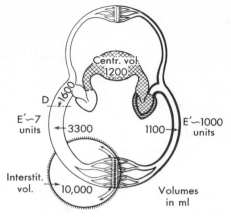

FIGURE 1.

Estimated capacity of the major compartments of the circulation. The resistance to stretch has been indicated by the thickness of the walls. The cross-hatched area represents the central volume proper (1200 ml) consisting of the diastolic volume of the left ventricle (2 stroke volumes) plus the pulmonary blood volume. By adding 400 ml for the right heart and the intrathoracic veins, the intrathoracic blood volume (1600 ml) is obtained. D denotes the diaphragm. Estimating the extrathoracic volume of the capacitance vessels with 3300 ml, one arrives at a total capacity for the low-pressure system of 4800 ml. Allowing 1100 ml for the arterial tree brings the total blood volume to 5900 ml. The volume elasticity of the total circulation, including the contribution of the interstitial fluid space, is 7 units, as compared with 700–1400 (1000 approx.) units for the arterial system. The spike-marked circle represents the border line between the interstitial space and the intracellular volume. The rapid exchange of plasma and interstitial fluid in the capillary bed is indicated by two pairs of arrows.

thoracic blood volume to be approximately 25% of the total blood volume (Sjöstrand, 1952; Sjöstrand, 1953 and Piiper, 1958), who found a distribution ratio of venous and arterial volumes of 3:1 for the dog's paw.

The volume elasticity of the various compartments has been indicated by the thickness of their walls. A rough estimate of the volume elasticity E' (Frank) $= \dfrac{\Delta p}{\Delta v}$ for the arterial Windkessel is 1 mm Hg/1 ml or 1400 dynes/cm⁵. This value is probably too high, but even if we accept a very low value of 700 dynes/cm⁵ we still find it to be 100 times greater than the volume elasticity of the total circulation which is, as we shall see later, 7 dynes/cm⁵ (Gauer *et al.*, 1956). This means, if we transfuse 1000 ml into the circulation, we find only 10 ml in the arterial tree and 990 ml in the extra-arterial system. The pressure in the whole circulation would rise as a consequence of the one liter accession by 7 cm H_2O only.

In order to understand the function of the total circulation both in health and disease, we should realize that, regardless of its importance for the performance of work by the left ventricle, the blood storage capacity of the arterial elastic reservoir is really very small. If the left ventricle skips just two

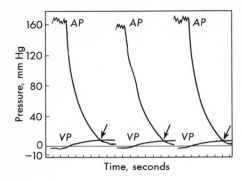

FIGURE 2.

Demonstration of the mean circulatory filling pressure (MCFP) of the circulation. Immediately after stopping of the heart by fibrillation, a pump transports blood from the arterial tree into the low-pressure system. The intersection of the two pressure curves (arrow) indicates the MCFP. The slope of the pressure curves gives a fair impression of the relative distensibilities of the two systems. (From Guyton et al., 1954. *Am. J. Physiol. 179*, 261.)

or three beats the arterial pressure falls instantaneously to nearly 30 mm Hg, while two or three stroke volumes run off. The concurrent increase in pressure in the extra-arterial system is negligible. Guyton et al. (1956), found that in a 12 kg dog only about 60 ml of blood, that is, 5% of the estimated blood volume is held in the arterial tree by the activity of the left ventricle. Flow resistance in the arterial system is at least 3 times as high as in the venous system and more than 8 times as high as in the pulmonary circulation. These considerations show that the homeostatic control of the arterial blood pressure is effected dynamically by the adaptation of cardiac output to peripheral flow resistance.

Besides the pressures, which result from the *vis a tergo* and *vis a fronte* in a dynamic system, we have to consider a hidden static pressure component, the so-called "mean circulatory filling pressure" (Guyton et al., 1954) or "the static blood pressure" (Starr, 1940). This pressure can be measured (with appropriate precaution) when the heart is stopped (Fig. 2). It is of course the same in all sections of the circulatory system and depends on the magnitude of the blood volume and the pressure-volume relationship of the total vascular space. The static blood pressure in man is 7.6 cm H_2O (Starr, 1940), the mean circulatory filling pressure (MCFP) of the dog (Guyton et al., 1954) 6.3 mm Hg ($\pm$ 0.94 mm Hg). Thus the MCFP in man and dog are almost identical. This remarkable observation together with the small scatter of Guyton's figures for the dog may indicate that the two species use the same principle in the homeostatic adaptation of the total blood volume to the capacity of the vascular system. Severe vasoconstriction (adrenalin) raises the MCFP to 16-18 mm Hg; spinal anaesthesia reduces it to 4.9 mm Hg (Guyton et al., 1954). These maximal deviations from the normal MCFP due to contraction or relaxation of the walls of the capacitance vessels are relatively small. Any higher or lower MCFP must be attributed to increase or loss in blood volume.

Since flow resistance is so relatively small in the low-pressure system and since only a minute fraction of the blood volume is transferred and held in the arterial tree by the action of the ventricle, we may expect that the physiological laws prevailing in the static circulation also play the dominant role in the extra-arterial portion of the circulation in life. Figure 3 shows that the pressures in the central veins, the pulmonary artery, and the left atrium rise and fall in parallel as the blood volume is changed by bleeding or transfusion (Henry *et al.*, 1956). With these moderate changes of blood volume the arterial pressure changes insignificantly and inconsistently. Each point in the diagram is a mean value derived from 12-15 dogs under light chloralose anaesthesia. The same relationship was found for men by measuring central venous pressure (Warren *et al.*, 1945; Warren *et al.*, 1948), pulmonary arterial pressure, and wedge pressure (Doyle *et al.*, 1951).

In Figure 3 particular attention should be drawn to the following observations.

(1) With total blood volume changes not exceeding ± 30%, the mean central venous pressure and mean pulmonary artery pressure rise and fall in parallel. This means that the right ventricle imparts a constant and relatively small amount of energy to the blood, boosting the mean pressure in the pulmonary artery by approximately 14 cm of water above the central venous pressure. This lack of temperament of the right ventricle, whose valves seem to be more important for the proper functioning of the circulation than its myocardium (Donald and Essex, 1954), together with the ease and rapidity with which 10% of the total blood volume can be exchanged between the

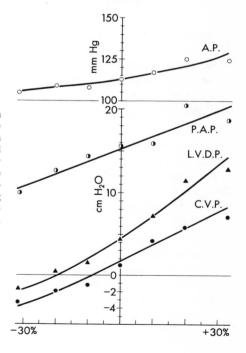

FIGURE 3.
Multiple curves showing the relation between changes of estimated blood volume (abscissa) and mean intrathoracic vascular pressures in 15 cases. Reading from below upward: central venous, left ventricular diastolic, pulmonary arterial, and systemic arterial pressures. The decreasing pressure differential between pulmonary artery and left atrium with increasing blood volume suggests a decreased flow resistance in the pulmonary vascular bed. (From Henry *et al.*, 1956. *Circulation Research* 4: 91.)

intrathoracic circulation and the peripheral capacitance vessels (Gauer, 1942) led us to consider the pulmonary circulation, the right heart, and the peripheral veins as a functional unit (Gauer and Henry, 1956). The salient point which distinguishes this so-called "low-pressure system" from the systemic arterial circulation is, however, not so much the characteristic low pressure, but the very different principles underlying the respective homeostatic control mechanisms.

In the arterial system the problem of homeostasis revolves around the dynamic equilibrium of cardiac output and peripheral resistance for the control of the blood flow and its distribution.

In the low-pressure system homeostasis is based on the proper adjustment of vascular capacity, blood volume, and blood volume distribution.

(2) The arterio-venous pressure difference across the pulmonary bed falls as the filling of the circulation increases. This could either be due to a reduction of cardiac output or of flow resistance. Since there is a tendency for cardiac output to increase with a transfusion, the only possible explanation rests in a reduction of flow resistance as the pulmonary bed gets more distended. This mechanism also explains the remarkable fact that the pressure gradient with change of total blood volume is steeper in the left atrium than in any other section of the extra-arterial system.

HOMEOSTATIC CONTROL OF VOLUME

The long lasting change of pressure and, hence, tension in the vessel walls of the low-pressure system could represent the adequate stimulus for the homeostatic control of volume. Although the control of blood cell volume and blood protein mass are important, the fastest component of a volume regulatory mechanism could be expected to affect water balance. If this were true, the kidney could be regarded as an indicator organ for a homeostatic mechanism of volume control. As could be expected of this working hypothesis, as iso-osmotic expansion of the blood volume (transfusion of whole blood, plasma, saline, packed red cells) results in a diuresis (Schwalm and Göltner, 1956; Zuidema et al., 1956). This diuresis cannot be attributed to osmotic changes of the plasma or to changes in renal hemodynamics. It is probably mediated through hormonal mechanisms (Zuidema et al., 1956).

As to the possible location of the sensing elements of this homeostatic reflex the following arguments encouraged a search within the intrathoracic vascular compartments.

(1) Whether one adheres to Starling's concept or subscribes to more modern views, one cannot deny the great importance of intrathoracic blood volume for the adequacy of cardiac function. Of particular importance, as the

elastic reservoir keeping the left ventricle full, is the central blood reservoir proper, extending between the pulmonary and aortic valves (Fig. 1).

(2) There is ample anatomical evidence of an abundant supply of sensory fibers to both atria of the heart and to the great veins within the pericardium (Nonidez, 1937).

(3) By recording action potentials from single nerve fibers in the afferent vagus, receptors could be identified as "Type B" (Paintal, 1953), which are particularly sensitive to changes in total blood volume (Henry and Pearce, 1956).

(4) With regard to stimulation of baroreceptors, it seems interesting that the greatest change of pressure and, hence, of wall tension with change of total blood volume, is found in the left atrium (Henry et al., 1956).

It could be shown that any measure leading to an expansion of this region caused diuresis, while depletion of the blood within the intrathoracic vascular bed was followed by oliguria (Fig. 4) (Gauer et al., 1954). In an attempt to define the sensitive area more precisely, it was found that inflation of a balloon

Procedure	Urine flow	Filling of intrathoracic circulation	Filling of extrathoracic circulation	Pressure in renal veins
Hemorrhage	↘	↘	↘	↘
Pos. pressure breathing man, anesth. dog	↘	↘	↗	↗
Balloon in inf. v. cava above renal veins	↘	↘	↗	↗
Balloon in inf. v. cava below renal veins	↘	↘	↗	↘
Orthostasis	↘	↘	↗	↗
Sequestering of blood by cuffs	↘	↘	↗	↘
Sequestering of blood by cuffs plus infusion of 1500 cc. of blood	normal	normal?	↗	normal?
Blood transfusion	↗	↗	↗	↗
Neg. pressure breathing man, anesth. dog	↗	↗	↘	↘
Head down tilt	↗	↗	↘	↘
Immersion of trunk in warm bath	↗	↗	↘	↗
Exposure to cold	↗	↗	↘	↗

FIGURE 4.

Procedures changing urine flow. (Condensed tables from Gauer et al. 1954. J. Clin. Invest. 33: 287)

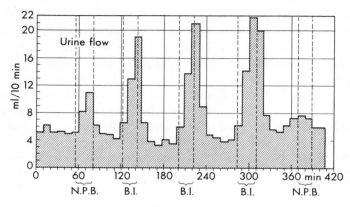

FIGURE 5.

Urine flow during negative pressure breathing (NPB) and inflation of a balloon (B.I.) in the left atrium. (From Gauer and Henry. 1956. *Klin. Woch.*, 34, 356)

inserted in the left atrium by an operation, provoked profuse diuresis (Fig. 5) (Henry *et al.*, 1956) which could be eliminated by cold block of the vagus nerve (Henry and Pearce, 1956). The right atrial pressure did not change in these experiments (Henry *et al.*, 1956). The evidence presented supports the conclusion that the central blood volume proper is homeostatically controlled. Since during a period of sleep in the horizontal position the relationship between the central and peripheral blood volumes is well defined, correction of the central blood volume would under this special condition also involve a correction of the total blood volume (and extra-cellular fluid?).[1] One must however realize that very probably additional mechanisms exist for the control of blood volume, because it is unlikely that the homeostasis of such an important physiological parameter depends on one reflex only.

THE INTERSTITIAL FLUID SPACE

Due to the free exchange of electrolytes and fluids through the capillary walls the interstitial fluid space is integrated into the low-pressure system in a rather complicated way. In a gross overestimation of the size of this pool, which is only about twice as large as the blood volume, the cardiovascular physiologists have been prone to assume that small blood losses could easily be replaced from this space. However, according to the principles of Starling (1909), even a minute inflow of interstitial fluid into the vascular compartment results in a fall of the colloid osmotic pressure in the plasma. A new physical

[1] From reports of pilots in cross country flight, we know that fatigue can often be combated by occasional inflation of a G-suit. This fatigue need not necessarily be attributed to an inadequate brain circulation. It could be caused reflexly via the central receptors as an attempt of the autonomic nervous system to enforce the condition of rest and horizontal posture, which may from time to time be necessary for the body to assess and correct fluid balance and other trophic functions.

equilibrium is thus obtained, which is different from normal conditions (Pappenheimer, 1953). The ensuing reduction of filtration pressure across the capillary walls permits only a partial replacement of the loss. A rapid replacement of plasma protein, restoring colloid osmotic pressure to normal, does not occur. Thus after heavy blood losses it takes from 48 to 72 hours until the composition of the plasma is normal again (Ebert *et al.*, 1941). Adolph *et al.* (1933) estimated from experiments in severely operated dogs, that about 36% of a plasma loss can be replenished within 20 minutes by interstitial fluid. Recent investigations gave higher figures of 40–50% replacement of the blood volume taken (Kaufmann and Müller, 1958) (Fig. 6). This predominantly physical process, which leads only to a partial restitution of the volume, is terminated after approximately 20 minutes (Kaufmann and Müller, 1958). Later an active homeostatic volume regulatory mechanism must necessarily take over to achieve a *restitutio ad integrum* by an effect on protein metabolism and water balance.

THE CENTRAL VENOUS PRESSURE

If we continuously record the changes of central venous pressure (CVP) in man during moderate changes of blood volume (Gauer *et al.*, 1956), they seem to reflect the volume changes due to bleeding and transfusion and the concurrent movements of electrolyte fluid across the capillary walls. For example, if we draw 500 cc of blood within 4 to 5 minutes the CVP falls pre-

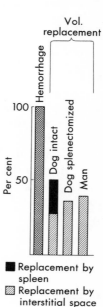

FIGURE 6.

Volume replacement by the interstitial space and the spleen after hemorrhage in intact and splenectomized dogs and in man. Twenty minutes after hemorrhage, 40–50% of the blood volume taken has been replaced. (After Kaufman *et al.* 1958. Kreislauf 47: 719)

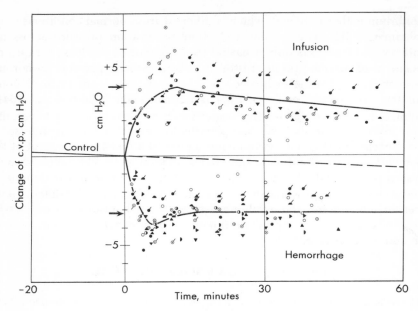

FIGURE 7.

Change of central venous pressures during hemorrhage (6,5 cc/kg) and transfusion (8,1 cc/kg) in 12 subjects. An initial 15–20 minute period of rapid pressure change (see text) is followed by relative constancy of pressure. The arrows indicate the intersection of the regression lines with the pressure axis at zero time. For the 70 kg man we find a pressure change of 7 cm H_2O for a volume change of 1000 ml. Extrapolation of the regression lines to the left yields recovery times of pressures of many hours. The long-lasting imbalance of volume and pressure may represent the adequate stimulus for a volume regulatory mechanism, acting through receptors in the low-pressure system. (From Gauer *et al.* 1956. *Circulation Research* 4: 79)

cipitously. After venesection the pressure rises fast at first, then more slowly, and after 20 minutes reaches a new level which deviates from the initial pressure by approximately 7 cm H_2O for a blood loss of 1000 ml (Gauer *et al.*, 1956). A comparison with Kaufmann's data (Kaufmann and Müller, 1958), shows that the fast recovery phase of CVP coincides with the phase of partial replacement of the blood loss by interstitial fluid. A transfusion represents a mirror image of this behavior (Fig. 7). Extrapolation from one-hour diagrams indicates that this new pressure level is held for a considerable period of time. It seems very likely that the normal pressure is finally attained by a rectification of volume rather than by a change of vascular tone.

VASOMOTOR CONTROL OF THE SIZE
OF THE CENTRAL RESERVOIR

It is well known that the pulmonary circulation represents the most distensible part of the low-pressure system and that its vasomotor activity is not very pronounced. In the upright posture with occluding venous cuffs around the limbs more than 10% of the estimated blood volume can be pooled in the peripheral vessels. With a combination of spirometric and plethysmographic methods, it was possible to show that, on release of the cuffs in the horizontal posture, 80% of the pooled volume was accommodated in and, by implication, came from the intrathoracic reservoirs (Sjöstrand, 1953). Other experiments suggested that 50% of the blood drawn from a vein during a moderate vene- section came from the intrathoracic pool (Glaser *et al.*, 1954). Its distensibility is therefore about the same as the distensibility of the rest of the circulation, which holds 75% of the total blood volume. The great distensibility and the lack of pronounced vasomotor control make the size of the central reservoir dependent on the give and take of the peripheral capacitance vessels, whose diameters may be changed either passively by external forces (gravity, pres- sure breathing), or actively by contraction or relaxation of their walls.

The control of venomotor tone has been extensively discussed in the past particularly in relation to the control of cardiac output through venous return (Fleisch, 1930; Franklin, 1937; Gollwitzer-Meier, 1932; Landis and Horten- stine, 1950). The effect of oxygen deficiency, high CO_2, stimulation of the ca- rotid sinus, or hemorrhage were investigated (Landis and Hortenstine, 1950). The results obtained, often with overwhelmingly strong stimuli in anesthetized animals suffering from severe operations, were ambiguous. In general, they were interpreted as indicating that the venomotor system was rather active in this matter of the control of venous return.

We were, therefore, very much surprised to find in moderate bleeding and transfusion experiments in men (Fig. 7) that the circulation behaved like an elastic container, with a linear pressure-volume relationship in the normal range of pressures. When pooling blood in extremities by occlusive cuffs, the CVP also fell without any apparent sign of a regulatory countermeasure (Gauer and Sieker, 1956).

When tilting a subject into the upright position, the passive displacement of blood volume into the dependent region due to gravity is combined with a stimulation of the carotid sinus. Page *et al.*, showed that immediately after return of the subject to the horizontal position, the pressures in the central compartments (CVP, pulmonary artery pressure, and wedge pressure) are elevated, and that during the tilt a fleeting constriction of an isolated vein segment can be observed (Page *et al.*, 1955). The tensing of the peripheral capacitance vessels indicated by these experiments may prevent circulatory collapse, but it is certainly not sufficient to prevent pooling of a considerable volume of blood in the periphery. The results obtained in isolated vein seg- ments (Salzman and Leverett, 1956) are at variance with findings in our own experiments in which blood flow was recorded and complete pressure-volume diagrams of the vascular bed of a hand were taken (Gauer *et al.*, 1958) (com- bined pressure and plethysmographic recording). While a reduced blood flow in the presence of a constant or slightly elevated arterial pressure indicated

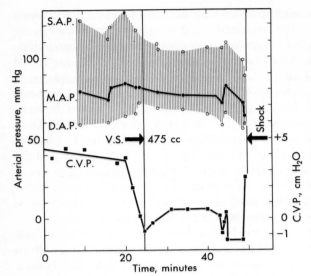

FIGURE 8.
Bleeding experiment. Arterial pressure (*top*) central venous pressure (CVP) (*below*). Between 20–24 minutes there is a hemorrhage of 475 ml, with a sharp fall of venous pressure and then a partial recovery by 1.5 cm H_2O. After a symptom-free interval of 20 minutes, nausea and shock develop with the subject in the horizontal posture. Note the rapid rise of CVP. The normal pressure-volume relationship is suddenly disturbed by an interference of venomotor activity as an emergency situation arises.

arteriolar constriction in the upright position, the state of contraction of the capacitance vessels did not change. Experiments on the effect of low oxygen and high CO_2 in the inspired air using the same procedure had the following results (Hintze and Thron, 1959).

Low O_2: There was a threshold at 10-11% O_2. Below this value, the tone of the capacitance vessels increased consistently. Flow resistance was decreased in 30%, increased in 60%, and did not change in 10% of the experiments.

5-6% CO_2 + 30% O_2: Flow resistance was consistently increased, while the tone of the capacitance vessels did not change.

There is a question as to whether the behavior of the hand veins is typical for the capacitance vessels of other vascular beds (Donegan, 1921).

Direct information on the vasomotor behavior of intestinal vessels, which have always been considered to be of particular importance for the homeostatic control of the circulation, has mostly been obtained in anaesthetized, operated animals (Alexander, 1954; Greer *et al.*, 1954). The results of Sjöstrand (1953), who found in tilt experiments in man that only 2.5% of the recorded volume shift could be assigned to the abdominal compartments, challenge the classical view. Wheeler *et al.* (1956), however, observed a drastic reduction of splanchnic blood volume with exercise in man. The latter findings need not exclude one another, but may point to the variability of vasomotor reaction of the capacitance vessels.

While we may conclude from these experiments that the low-pressure system behaves more or less like an elastic bag with a linear pressure volume characteristic, we must at the same time emphasize that this is probably only true if the changes of central blood volume induced are moderate and not greater than those which the circulation has been accustomed to in everyday life. With strong stimuli such as a Valsalva maneuver (Page *et al.*, 1955), asphyxia, high G (Salzman and Leverett, 1956) or relatively large blood losses the veins constrict in what we may consider an emergency reaction (Fig. 8). In this case a simple relationship between blood volume and central pressure can no longer be expected, so that after a severe blood loss we may find a normal or even an elevated CVP.

The available experience in man seems to indicate that the vascular reaction due to changes of the total blood volume is a threshold type, and that stimuli, whose intensity do not exceed the one imposed on the circulation by normal stresses, do not cause relaxation or strong contraction of the peripheral capacitance vessels. The same stresses, however, have a pronounced effect on the diuretic reflex (Gauer and Henry, 1956; Smith, 1957).

If we accept this reflex as part of a true volume control mechanism, we may conclude that the homeostatic control of the central blood volume automatically affords the adaptation of the blood volume to the total capacity of the vascular bed, regardless of its absolute size and the more or less fortuitous distribution of the blood in the periphery. As an example, the seasonal fluctuations of plasma volume (Doupe *et al.*, 1957) can easily we explained by this mechanism, which serves to produce adaptive changes rather than constancy of blood volume.

MULTIPLE FACTORS IN VOLUME CONTROL

The changes of blood volume associated with acute adjustments and acclimatization to chronic O_2 deficiency, high CO_2, hard labor, or cardiac insuf-

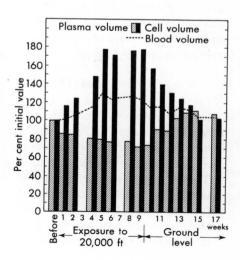

FIGURE 9.
Plasma, cell, and blood volume in a group of 8 dogs before, during, and after adaptation to 20,-000 feet (expressed as percentage of base-line value). During the first two weeks, plasma volume is reduced corresponding to the increase of the cell volume. Later this reduction does not keep pace with the change of cell volume; consequently the total blood volume finally rises by approximately 25%. (From Reissmann. 1951. *Am. J. Physiol.* 167: 52)

ficiency resist a simple explanation. They pose problems not only in hemo-mechanics, but also in the transport function of the blood.

Experiments on the acclimatization of dogs to high altitude (Reissmann, 1951) may serve as an example of a condition where several factors influ-ence blood volume (Fig. 9). The chain of events starts at once with an in-crease in red cell volume; the most likely explanation is the attempt to neu-tralize the effects of low oxygen tension by increasing the oxygen carrying ca-pacity of the blood. During the first two weeks, the ensuing increase in total blood volume is offset by a corresponding decrease of plasma volume. This reduction in plasma volume may be achieved through a volume regulatory mechanism. Later on, the reduction of plasma volume does not keep pace with the increase in red cell volume, and in the sixth week we end up with a net gain of total blood volume of 25% at an increase of red cell volume of 70%.

The argument that the organism has to abandon the homeostasis of blood volume in order to avoid too high a hematocrit and, hence, blood viscosity, cannot be upheld (Reissmann 1951). However, it may well be that after the second week a working hypertrophy of the organ "circulation" becomes ap-parent with an increased vascularization and perhaps a slightly enlarged heart. This event would call for a moderate increase in total blood volume. So in the course of the acclimatization process we have at least three factors influenc-ing blood volume and its components: the hypoxic stimulus on red cell for-mation, the volume regulatory mechanism which leads to a concurrent reduc-tion of plasma volume and, finally, the influence of a more hypothetical trophic center which sets the standard of blood volume at a different level.

As to the effector mechanisms, it seems worthwhile to note that the classi-cal vascular hormones such as adrenalin and noradrenalin do not seem to play the predominant role which they probably have in the arterial circulation. ADH, aldosterone, probably other hitherto unknown factors influencing water and salt metabolism (Smith, 1957), and other trophic functions occupy key positions in the homeostasis of the low-pressure system. Research on the cen-tral representation of these controls is just beginning (Folkow, 1955).

SUMMARY AND CONCLUSIONS

Experimental evidence is presented which supports the view that the pul-monary circulation and the capacitance vessels of the systemic circulation form a functional unit. The main goal of the homeostatic control of the low pressure system is the maintenance of an adequate central blood volume.

This central reservoir, consisting of the pulmonary vascular bed plus the diastolic blood volume of the left heart, gives the left ventricle freedom to adjust the output to varying requirements of the systemic arterial circulation within one heart beat, independent of fleeting changes of venous return.

Homeostasis of the central blood volume theoretically could be achieved either by the homeostatic control of total blood volume or by appropriate vasomotor activity of the peripheral vascular bed.

Diuresis induced by a distension of this central reservoir including the left atrium is interpreted as an expression of a reflex mechanism for the homeostatic control of the central blood volume and, under conditions of rest and horizontal body position, of total blood volume also. This volume regulatory reflex, which is mediated through sensing elements in the walls of the atria and the great veins within the pericardium, has a low threshold.

In contrast, the vasomotor reaction of the capacitance vessels can only be elicited by relatively strong stimuli. Normal stresses to which the circulation is adapted, such as moderate changes in blood volume up to ±10%, or changes in central blood volume associated with a change in posture, do not have a sufficient effect on the state of contraction of the peripheral capacitance vessels to prevent a fall in central pressure and volume. In the normal resting state, the elastic tension of the circulation is therefore rather stable. This means that in those conditions in which a homeostatic correction of the central blood volume could theoretically be achieved, either by volume control or by control of peripheral vascular tone, the more sensitive volume control takes the lead, adjusting the blood volume to the capacity of the vascular bed.

REFERENCES

Adolph, E. F., M. J. Gérbasi, and M. J. Lepore. 1933. "The rate of entrance of fluid into the blood in hemorrhage," Am. J. Physiol. 104: 502.

Alexander, R. 1954. "Participation of the venomotor system in pressor reflexes," Circ. Research 2: 405.

Bazett, H. C. 1949. "Factors regulating blood pressure," Transactions of Third Conference, Josiah Macy Jr., Fndn., New York.

Donald, D. E., and H. D. Essex. 1954. "Massive destruction of the myocardium of the canine right ventricle. A study of the early and late effects," Am. J. Physiol. 177: 477.

Donegan, S. E. 1921. "The physiology of the veins," J. Physiol. 55: 226.

Doupe, J., M. H. Ferguson, and J. A. Hildes. 1957. "Seasonal fluctuations in blood volume," Can. J. Biochem. Physiol. 35: 201.

Doyle, J., J. Wilson, H. Estes, and T. Warren. 1951. "The effect of intravenous infusions of physiologic saline solution on the pulmonary arterial and pulmonary capillary pressure in man," J. Clin. Invest. 30: 345.

Ebert, R. V., E. A. Stead, Jr., and J. G. Gibson. 1941. "Response of normal subjects to acute blood loss," Arch. Int. Med. 68: 578.

Fleisch, A. 1930. "Venenmotorenzentrum und Venenreflexe," Pflüger's Arch. ges. Physiol. 225: 26.

Folkow, B. 1955. "Nervous control of the blood vessels," Physiol. Rev. 35: 629.

Franklin, K. I. 1937. A Monograph on Veins, Charles C. Thomas, Springfield, Illinois.

Gauer, O. H. 1942. X-ray motion picture: "Beschleunigungswirkung auf den Kreislauf."

Gauer, O. H., and J. P. Henry. 1956. "Beitrag zur Homöostase des extra-arteriellen Kreislaufs. Volumenregulation als unabhängiger physiologischer Parameter," Klin. Woch. 34: 356.

Gauer, O. H., J. P. Henry, H. O. Sieker, and W. E. Wendt. 1954. "The effect of negative pressure breathing on urine flow," J. Clin. Invest. *33:* 287.

Gauer, O. H., R. Edelberg, J. P. Henry, and H. O. Sieker. 1956. "Changes in central venous pressure after moderate hemorrhage and transfusion in man," Circ. Research *4:* 79.

Gauer, O. H., and H. O. Sieker. 1956. "The continuous recording of central venous pressure changes from an arm vein," Circ. Research *4:* 71.

Gauer, O. H., H. L. Thron, and K. D. Scheppokat. 1958. (abstr.) "Das Verhalten der kapazitiven und der Widerstandsgefäße der menschlichen Hand unter orthostatischer Belastung," Pflüger's Arch. ges. Physiol. *268:* 26.

Glaser, E. M. 1949. "Effects of cooling and warming on vital capacity, forearm and hand volume and skin temperature of man," J. Physiol. *109:* 421.

Glaser, E. M., D. R. McPherson, K. M. Prior, and E. Charles. 1954. "Radiological investigation of the effects of hemorrhage on the liver, lungs, and spleen with special reference to blood storage in man," Clin. Sci. *13:* 461.

Gollwitzer-Meier, K. 1932. "Venensystem und Kreislaufregulierung," Ergeb. Physiol. *34:* 1145.

Greer, K., J. Koch, W. Plewa, and R. Thauer. 1954. "Zur Analyse der quantitativen Beziehungen zwischen Blutverlusten und Entspeicherungsvorgängen der Milz," Pflüger's Arch. *259:* 454.

Guyton, A. C., G. G. Armstrong, and P. L. Chipley. 1956. "Pressure-volume curves of the arterial and venous circulation," Am. J. Physiol. *184:* 253.

Guyton, A. C., D. Polizo, and G. G. Armstrong. 1954. "Mean circulatory filling pressure measured immediately after cessation of heart pumping," Am. J. Physiol. *179:* 261.

Henry, J. P., O. H. Gauer, and H. O. Sieker. 1956. "The effects of moderate changes in blood volume on left and right atrial pressures," Circ. Research *4:* 91.

Henry, J. P., O. H. Gauer, and J. L. Reeves. 1956. "Evidence of the atrial location of receptors influencing urine flow," Circ. Research *4:* 85.

Henry, J. P., and J. W. Pearce. 1956. "The possible role of cardiac atrial stretch receptors in the induction of changes in urine flow," J. Physiol. *131:* 572.

Hintze, A., and H. L. Thron. 1959 (in press). "Der Einfluss akuter Hypoxie und Hyperkapnie auf Durchblutung und Venentonus der menschlichen Hand," Verhbandl. Ber. deut. Ges. Kreisl. Forsch.

Kaufmann, W., and A. A. Müller. 1958. "Expansion des Plasmavolumens nach rascher Verminderung der zirkulierenden Blutmenge," Z. Kreisl. *47:* 719.

Landis, E. M., and J. C. Hortenstine. 1950. "Functional significance of venous blood pressure," Physiol. Rev. *30:* 1.

Nonidez, J. F. 1937. "Identification of the receptor areas in the venae cavae and pulmonary veins which initiate reflex cardiac acceleration (Bainbridge's reflex)," Am. J. Anat. *61:* 203.

Page, E. B., J. B. Hickam, H. O. Sieker, H. D. McIntosh, and W. W. Pryor. 1955. "Reflex venomotor activity in normal persons and in patients with postural hypotension," Circulation *11:* 262.

Paintal, A. S. 1953. "A study of right and left atrial receptors," J. Physiol. *120:* 596.

Pappenheimer, J. R. 1953. "Passage of molecules through capillary walls," Physiol. Rev. *33:* 387.

Püper, J. 1958. "Eine Methode zur Lokalisierung des Strömungswiderstandes," Pflüger's Arch. ges. Physiol. *266:* 199.

Reissmann, K. R. 1951. "Blood volume in the dog during altitude acclimatization," Am. J. Physiol. *167:* 52.

Salzman, E. W., and S. D. Leverett. 1956. "Peripheral venoconstriction during acceleration and orthostasis," Circ. Research *4:* 540.

Schwalm, H., and E. Göltner. 1956. "Bluttransfusion und diurese," Bibl. Haematol. Suppl. ad. Acta, Haematol. *172.*

Sjöstrand, T. 1952. "The regulation of the blood distribution in man," Acta Physiol. Scand. *26:* 312.

Sjöstrand, T. 1953. "Significance of the volume and distribution of the blood for the circulation," Physiol. Rev. *33:* 202.

Smith, H. W. 1957. "Salt and water volume receptors. An exercise in physiologic apologetics," Am. J. Med. *23:* 623.

Starling, E. H. 1909. *The Fluids of the Body*, The Herter Lectures, W. T. Keener and Co., Chicago.

Starr, I. 1940. "Role of the 'static blood pressure' in abnormal increments of venous pressure, especially in heart failure. II. Clinical and experimental studies," Am. J. Med. Sci. *199:* 40.

Warren, J. V., E. S. Brannon, E. A. Stead, and A. J. Merrill. 1945. "The effect of venesection and the pooling of blood in the extremities on the atrial pressure and cardiac output in normal subjects with observations on acute circulatory collapse in three instances," J. Clin. Invest. *24:* 337.

Warren, J. V., E. S. Brannon, H. S. Weens, and E. A. Stead, Jr. 1948. "Effect of increasing blood volume and right atrial pressure on circulation of normal subjects by intravenous infusion," Am. J. Med. *4:* 193.

Wheeler, H. O., O. L. Wade, B. Combes, A. W. Childs, A. Cournand, and S. E. Bradley. 1956. "Effect of exercise on splanchnic blood flow and splanchnic blood volume in man," Fed. Proc. *15:* 198 (abstract 645).

Zuidema, G. D., N. P. Clarke, J. L. Reeves, O. H. Gauer, and J. P. Henry. 1956. "Influence of moderate changes in blood volume on urine flow," Am. J. Physiol. *186:* 89.

215   Homeostasis of the Extra-Arterial Circulation

Homeostasis of the Arterial Circulation

DONALD E. GREGG

Department of Cardiorespiratory Diseases, Walter Reed Army Institute of Research, Washington, D.C.

Two aspects of the problem of arterial homeostasis in space which deserve emphasis have been selected. The first is a consideration of some of the existing basic data relating to arterial homeostasis on earth which may point up the necessary physiological adjustments of the arterial system in space. The second is a consideration of practical means whereby man's tolerance to at least one possible condition in space, i.e., carbon dioxide, may be extended.

BASIC DATA RELATING TO ARTERIAL HOMEOSTASIS

Arterial blood pressure is maintained within moderate limits by a balance effected through simultaneous adjustments of the caliber of the peripheral vessels and cardiac output. The cardiac output is controlled by heart rate and stroke volume. The factors controlling stroke volume include ventricular filling pressure, ventricular diastolic volume, blood volume distribution (especially the size of the thoracic blood reservoir), ventricular distensibility and contractility, and the venous return pumping mechanisms. In addition, an over-all central control is exerted by cerebral, hypothalamic, and medullary centers. In general, if peripheral resistance falls, arterial blood pressure is maintained by increased cardiac output. If cardiac output falls, arterial blood pressure is maintained by increased resistance in the peripheral circulation. Our purpose is briefly to evaluate some of these factors.

High pressoreceptors

One of the first major advances in conceptual thinking on this problem arose through the work of Heymans *et al.* (1933), who showed in the dog that occlusion of the carotid arteries resulted in an augmentation of heart rate, peripheral resistance, and arterial blood pressure, thereby demonstrating the potential importance in man of the carotid sinus and aortic arch baroreceptors in the reflex regulation of the bore of peripheral arterioles. One way of getting at this in man is a study of change in posture. Some of the observed physiological changes are illustrated in Fig. 1. Presumably, as man goes from the supine to the erect position arterial blood pressure decreases mildly at the carotid sinus level. The heart becomes smaller; about 400 cc of blood leaves the thoracic portion of the central blood pool to accumulate mainly in the veins of the extremities; the pressure in them increases and the filling pressure of the heart falls. Cardiac output decreases mildly, stroke volume decreases considerably; the heart rate rises. One can also observe a decrease in blood flow through skin, skeletal muscle, liver, and kidney (Stead *et al.*, 1945; Brigden *et al.*, 1950; Culbertson *et al.*, 1951; Lagerlöf *et al.*, 1951; Wilkins *et al.*, 1951).

These changes are at least partially explainable on a mechanical basis, i.e., tipping into the erect position might be regarded as a functional hemorrhage into the lower portions of the body. The flow alterations could also be related to vasoconstriction of the arterial and/or venous vessels. Since the pressure in a superficial arm vein maintained at heart level rises considerably (about

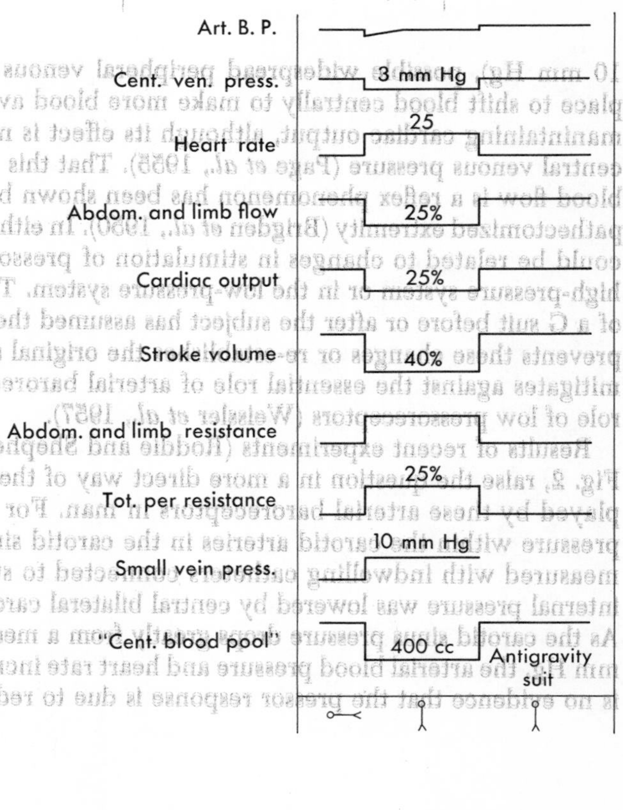

FIGURE 1.
Effect on various cardiovascular parameters in man of changing from the supine to the upright position.

Art. B. P.	
Cent. ven. press.	3 mm Hg
Heart rate	25
Abdom. and limb flow	25%
Cardiac output	25%
Stroke volume	40%
Abdom. and limb resistance	
Tot. per resistance	25%
Small vein press.	10 mm Hg
"Cent. blood pool"	400 cc Antigravity suit

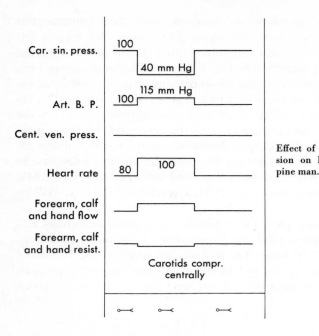

Car. sin. press.

100

40 mm Hg

Art. B. P.

115 mm Hg

100

Cent. ven. press.

Heart rate

80   100

Forearm, calf
and hand flow

Forearm, calf
and hand resist.

Carotids compr.
centrally

FIGURE 2.
Effect of central carotid artery compression on hemodynamic responses in supine man.

10 mm Hg), possible widespread peripheral venous constriction has taken place to shift blood centrally to make more blood available to the heart for manintaining cardiac output, although its effect is not enough to maintain central venous pressure (Page *et al.*, 1955). That this limitation of peripheral blood flow is a reflex phenomenon has been shown by its absence in a sympathectomized extremity (Brigden *et al.*, 1950). In either case these alterations could be related to changes in stimulation of pressoreceptors either in the high-pressure system or in the low-pressure system. The fact that application of a G suit before or after the subject has assumed the upright position either prevents these changes or re-establishes the original state of the circulation, mitigates against the essential role of arterial baroreceptors, and favors the role of low pressoreceptors (Weissler *et al.*, 1957).

Results of recent experiments (Roddie and Shepherd, 1957) illustrated in Fig. 2, raise the question in a more direct way of the importance of the role played by these arterial baroreceptors in man. For these observations the pressure within the carotid arteries in the carotid sinus region was directly measured with indwelling catheters connected to strain gauges, while the internal pressure was lowered by central bilateral carotid artery compression. As the carotid sinus pressure drops greatly from a mean pressure of 100 to 40 mm Hg, the arterial blood pressure and heart rate increase only mildly. There is no evidence that the pressor response is due to reduction in caliber of the limb and skeletal muscle vessels. Actually the resistance to flow which they offer is slightly less than in the control state as the result of a mild increase in blood flow through the limbs and in systemic blood pressure. Presumably, the slight reduction in resistance is caused by passive dilatation from the increased perfusion pressure. Simultaneous measurements of cardiac output would have been helpful here since the increase in arterial blood pressure could arise from the increased cardiac output or from increased vessel resistance in another area.

Similarly, when a sizeable increase in carotid sinus pressure is produced by applying suction to the neck area, there is no evidence that the small hypotensive response arises from an increase in the caliber of the limb blood vessels since their caliber actually decreases slightly (Ernsting and Parry 1957). Since in this instance the measured cardiac output was found to be maintained, the mild blood flow decrease in hand, forearm, and calf is also probably on a mechanical basis and the decreased arterial blood pressure probably results from mild splanchnic dilatation. Here again only mild changes in blood pressure, heart rate, and peripheral resistance are associated with large changes in carotid sinus pressure.

In these experiments one must not lose sight of the fact that other pressure sensitive intra-arterial areas exist that may have contributed significantly to the regulation of arterial blood pressure and which may have been dominant. I refer to those in the aortic arch and to the abdominal pressoreceptors or Pacinian corpuscles which are especially abundant in the pancreas (Sarnoff and Yamada, 1958).

I should like to close this discussion of the role of the arterial baroreceptors on arterial blood pressure by referring to some recent observations in the dog which indicate that stimulation of the caotid sinus baroreceptors exerts a powerful reflex effect on arterial blood pressure which is mediated largely through enhanced cardiac action and to a lesser extent through changes in peripheral resistance.[1] In these experiments in the open chest dog both carotid sinuses were perfused under controlled pressure in the presence of a constant but high heart rate. When mean perfusion pressure and pulse pressure were greatly decreased, both right and left atrial pressures dropped while arterial blood pressure, cardiac output, and stroke volume rose. The calculated stroke work increased approximately 10 times while the peripheral resistance was only about doubled. This indicates that the circulatory response to carotid sinus baroreceptor stimulation is dominantly an increased cardiac action and secondarily an increase in peripheral resistance. Finally, the effector portion of this reflex appears to be the sympathetic fibers from the stellate ganglion to the heart, since following their section these effects disappeared or could not again be induced.

[1] Information kindly supplied by Dr. Stanley Sarnoff.

From the preceding I think it is fair to say that how important a role the carotid sinuses play in man in controlling arterial blood pressure through variations in peripheral resistance is not yet settled.

Low pressoreceptors

In dealing with this subject the importance of the thoracic portion of the central blood pool for maintaining arterial blood pressure should be stressed. In the supine position a sizeable blood reservoir has been identified in the thorax, residing mainly on the left side of the circulation in the pulmonary veins, atria, and the left ventricle (Sjöstrand, 1953; Gauer, 1955). Actually, only about half the blood volume of the left ventricle is ejected during systole (Nylin, 1943). An idea of the magnitude of these reserves is given by the observations that arterial blood pressure can be effectively maintained in the presence of very large changes in heart rate, peripheral resistance, and stroke volume when these are induced artificially in man, i.e., without significant changes in those factors that would actively promote venous return. The effect of change of heart rate is shown in Fig. 3. If atropine is given intra-

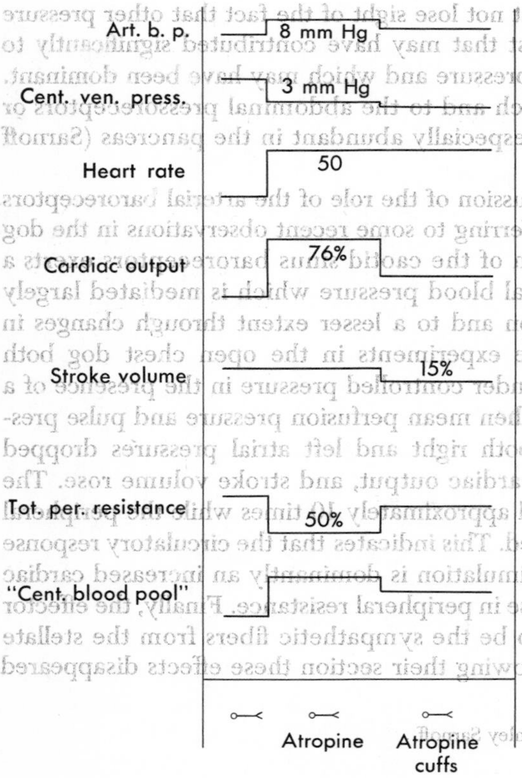

Art. b. p.	8 mm Hg
Cent. ven. press.	3 mm Hg
Heart rate	50
Cardiac output	76%
Stroke volume	15%
Tot. per. resistance	50%
"Cent. blood pool"	

Atropine   Atropine cuffs

FIGURE 3. Effect of atropine on hemodynamic responses in supine man.

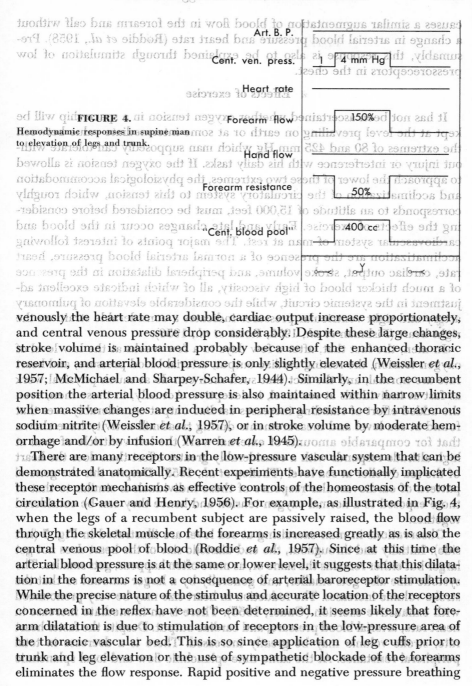

Art. B. P.

Cent. ven. press.   1 4 mm Hg

Heart rate

Forearm flow   150%

Hand flow

Forearm resistance   50%

"Cent. blood pool"   400 cc

FIGURE 4.
Hemodynamic responses in supine man to elevation of legs and trunk.

venously the heart rate may double, cardiac output increase proportionately, and central venous pressure drop considerably. Despite these large changes, stroke volume is maintained probably because of the enhanced thoracic reservoir, and arterial blood pressure is only slightly elevated (Weissler *et al.*, 1957; McMichael and Sharpey-Schafer, 1944). Similarly, in the recumbent position the arterial blood pressure is also maintained within narrow limits when massive changes are induced in peripheral resistance by intravenous sodium nitrite (Weissler *et al.*, 1957), or in stroke volume by moderate hemorrhage and/or by infusion (Warren *et al.*, 1945).

There are many receptors in the low-pressure vascular system that can be demonstrated anatomically. Recent experiments have functionally implicated these receptor mechanisms as effective controls of the homeostasis of the total circulation (Gauer and Henry, 1956). For example, as illustrated in Fig. 4, when the legs of a recumbent subject are passively raised, the blood flow through the skeletal muscle of the forearms is increased greatly as is also the central venous pool of blood (Roddie *et al.*, 1957). Since at this time the arterial blood pressure is at the same or lower level, it suggests that this dilatation in the forearms is not a consequence of arterial baroreceptor stimulation. While the precise nature of the stimulus and accurate location of the receptors concerned in the reflex have not been determined, it seems likely that forearm dilatation is due to stimulation of receptors in the low-pressure area of the thoracic vascular bed. This is so since application of leg cuffs prior to trunk and leg elevation or the use of sympathetic blockade of the forearms eliminates the flow response. Rapid positive and negative pressure breathing causes a similar augmentation of blood flow in the forearm and calf without a change in arterial blood pressure and heart rate (Roddie *et al.*, 1958). Presumably, this response is also to be explained through stimulation of low pressoreceptors in the chest.

Effects of exercise

It has not been ascertained whether oxygen tension in a space ship will be kept at the level prevailing on earth or at some intermediate value between the extremes of 80 and 425 mm Hg which man supposedly can tolerate without injury or interference with his daily tasks. If the oxygen tension is allowed to approach the lower of these two extremes, the physiological accommodation and acclimatization of the circulatory system to this tension, which roughly corresponds to an altitude of 15,000 feet, must be considered before considering the effects of exercise. Early and late changes occur in the blood and cardiovascular system of man at rest. The major points of interest following acclimatization are the presence of a normal arterial blood pressure, heart rate, cardiac output, stroke volume, and peripheral dilatation in the presence of a much thicker blood of high viscosity, all of which indicate excellent adjustment in the systemic circuit, while the considerable elevation of pulmonary artery and right ventricular pressures indicates a considerable strain on the right heart (Fishman *et al.*, 1952; Rotta *et al.*, 1956).

In men, the fact that, after a few days to a few weeks at the low level of oxygen tension, the resting cardiac output, arterial blood pressure, and heart rate are normal, and the fact that such men can do as much physical work as fast as individuals at sea level, is deceptive. Actually, in these men, even the added effort of standing increases cardiac output considerably over that found at sea level and measurements during treadmill activity have shown that for comparable amounts of external work the left ventricle of man at high altitude responds with a considerably greater effort than does the heart of the sea dweller at sea level (Theilen *et al.*, 1955). Despite this the general pattern of cardiovascular response of these individuals is similar to that of those exposed to a normal oxygen tension and hence they can be considered together.

Observations in man exercising at sea level are illustrated in Fig. 5 (left side). Initially and throughout, the end diastolic size of the heart does not get larger but either remains the same or, as more often happens, gets smaller. The systolic size also gets smaller, and generally by a larger amount so that the stroke volume increases. The reduction in heart size may be very pronounced with exhaustive exertion (Gauer, 1955). There is an immediate increase in heart rate, arterial blood pressure, and cardiac output. Despite the faster heart rate, stroke volume may be greatly increased. There is a decrease in total peripheral resistance. At the same time splanchnic flow and local splanchnic

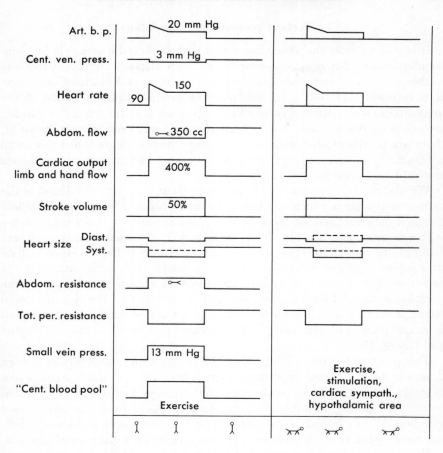

FIGURE 5.

Left side: hemodynamic responses in exercising man. *Right side:* hemodynamic responses in the unanesthetized dog to exercise, to stimulation of the cardiac sympathetic fibers and of the hypothalamic area. Dotted lines represent the less usual responses.

blood volume are decreased (Wade *et al.*, 1956) and the pressure in superficial veins (in a nonexercising area) increases by 10 to 13 mm Hg (Page *et al.*, 1955). By calling upon the increased reserve in the thoracic blood pool and sacrificing its own end diastolic volume the left ventricle pays for the deficit between failing return and normal output. This period of dynamic imbalance lasts only a few seconds until increased venous return, as a result of increased cardiac output, restores equilibrium on a higher flow level. In normal dogs exercised on a treadmill similar results are generally obtained (Rushmer and West, 1957). This is illustrated in Fig. 5 (right side).

Effects of sympathetic stimulation

It is evident from the above discussion that a marked increase in left ventricular contractility occurs in exercise, since the stroke volume may increase in the presence of reduced central venous pressure and diastolic heart size. It is believed that this is caused by reflex sympathetic stimulation of the myocardium with release of sympathin and possibly later the release of catechol amines from the adrenals. Such observations do not exist in man; however, there are pertinent observations in the dog which indicate that myocardial contractility can play a large role in determining cardiac output and hence arterial blood pressure.

We observed many years ago in the open chest dog that stimulation of the cardiac nerve fibers which had been previously isolated from the left stellate ganglion increased systolic blood pressure, cardiac output, and stroke volume with a decrease in heart size. The heart rate did not necessarily change. These findings are similar to those on the right-hand side of Fig. 5. Since stellate stimulation largely elevated arterial blood pressure and cardiac output in the presence of a constant heart rate and after all known connections to the peripheral vasculature had been severed, it follows that the rise of arterial blood pressure was caused by the augmented force of contraction, giving an increased cardiac output, and not by increased peripheral resistance (Shipley and Gregg, 1945).

This positive inotropic effect has been demonstrated recently in a more dramatic way.[2] In these experiments left ventricular function curves (a plot of stroke volume or stroke work against left atrial pressure) were determined before and during stimulation of the cardiac fibers from the left stellate ganglion. With stimulation the ventricular function curve shifts to the left, i.e., stroke work or stroke volume increases greatly for a given atrial pressure.

Finally, it has been demonstrated that stimulation of the left stellate ganglion or the hypothalamic area in the unanesthetized dog gives cardiovascular responses similar to those occurring with treadmill exercise in the same dog on the same day (Fig. 5) (Anzola and Rushmer, 1956; Rushmer and Smith, 1958).

Effects of removal of gravity

The preceding displays in part our meager knowledge of the control of the arterial blood pressure on earth. Projection of things to come in space is precarious. Mechanical effects from the surrounding tissues can alter the circulation mildly. The circulatory changes caused by gravity are due to elastic deformation which body organs and blood vessels undergo. In the weightless state the organs are without support and hence this leads to mild derangement of body organs as they seek slightly altered positions.

Direct disturbances of the circulation, however, by absence of gravity would

[2] Information kindly supplied by Dr. Stanley Sarnoff.

not be anticipated. The circulation operates by elastic forces delivered by the heart and the elasticity of the blood vessels. Although the blood loses its weight it retains its mass, inertia, and other properties of a liquid. In general, it is believed it would resemble that of a man at sea level in the horizontal position except that flattening of the veins would not occur and the distribution of the blood would be the same in the horizontal and vertical head up or down position, or indeed in any position.

One might expect diminution of activity of the vasomotor system and reflexes that have so much to do with compensatory responses of the circulatory system to stress. This is so since the execution of locomotion takes place under continuous guidance of a complex system of sensory receptors widely distributed over the body. Since the degree of activation of muscle is related to the weight of the body and since this depends mainly on muscle proprioceptors, one could expect that muscle tonus would be reduced and the limbs relaxed and flaccid. In addition, since it will take no more energy to move a large object than a small object, and very little energy in either case, one might expect a further reduction in skeletal muscle activity with a fall in cardiac output and even atrophy of the heart and skeletal muscle. Some form of standard exercise might be needed to prevent this.

EXTENSION OF MAN'S TOLERANCE TO CARBON DIOXIDE

Effects of hypercapnia

I should now like to consider the effects of CO_2 accumulation on arterial homeostasis in the body and possible means of extending man's tolerance to it. It is considered that sustained exposure to a level higher than about 1.5% CO_2 in the inspired air is unsafe for man (White, 1948).

Dr. Nahas, of our department, has been experimenting with an organic buffer base which in the dog tends to neutralize the effects of high blood CO_2 tensions. Hypercapnia was induced in dogs via apneic oxygenation (Holmdahl, 1956), a condition of ventilatory arrest induced with succinyl choline (following one hour of ventilation with 100% oxygen). After one hour of apnea there occurs a large fall in arterial oxygen saturation and arterial pH; a large rise in arterial pCO_2 and cerebrospinal fluid pressure; bradycardia, cardiac arrythmias, and wide fluctuation in blood pressure and anuria; 40% of all dogs die within the apneic hour. In dogs given buffer base intravenously at the onset of apneic oxygenation the above physiological parameters remain within the normal range; about 25% of the CO_2 estimated to be produced is recovered in the urine, and all dogs have survived without apparent ill effects. These exploratory experiments furnish an interesting lead with possible practical applications in acute and chronic respiratory acidosis induced in a sealed cabin or submarine, during the course of or after surgery, and in emphysema.

REFERENCES

Anzola, J., and R. F. Rushmer. 1956. "Cardiac responses to sympathetic stimulation," Circ. Research 4: 302.

Brigden, W., S. Howarth, and E. P. Sharpey-Schafer. 1950. "Postural changes in the peripheral blood flow of normal subjects with observations on vasovagal fainting reactions as a result of tilting, the lordotic posture, pregnancy and spinal anesthesia," Clin. Sci. 9: 79–90.

Culbertson, J. W., R. W. Wilkins, F. J. Ingelfinger, and S. E. Bradley. 1951. "The effect of the upright posture upon hepatic blood flow in normotensive and hypertensive subjects," J. Clin. Invest. 30: 305–311.

Ernsting, J., and D. J. Parry. 1957. "Some observations on the effects of stimulating the stretch receptors in the carotid artery of man," J. Physiol. 137: 45–46P.

Fishman, A. P., J. McClement, A. Himmelstein, and A. Cournand. 1952. "Effects of acute anoxia on the circulation and respiration in patients with chronic pulmonary disease studied during the steady state," J. Clin. Invest. 31: 770–781.

Gauer, O. H. 1955. "Volume changes of the left ventricle during blood pooling and exercise in the intact animal. Their effects on left ventricular performance," Physiol. Revs. 35: 143–155.

Gauer, O. H., and P. Henry. 1956. "Beitrag zur Homöostase des extra arteriellen Kreislaufs. Volumenregulation als unabhängiger physiologischer Parameter," Klin. Woch. 34: 356–366.

Heymans, C., J. J. Bouckaert, and P. Regniers. 1933. Le sinus carotidien et la zone homologue cardioaortique, Doin, Paris.

Holmdahl, M. H. 1956. "Pulmonary uptake of oxygen, acid-base metabolism, and circulation during prolonged apnoea," Acta chir. scand. Suppl. 212: 1–128.

Lagerlof, H., H. Eliasch, L. Werko, and E. Berglund. 1951. "Orthostatic changes of the pulmonary and peripheral circulation in man. A preliminary report," Scand. J. Clin. & Lab. Invest. 3: (2) 85–91.

McMichael, J., and E. P. Sharpey-Schafer. 1944. "Cardiac output in man by direct Fick method; Effects of posture, venous pressure change, atropine, and adrenaline," Brit. Heart J., 6: 33–40.

Nylin, G. 1943. "On the amount of, and changes in, the residual blood of the heart," Am. Heart J. 25: 598–607.

Page, E. B., M. B. Hickam, H. O. Sieker, H. D. McIntosh, and W. W. Pryor. 1955. "Reflex venomotor activity in normal persons and in patients with postural hypotension," Circulation 11: 262–270.

Roddie, I. C., J. T. Shepherd, and R. F. Whelan. 1957. "Reflex changes in vasoconstrictor tone in human skeletal muscle in response to stimulation of receptors in a low-pressure area of the intrathoracic vascular bed," J. Physiol. 139: 369–376.

Roddie, I. C., J. T. Shepherd, and R. F. Whelan. 1958. "Reflex changes in human skeletal muscle blood flow associated with intrathoracic pressure changes," Circ. Research 6: 232–238.

Roddie, I. C., and J. T. Shepherd. 1957. "The effects of carotid artery compression in man with special reference to changes in vascular resistance in the limbs,"J. Physiol. 139 (3): 377–384.

Rotta, A. A. Cánepa, A. Hurtado, T. Valásquez, and R. Chavez. 1956. "Pulmonary circulation at sea level and at high altitudes," J. Appl. Physiol. 9: 328–336.

Rushmer, R. F., and O. Smith. 1957. "Hypothalamic influence on left ventricular performance," Fed. Proc. 17 (1) 137 (abstract 544).

Rushmer, R. F., and T. C. West. 1957. "Role of autonomic hormones on left ventricular performance continuously analyzed by electronic computers," Circ. Research 5: 240.

Sarnoff, S. J., and S. I. Yamada. 1958. "Evidence for abdominal pressoreceptors with special reference to the pancreas," Fed. Proc. 17 (1): 141 (abstract 559).

Shipley, R. E., and D. E. Gregg. 1945. "The cardiac response to stimulation of the stellate ganglia and cardiac nerves," Am. J. Physiol. 143: 396.

Sjöstrand, T. 1953. "Volume and distribution of blood and their significance in regulating the circulation," Physiol. Rev. 33: 202–228.

Stead, E. A., Jr., J. V. Warren, A. J. Merrill, and E. S. Brannon. 1945. "The cardiac output in male subjects as measured by the technique of right atrial catheterization. Normal values with observations on the effect of anxiety and tilting," J. Clin. Invest. 24: 326–331.

Theilen, E. O., D. E. Gregg, and A. Rotta. 1955. "Exercise and cardiac work response at high altitude," Circulation 12: 383–390.

Wade, O. L., B. Combes, A. W. Childs, H. O. Wheeler, A. Cournand, and S. E. Bradley. 1956. "The effect of exercise on the splanchnic blood flow and splanchnic blood volume in normal man," Clin. Sci. 15: 457–463.

Warren, J. V., E. S. Brannon, E. A. Stead, Jr., and A. J. Merrill. 1945. "The effect of venesection and the pooling of blood in the extremities on the atrial pressure and cardiac output in normal subjects with observations on acute circulatory collapse in three instances," J. Clin. Invest. 24: 337–345.

Weissler, A. M., J. V. Warren, E. H. Estes, H. D. McIntosh, and J. J. Leonard. 1957. "Vasodepressor syncope. Factors influencing cardiac output," Circulation 15: 875–882.

Weissler, A. M., J. J. Leonard, and J. V. Warren. 1957. "Effects of posture and atropine on cardiac output," J. Clin. Invest. 36: 1656–1662.

White, C. S. 1948. Estimated Tolerance of "Human Subjects to Various CO_2 Time Concentrations," Lovelace Foundation Project No. 200, Report No. 2, Aviation Medical Consultants' Report to Douglas Aircraft Company, Inc.

Wilkins, R. W., J. W. Culbertson, and F. J. Ingelfinger. 1951. "The effect of splanchnic sympathectomy in hypertensive patients upon estimated hepatic blood flow in the upright as contrasted with the horizontal position," J. Clin. Invest. 30: 312–317.

Pulmonary Circulatory Effects of Carbon Dioxide and Oxygen

ROBERT C. STROUD

U. S. Naval Medical Research Laboratory, New London, Connecticut

Most of the investigators engaged in studies of pulmonary circulation would agree that this field constitutes one of the more complex entities facing physiologists today. The factors complicating the study of blood flow through the lungs probably have received, during the past two or three years, more attention than the pulmonary circulation itself. It would therefore seem worthwhile to review very briefly the present status of studies concerned with the effects of oxygen and carbon dioxide on the pulmonary circulation; to outline the major factors which must be clarified before further significant advances can be reasonably expected; and finally, to report on several preliminary experiments of my own concerned with one of these factors, namely pulmonary arterio-venous anastomoses or shunts.

A major part of the efforts expended on the study of the pulmonary circulation have centered about the basic question of whether or not pulmonary blood vessels exhibit active vasomotion. For obvious reasons, emphasis has been placed, in these studies, upon the effects of changes in inspired oxygen or carbon dioxide tension. Thus, research in this area has been concerned primarily with the following problems.

1. Does altering the concentration of these gases result in pulmonary vasomotion? Today, few physiologists would disagree with an affirmative answer. Low O_2 and high CO_2 both increase the resistance to blood flow through the lungs. The effect of O_2 is, however, stronger and more definite. There remains little doubt that this increased resistance is due to vasoconstriction. (See References for a partial list of publications on this subject.)

2. If altering the gas tensions does result in vasomotion, is there a neurogenic mechanism involved? What are its anatomical and physiological characteristics? In this respect, evidence exists that at least part of the vasomotor

228

response to changes in gas tensions is neurogenic and both the thoracic sympathetic outflow and the vagus nerves have been implicated. (Stroud and Rahn, 1953; Daly and Hebb, 1952.)

3. In what part of the lesser circulation does this vasomotion occur? This question remains essentially unanswered although perfused lung experiments seem to indicate that the pulmonary arteries or arterioles and veins may show vasomotion independently of each other. (Nisell, 1948–1949; Nisell, 1950.)

4. If vasomotion occurs within the pulmonary circulation, does it serve a useful purpose and what is this purpose? Concerning this problem we may only speculate, particularly since the third question remains unanswered. Probably the most favored hypothesis is that pulmonary circulatory vasomotion serves to help regulate the ventilation-perfusion ratio distribution throughout the lungs. (Stroud and Rahn, 1953; Liljestrand, 1958; Lilienthal and Riley, 1954.) However, this attractive theory awaits really good supporting evidence.

The major complexity involved in attempting to approach these problems experimentally is the fact that most of the pulmonary circulation is imbedded in lung tissue which, in turn, is enclosed within the thoracic space. This not only means that the circulation is relatively inaccessible for in vivo measurements, but also that it is acted upon by a variety of forces such as changes in transpulmonary pressure and in lung tissue characteristics (Lilienthal and Riley, 1954).

It would seem that this problem could be overcome relatively easily by utilization of an isolated heart-lung profusion system which leaves the nerve fibers to the pulmonary vessels intact. A strong argument was presented for this general approach by I. deBurgh Daly in a review article in 1958. However, interpretation of results obtained with these methods present certain difficulties. It is quite difficult to be absolutely certain that the vascular nerve supply remains competent. Moreover, the pulmonary vascular resistance usually increases rather rapidly during perfusion, often making it necessary to undertake experiments with abnormal pressure-flow relationships. Partly for this reason quantitative pressure-flow and pressure-volume curves have not been obtained as yet, thus making it more difficult to interpret in vivo experiments in which both pressure and flow change.

As if these complexities were an insufficient plague on the pulmonary physiologist, the bronchial circulation with its pre- and post-pulmonary capillary anastomoses was installed into the system. Experiments must therefore take into account any possible effects on the pulmonary circulation of changes in bronchial circulatory hemodynamics due to alterations in systemic arterial pressure or flow or due to vasomotion within the bronchial circulation itself. The effects of changes in bronchomotor tone also cannot be ignored as pointed out by Rodbard (1950). These changes may result in the trapping of air in the alveoli due to bronchoconstriction, thus increasing pulmonary capillary pressure. It has also been shown that changes in bronchomotor tone may

alter lung viscance and elastance (Rodbard, 1953) with resulting effects on
the pulmonary circulatory pressures.

There is at least one additional factor previously mentioned; although there
has been a scattered interest in the investigation of pulmonary arterio-venous
shunting, relatively little work has been done on this aspect of the lesser circulation. That these shunts exist anatomically has been shown for the human
lung by Tobin and Zariquiey (1951) who utilized a post-mortem injection procedure. Among the *in vivo* demonstrations of the presence of pulmonary arterio-
venous anastomoses in animals have been those of Prinzmetal *et al.* (1948), who
made use of the injection of glass microspheres as did Sirsi and Bucher (1953)
who had their beads radioactively labeled, and those of Irwin and his colleagues (1954) who transilluminated the edge of intact lungs for microscopic
study. None of these reports indicated whether or not these shunts could accommodate more than about 2% of the cardiac output as indicated by gas
tension gradient analyses (Riley and Cournand, 1949). All indications are that
in man or animals under normal conditions only a very small percentage of
the total flow bypasses the pulmonary capillaries.

The first indication which we encountered that these shunts might accommodate, under certain conditions, a fairly large proportion of the total flow
was during the experiments reported by Rahn, Stroud, and Tobin (1952). At
that time we were taking cinefluorographic pictures of thorotrast injected into
the right heart or pulmonary artery of dogs. It was also at that time that considerable discussion was being held concerning the interpretation of pulmonary
artery wedge pressures. We thought that it would be interesting to see the result of a thorotrast injection through a cardiac catheter wedged into a pulmonary artery. Thus, we jammed the catheter in and out several times to
make certain that it was completely wedged and then made the injection.
The resulting pictures dramatically indicated that a major part of the injection
passed through a shunt directly to a pulmonary vein. This rather large shunt
was observed in three of four dogs thus studied, but only after irritation of
the vessels by pulling the catheter back and forth. I will return to this point
in a moment. The passage of a thorotrast through a true arterio-venous
anastomoses was verified on post-mortem injection of the pulmonary vessels
by Dr. Tobin of the anatomy department at the University of Rochester School
of Medicine.

Largely because of my interest in the pulmonary vascular effects of altering
the inspired gas tensions, I sought a method for investigating the possibility
that these shunts might also respond in some manner to alterations in oxygen
or carbon dioxide tensions. An approach was attempted utilizing 75–180 micron diameter glass beads. Twenty-one experiments were undertaken on 10–15
kg dogs.

This method consists of passing a short cardiac catheter into the pulmonary
conus of an anesthetized dog. Suitable arrangements are also made for measur-

ing left atrial and femoral arterial pressures. After preparations are complete, one-half gram of 75 micron glass microspheres is injected under minimum pressure into the pulmonary conus. Simultaneously and for 10 seconds following the completion of the injection, blood is allowed to run freely from a large polyethylene tube inserted in a carotid artery. This blood (about 30 ml) is collected in a large test tube and examined for the presence of microspheres. Pressure measurements are made immediately before and after injection.

Of the total number of experiments undertaken, ten could be considered complete and the average results are shown in Fig. 1. In these experiments 75 micron glass beads were injected with the animal alternately breathing air and 100% O_2. The upper diagram indicates the results obtained when the first injection was made with the animal breathing oxygen, while in the lower the animal breathed air prior to and during the first injection.

It is interesting to note that in every case more beads were recovered when the dog breathed oxygen than when air was breathed. It may also be noted that more beads were recovered throughout the experiment when oxygen was breathed during the first injection.

With regard to pressures, apparently as we might now suspect, the effect of a bead injection upon the pulmonary artery pressure is greater when air is being breathed. However, it can also be noted that the effect upon this pressure of three or four successive injections is greater when O_2 is breathed

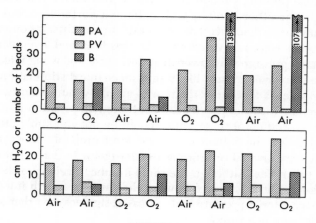

FIGURE 1.

Top: average measurements obtained in 5 experiments in which dogs breathed O_2 or air in the order indicated. Control measurements were made immediately before and experimental measurements immediately following each bead injection. *Bottom:* average measurements obtained in 5 experiments in which the dogs breathed air and O_2 in the opposite order to those represented in the upper diagram. P.A. = Pulmonary arterial pressure, P.V. = Pulmonary venous pressure, B. = Number of beads recovered.

prior to the first injection. This latter observation is particularly difficult to explain.

Although not indicated in this figure, the systemic arterial pressure fell by about 10–20 mm Hg during the experiments in which it was measured. Although respiration was not recorded, no obvious respiratory embarrassment occurred in any dog until after the third or fourth injection.

We must be careful concerning the inferences which we may draw from experiments of this type. Our method of sampling from a carotid artery told us only how many beads could be recovered from that particular small unit of the circulation. Any factor tending to change the proportion of flow through this artery would certainly be reflected in our bead count. Bearing these factors in mind, it is nevertheless interesting to see what our results suggest in regard to the functioning of pulmonary arterio-venous shunts. At least three theories have been suggested: (1) that impaction of emboli downstream from afferent nerve endings causes a reflex vasoconstriction upstream, thus diverting more blood through shunts (Whitteridge, 1950); (2) that these shunts are opened whenever the pulmonary arterial pressure becomes elevated (Rahn et al., 1952); and (3) that direct mechanical stimulation of afferent nerve endings causes a reflex vasodilatation of arterio-venous shunts in the lung. In view of our data, it also seems possible that oxygen tension affects these shunts either directly or indirectly.

In considering these theories, it would seem that if reflex vasoconstriction occurred upstream from impacted emboli, it would be unlikely that the pulmonary arterial pressure would fall during the recovery period following each injection. On the other hand, if high pulmonary arterial pressure were the sole factor involved, then it is difficult to explain the observation that in every case more beads were recovered when O_2 was breathed, even when the pulmonary arterial pressure was lower than during the following injection on air. It therefore would seem most likely that mechanical stimulation of afferent nerve endings leads to a reflex dilation of arterio-venous shunts. This would be in agreement with the previously mentioned observation that cinefluorographic demonstration of these shunts could be obtained only after irritation of the distal end of the pulmonary artery. Most probably, however, the level of the pulmonary arterial pressure is a major factor in determining the effectiveness of this reflex. Although the same number (weight) of beads was injected each time, it was only following the third or fourth injection, when the pulmonary arterial pressure had increased significantly, that a large number of beads were recovered.

In conclusion, it might be noted that the existence of these shunts probably adds only a relatively minor complexity to the interpretation of pressure-flow changes in the normal pulmonary circulation as a result of altering the inspired gas tensions. This is true because relatively simple calculations based on the classical relationships between parallel resistances and the proportional flow through them indicate that a very large drop in the normal shunt resistance would have to occur before it would become significantly reflected in measurements concerned with the total pulmonary circulation. However, following embolization or other forms of pulmonary artery irritation, these shunts may play a significant role.

REFERENCES

Atwell, R. J., J. B. Hickman, W. W. Pryor, and E. B. Page. 1951. Am. J. Physiol. *166*: 37.
Burchell, H. B., and E. H. Wood. 1951. Fed. Proc. *10*: 21.
Daly, I. deBurgh. 1958. Quart. J. Exptl. Physiol. *43*: 2.
Daly, I. deBurgh, and C. O. Hebb. 1952. Quart. Exptl. Physiol. *37*: 19.
Dirken, M. N. J., and H. Heemstra. 1947–48. Quart. J. Exptl. Physiol. *34*: 193.
Dirken, M. N. J., and H. Heemstra. 1947–48. Quart. J. Exptl. Physiol. *34*: 213.
Doyle, J. T., J. S. Wilson, and J. V. Warren. 1952. Circulation *5*: 263.
Duke, H. N., and E. M. Killick. 1952. J. Physiol. *117*: 303.
Duke, H. N. 1950. J. Physiol. *111*: 17P.
Euler, U. S. von, and G. Liljestrand. 1946. Acta Physiol. Scand. *12*: 301.
Fishman, A. P., A. Himmelstein, H. W. Fritts, Jr., and A. Cournand. 1955. J. Clin. Invest. *34*: 637.
Hall, P. W., III. 1953. Circ. Research *1*: 238.
Hebb, C. O., and R. H. Nimmo-Smith, 1947–48. Quart. J. Exptl. Physiol. *34*: 159.
Heemstra, H. 1954. Quart. J. Exptl. Physiol. *39*: 83.
Irwin, J. W., W. S. Barrage, C. E. Aimer, and R. W. Chesnut, Jr. 1954. Anat. Rec. *119*: 391.
Lewis, B. M., and R. Gorlin. 1952. Am. J. Physiol. *170*: 574.
Lilienthal, J. L., and R. L. Riley. 1954. Ann Rev. Med. *5*: 237.
Liljestrand, G. 1948. Arch. Int. Med. *81*: 162.
Liljestrand, G. 1958. Acta Physiol. Scand. *44*: 216.
Logaras, G. 1947. Acta Physiol. Scand. *14*: 120.
McGregor, M., H. Borst, J. L. Whittenberger, and E. Berglund. 1955. Am. J. Physiol. *183*: 643.
Nisell, O. 1948–49. Acta Physiol. Scand. *16*: 14.
Nisell, O. 1950. Acta Physiol. Scand. *21*: Suppl. 73.
Nisell, O. 1951. Acta Physiol. Scand. *23*: 85.
Peters, R. M., and A. Roos. 1952. Am J. Physiol. *171*: 250.
Peters, R. M. 1957. Am. J. Physiol. *191*: 399.
Prinzmetal, M., E. M. Ornitz, Jr., B. Simkin, and H. C. Bergman. 1948. Am. J. Physiol. *152*: 48.
Rahn, H., and H. T. Bohnson. 1953. J. Appl. Physiol. *6*: 105.
Rahn, H., R. C. Stroud, and C. E. Tobin. 1952. Proc. Soc. Exptl. Biol. & Med. *80*: 239.
Riley, R. L., and A. Cournand. 1949. J. Appl. Physiol. *1*: 825.
Rodbard, S. 1950. J. Lab. Clin. Med. *36*: 980.
Rodbard, S. 1953. Am. J. Med. *15*: 356.
Rotta, A., A. Conepa, A. Hurtado, T. Velasquez, and R. Chavez. 1956. J. Appl. Physiol. *9*: 328.
Sirsi, M., and K. Bucher. 1953. Experientia *9*: 217.
Stroud, R. C., and H. Rahn. 1953. Am. J. Physiol. *172*: 211.
Stroud, R. C., and H. L. Conn, Jr. 1954. Am. J. Physiol. *179*: 119.
Tobin, C. E., and M. O. Zariquiey. 1951. Proc. Soc. Exptl. Biol. & Med. *75*: 827.
Westcott, R. N., N. O. Fowler, R. C. Scott, V. D. Havenstein, and J. McGuire. 1951. J. Clin. Invest. *20*: 957.
Whitteridge, D. 1950. Physiol. Rev. *30*: 475.

Regulation of Brain Oxygen and Acid-Base Environment

CHRISTIAN J. LAMBERTSEN

Department of Pharmacology, School of Medicine, University of Pennsylvania, Philadelphia, Pennsylvania

This paper will present information regarding the interactions of pCO_2 and pO_2 in establishing the oxygen and acid-base environment of the human brain. I will conclude from this information that in studies of anoxia or hyperoxia, and hypo- or hypercapnia, both carbon dioxide and oxygen tensions must be considered because of their potent interactions with respiration, blood gas transport, cerebral blood flow, and cerebral metabolism.

OXYGEN, CO₂, AND BRAIN CIRCULATION

We can begin with the well-known effects of carbon dioxide upon the cerebral circulation as shown in Fig. 1, which is derived from studies of Kety and Schmidt (1946) and from results obtained with my co-workers (Lambertsen *et al.,* 1953). During administration of carbon dioxide an elevation of pCO_2 produces a cerebral vasodilatation, with a consequent increase in brain blood flow. Hyperventilation hypocapnia causes a cerebral vasoconstriction and reduction of brain blood flow. No other condition or "drug" is as potent as CO_2 in relaxing cerebral vessels. While it is not known whether CO_2 or pH changes are responsible for vasodilatation, it does appear clear that the action of CO_2 is exerted on the arterial, rather than on venous or capillary components of the cerebral circulation. The dominance of carbon dioxide effects upon cerebral vascular smooth muscle makes it necessary to exclude it as a variable in studying other factors in cerebral circulatory control.

The effects of low and high oxygen tensions upon the brain circulation are also known (Fig. 2). Inhalation of low oxygen gas mixtures at sea level causes cerebral vasodilatation (Kety and Schmidt, 1946; Lambertsen, 1958). Oxygen tensions above normal result in cerebral vasoconstriction (Kety and Schmidt,

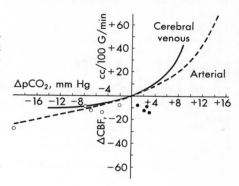

FIGURE 1.

Curves derived from data obtained in hyperventilation and CO_2 inhalation by Kety and Schmidt (1946). Open circles are mean relationships between CBF and Art. pCO_2 during oxygen inhalation at 1.0, 3.0, and 3.5 atmospheres (Lambertsen et al., 1953). Black points represent simultaneously obtained relationships between CBF and internal jugular venous pCO_2. The figure indicates that CBF is affected by changes in arterial rather than venous pCO_2, that CBF reduction by O_2 is due to the concomitant arterial hypocapnia and that oxygen inhalation produces simultaneous arterial hypocapnia and venous hypercapnia.

1946; Lambertsen et al., 1953). We are therefore faced with the possibility of combined effects of varying degrees of hypocapnia with low, normal or high pO_2, and varying degrees of hypercapnia with low, normal, or high pO_2.

Figure 3 indicates that this complex situation can be simplified. In the studies illustrated, the hypocapnia which normally accompanies both anoxemia and hyperoxemia was prevented by artificially regulating alveolar (arterial) pCO_2 at 44 mm Hg (Lambertsen, 1958; Turner et al., 1957) (4). Under this condition administration of oxygen at 0.8 atmosphere produces no cerebral vasoconstriction. It thus appears that oxygen tensions above normal do not have a direct cerebral vasoconstrictor action. Rather, the well-known ability of oxygen to constrict cerebral vessels should be considered as an indirect effect, related to the hypo-

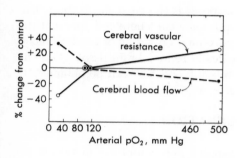

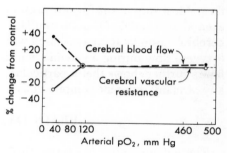

FIGURE 2 (left).

Plot of mean values in eight subjects breathing 8% O_2 in N_2, air, and 85% O_2, each with 15% N_2O, at one atmosphere with "natural" pCO_2. Figure shows anoxic cerebral vasodilatation and cerebral vasoconstriction associated with oxygen inhalation.

FIGURE 3 (right).

Plot of mean values in eight subjects during inhalation of 8% O_2 in N_2, air, and 80% O_2, each with 15% N_2O, at one atmosphere. Arterial pC_2O artificially controlled at 44 mm Hg. Anoxic cerebral vasodilatation persists but, in absence of pCO_2 change, oxygen exerts no cerebral vasoconstrictor action.

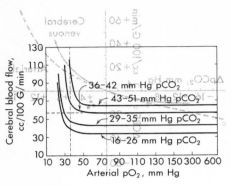

FIGURE 4.

Relationships among arterial pO_2, arterial pCO_2, and rate of brain blood flow, based upon 56 measurements in seven normal men (Lambertsen *et al.*, 1957). Above about 50 mm Hg, arterial pO_2 oxygen tension exerts no important effect upon blood flow. The vasodilator action of low arterial pO_2 becomes increasingly prominent as arterial pO_2 falls below 50 mm Hg. By varying arterial pCO_2, wide fluctuations in brain blood flow can be produced both in the absence and in the presence of anoxemia; actually hypocapnia is capable of reversing, and hypercapnia of exaggerating, the cerebral vasodilatation normally associated with anoxemia. The figure shows that a particular rate of cerebral blood flow can be obtained over a wide range of variation of arterial pO_2 and pCO_2.

capnia brought about by oxygen-induced hyperventilation. It should therefore be possible to ignore increased pO_2 as an independent factor affecting cerebral vessels. The anoxic, cerebral vasodilation during controlled arterial pCO_2 represents the result of exposure to low arterial pO_2, unmodified by changes in blood pCO_2.

An extension of these studies is shown in Fig. 4, in which pCO_2, pO_2, and cerebral blood flow interactions observed in 60 experiments are grouped into several ranges of pCO_2 (Lambertsen, 1958). The figure shows the absence of direct action of pO_2 changes above about 50 mm Hg when pCO_2 is held "constant." It also shows the considerable activity of pCO_2 at constant, elevated pO_2, and the striking ability of anoxemia to increase the rate of brain blood flow. Most important for our present purposes is the clear illustration that, even at an arterial pO_2 of 30 mm Hg, hypocapnia can completely prevent the cerebral vasodilatation associated with anoxemia. Lowering cerebral blood (oxygen) flow during anoxemia will drastically reduce brain tissue pO_2. The figure further shows that a particular cerebral blood flow can be obtained by any of many different combinations of arterial pCO_2 and pO_2.

BRAIN OXYGENATION

There is no reason to assume that brain cell pO_2 is uniform in various regions of the brain, or even at various points within a single brain cell. Certainly the mean brain pO_2 cannot be measured, since it is a mathematical expression of the average of many different oxygen tensions in many different parts of the brain. We have elected to measure arterial and internal jugular pO_2 as indices of the *highest* oxygen tensions to which undetermined brain cells are exposed. Mean brain capillary pO_2, calculated by integration, serves only as an expression of the average pO_2 level in the average brain capillary. Figure 5 illustrates diagramatically the probable change in blood pO_2 in its passage across the human brain. During air breathing at sea level or oxygen breathing at 33,000 feet, an arterial pO_2 of 100 mm Hg and a cerebral venous pO_2 of nearly 40 are thus associated with a mean brain capillary pO_2 of about 60 mm Hg. Oxygen inhalation at sea level, while markedly raising arterial pO_2, has only moderate effect upon mean capillary pO_2 and a minor influence upon venous pO_2.

The level of mean brain capillary pO_2 is affected by a number of interacting factors, as illustrated in the qualitative expression:

$$\text{mean brain capillary } pO_2 = \frac{\text{CBF} \times \text{Hb O}_2 \text{ capacity} \times \text{arterial } pO_2 \times \text{arterial [H}^+]}{\text{brain O}_2 \text{ consumption}}.$$

We are not yet ready to employ such an equation to predict brain capillary pO_2 in unusual situations of gaseous environment (Lambertsen, 1958). Hydrogen ions can affect not only blood flow and hemoglobin dissociation, but probably brain metabolism. In anoxia low pO_2 can alter not only brain blood flow but brain metabolism and blood hydrogen ion concentration. For such reasons, mean brain capillary pO_2 must be considered the passive end result of a series of dynamic interactions, not all of which are as yet clearly defined.

To aid in the definition of these interactions the several series of experiments illustrated in Table 1 were carried out. The table shows average results of altered ambient gaseous environment. Each series except the last (Lambertsen, 1953; Lambertsen, 1957) included 6 to 8 subjects. With each inspired oxygen tension, arterial carbon dioxide tension was varied, by hyperventilation and by carbon dioxide administration, to produce changes in brain circulation. Considering cerebral blood flow $\times$ arterial oxygen content as Brain Oxygen Flow (Lambertsen, 1958), alteration of pCO_2 thus permitted separate appraisal of the influence of oxygen flow and oxygen tension upon brain oxygenation. In each of the paired series except the last, the principle of artificial regulation of alveolar pCO_2 was employed.

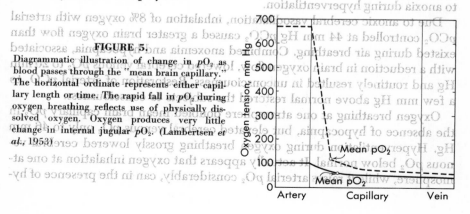

FIGURE 5.
Diagrammatic illustration of change in pO_2 as blood passes through the "mean brain capillary." The horizontal ordinate represents either capillary length or time. The rapid fall in pO_2 during oxygen breathing reflects use of physically dissolved oxygen. Oxygen produces very little change in internal jugular pO_2. (Lambertsen et al., 1953)

TABLE 1

Modification of brain oxygenation by alteration of arterial pO_2 and pCO_2.

Conditions			Brain O_2 flow	pO_2 (mm Hg)		
Gas breathed	Barometric pressure Atmos	Arterial pCO_2 mm Hg	cc/100 G/min	Art.	Mean Cap.	Venous
8% O_2	1	24	8.0	35	25	20
8% O_2 + CO_2	1	44	13.2	39	32	28
Air	1	24	7.1	95	50	21
Air + CO_2	1	44	12.2	112	64	40
O_2	1	24	7.4	500	75	22
O_2 + CO_2	1	44	14.1	500	122	46
O_2	3.5	37	11.2	2000	800	80
O_2 + CO_2	3.5	58	22.4	2000	1500	1000

Table 1 shows that during air breathing at one atmosphere an arterial pCO_2 of 44 mm Hg was associated with an essentially normal brain oxygen flow (12.2 cc/min/100G), a mean brain capillary pO_2 of 64 and a cerebral venous pO_2 of 40 mm Hg. Hypocapnia during air breathing reduced cerebral oxygen flow and lowered internal jugular venous pO_2 to about half its normal value. In these and similar experiments it was found that unconsciousness developed when the cerebral venous pO_2 fell below 19–20 mm Hg. This may, as suggested also by the work of others (Opitz and Schneider, 1950), indicate the minimum pO_2 required to assure oxygenation of cells supplied by diffusion of oxygen from the venous end of the brain capillary. Hyperventilation, even while breathing air at sea level, may therefore result in borderline anoxia of such cells. Certainly, since venous pO_2 cannot indicate the "tissue" pO_2, it is probable that cells supplied by diffusion from arterial regions of the brain capillary are not similarly exposed to anoxia during hyperventilation.

Due to anoxic cerebral vasodilatation, inhalation of 8% oxygen with arterial pCO_2 controlled at 44 mm Hg pCO_2 caused a greater brain oxygen flow than existed during air breathing. Combined anoxemia and hypocapnia, associated with a reduction in brain oxygen flow, lowered cerebral venous pO_2 to 20 mm Hg and routinely resulted in unconsciousness. Restoration of arterial pCO_2 to a few mm Hg above normal restored the subjects to consciousness.

Oxygen breathing at one atmosphere doubled mean brain capillary pO_2 in the absence of hypocapnia, but elevated cerebral venous pO_2 only to 46 mm Hg. Hyperventilation during oxygen breathing grossly lowered cerebral venous pO_2 below normal. It actually appears that oxygen inhalation at one atmosphere, while it raises arterial pO_2 considerably, can in the presence of hypocapnia fail to improve oxygenation of certain central nerve cells. Quite probably, hypocapnia of severe degree can result in cellular anoxia even during oxygen breathing at atmospheric pressure.

Finally, very high tensions of inspired oxygen can raise mean and internal jugular venous pO_2 even during hyperventilation hypocapnia (Lambertsen *et al.*, 1953; Lambertsen *et al.*, 1957), and elevation above normal of arterial pCO_2 causes dramatic elevations of central venous and mean brain capillary pO_2 to 1000 and 1500 mm Hg, respectively (Lambertsen *et al.*, 1955).

The great importance of arterial pCO_2, and its influence upon cerebral vessels, in determining brain oxygenation is evident from such studies. It even appears that certain cells may be better oxygenated during normocapneic arterial anoxemia than during air or oxygen breathing associated with vigorous hyperventilation.

BRAIN OXYGEN CONSUMPTION

Failure to maintain adequate oxygen tension levels in brain tissue must result in failure of brain oxygen consumption. Figure 6, in which each point represents the mean of at least six experiments in normal men, shows the effect upon brain oxygen utilization and mean brain capillary pO_2 of varying the inspired oxygen percentage from 8 to 80% at one atmosphere in the absence of supplementary hyperventilation (Lambertsen, 1958). The two solid dots indicate the control values obtained during air breathing at sea level. Oxygen, while it doubled mean brain capillary pO_2, did not affect brain oxygen consumption. A marked reduction in brain oxygen utilization resulted from administration of 8% oxygen and was accompanied by unconsciousness. Unconsciousness did not result from the administration of 10% oxygen, even though a significant lowering of brain oxygen consumption was produced. Of particular interest is the ability of carbon dioxide to increase brain oxygenation with 8% inspired oxygen above that found when 10% oxygen was inspired. This was accomplished by raising arterial pCO_2 from the level naturally associated with anoxemia to an artificially induced level of 44 mm Hg.

FIGURE 6.

Relationships between mean brain capillary pO_2 and cerebral oxygen consumption ($CMRO_2$). Points represent mean values in eight normal subjects. The figure shows the absence of change in $CMRO_2$ during oxygen administration, the reduction of $CMRO_2$ by 10 and 8% O_2 in N_2, and the improvement in both mean capillary pO_2 and $CMRO_2$ by restoring arterial pCO_2 to 44 mm Hg.

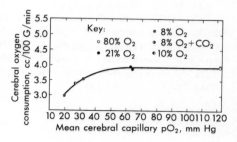

RELATIONSHIP TO CLOSED ENVIRONMENTS

We will not pretend that the sole basis for performing these studies was their potential relationship to submarine or other extra-atmospheric existence. An understanding of the regulation of brain circulation and internal gaseous environment is also necessary for studies of drug actions upon respiration and brain circulation. However, one of the primary questions in closed-system existence is the nature of the gaseous environments best suited to each of the situations in which such systems are to be employed (Opitz and Schneider, 1950). The studies reported suggest the practicability of maintaining the normal brain oxygenation and acid-base environment at considerably reduced inspired pO_2 or total pressure. The implications of this in permitting use of a single gas system (oxygen), in the elimination of pulmonary oxygen toxicity, in the requirement for studies of possible atelectasis during pure oxygen breathing at much reduced pressure, in the employment of metabolically produced CO_2 for useful purposes, and in improvement of radiation tolerance are presented elsewhere (Lambertsen, 1958).

REFERENCES

Kety, S. S., and C. F. Schmidt. 1946. "The effects of altered arterial tensions of carbon dioxide and oxygen on cerebral blood flow and cerebral oxygen consumption in normal, young men," J. Clin. Invest. 25: 107.

Lambertsen, C. J. 1958. "Pharmacology in Modern Medicine," In: Gases and Vapors, I: Oxygen, Carbon Dioxide and Helium, Ed. Drill, V. A., McGraw-Hill Company, Inc., New York, Part 16, Chap. 56.

Lambertsen, C. J., R. H. Kough, D. Y. Cooper, G. L. Emmel, H. H. Loeschcke, and C. F. Schmidt. 1953. "Oxygen toxicity. The effects in man of oxygen inhalation at 1 and 3.5 atmospheres upon blood gas transport, cerebral circulation and cerebral metabolism," J. Appl. Physiol. 5: 471.

Lambertsen, C. J. 1958. "From submarines to satellites," preface by C. F. Schmidt, an editorial, Circ. Research VI: 405.

Lambertsen, C. J., H. Wendel, H. Chiodi, and S. G. Owen. 1957. "Respiratory effects of 0.08 and 0.8 atmosphere of inspired pO_2 at a 'constant' alveolar pCO_2 of 43 mm Hg," Fed. Proc. 16: 76.

Lambertsen, C. J., J. H. Ewing, R. H. Kough, R. L. Gould, and M. W. Stroud, III. 1955. "Oxygen toxicity. Arterial and internal jugular blood gas composition in man during inhalation of air, 100% O_2 and 2% CO_2 in O_2 at 3.5 atmospheres ambient pressure," J. Appl. Physiol. 8: 255.

Opitz, E., and M. Schneider. 1950. "Uber die Sauerstoffversorgung des Gehirns und den Mechanismus von Mangelwirkungen," Ergeb. Physiol. 46: 126.

Turner, J., C. J. Lambertsen, S. G. Owen, H. Wendel, and H. Chiodi. 1957. "Effects of 0.08 and 0.8 atmosphere of inspired pO_2 upon cerebral hemodynamics at a 'constant' alveolar pCO_2 of 43 mm Hg," Fed. Proc. 16: 130.

Cardiovascular Responses Under Various Emotional States*

J. P. MEEHAN

University of Southern California, School of Medicine, Department of Physiology, Los Angeles, California

In everyday life, man's circulatory system is called upon to make constant adjustments to a multitude of environmental stimuli or physical stresses. Both the qualitative and quantitative nature of these responses to stress is influenced by, as well as mediated through, the central nervous system. The various factors that affect the over-all behavior of the central nervous system might reasonably be expected to play a role in determining both the qualitative and the quantitative response of the circulatory system to an acute stress. The emotional state of an individual does affect the over-all behavior of the central nervous system, and the physiological consequences of sustained emotional states have received considerable scientific attention (Wolff, 1953).

The possible role of emotion in modifying the cardiovascular response to acute physical stress was suggested by the results of investigations concerning both individual resistance to cold injury and studies of racial adaptations to a cold environment (Meehan *et al.*, 1954; Meehan, 1955; Meehan, 1955a). In order to establish some working hypothesis for the investigation of emotional state and an individual's reaction to cold stress, the schema depicted in Fig. 1 was developed (Meehan, 1957). This schema is not to be interpreted as an exact representation of anatomical entities within the central nervous system. Rather, it is a diagram of at least some of the major functions subserved by the central nervous system. Although the diagram of Fig. 1 is primarily pointed at the sensations of cold and the physiologic responses to this sensation, the general concept does permit a considerably wider extension.

In studying physiologic responses to acute physical stresses, an appropriate

* This research was supported in part by the United States Air Force under Contract No. AF 41(657)-218 monitored by the Arctic Aeromedical Laboratory, APO 731, Seattle, Washington; and by research grant No. B-1464 from the National Institutes of Health, Public Health Service.

241

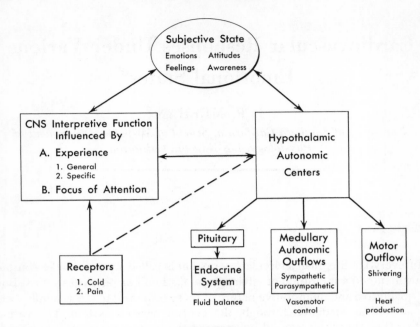

FIGURE 1.

Schema illustrating some major functions of the central nervous system in modifying or determining the physiologic response to applied physical stimuli.

stimulus is usually applied, and receptor organs respond and transmit information to the central nervous system. A response to the stimulus is recognized as an acute adjustment in bodily physiology that is mediated through one or more of the outflow paths of the hypothalamus. As is indicated in Fig. 1, various capabilities within the central nervous system may act to modify this over-all response. The afferent information may be subject to an interpretative process based on the experience of the individual. This in turn may affect quantitatively the physiologic response to the stimulating stress. The focus of attention may play a very similar role.

The emotional state of an individual has wide-spread effects on the activity of the central nervous system. The perception of stimuli may bear a relationship to emotional state. Further, the level of intrinsic activity of the hypothalamic centers may be influenced directly. Of importance for the present considerations is the fact that at any given time an individual has a certain mood, feeling, or emotional state with which he faces his environmental stresses. Mood or emotional state, then, may play a very important role in determining the physiological response of the normal individual to environmental stimuli.

From time to time it is possible to make chance observations on the effects of emotion in determining physiological responses to environmental stimuli.

The data presented in Fig. 2 were obtained from a number of experiments in which the phenomenon of cold vasodilatation was being investigated (Lewis, 1929). Each curve represents a separate experiment upon the same subject. These experiments were conducted under carefully controlled conditions, and due attention was given to all of the known factors that can modify cold vaso-dilatation (Yoshimura and Iida, 1951; Yoshimura and Iida, 1952; Hardy *et al.*, 1952). The experiments represented by the dotted lines indicate the usual response of this particular subject. The data represented by the solid line were obtained when the subject was fortuitously studied while in a state of extreme anxiety over what he considered to be an unfair classroom examination. On this occasion, the subject's response to the standard hand-cooling experiment was markedly different. He showed no rewarming of the fingers while in the ice water and, in addition, suffered a severe arthalgia of the joints of the fingers for several days (Meehan, 1957). This type of observation strongly suggests that the physiological response of a person to external stimuli may be markedly affected by his emotional state. Observations such as the foregoing indicate the desirability of having an experimental methodology that would permit manipulation and control of emotional state in the individual subject. Hypnosis was suggested as a potentially useful tool.

It has been well established that hypnotic suggestion can modify the perception of certain stimuli. Furthermore, it is also possible to modify the physiological response to these stimuli (Hardy *et al.*, 1952). A fairly simple experiment illustrating how hypnotic suggestion might influence the response of an individual to the hand-cooling experiment is shown in Fig. 3. The subject was hypnotized for both the experiments graphed in Fig. 3. In the experiment represented by the dotted line, it was hypnotically suggested to the subject that he was having a very uncomfortable and a very disturbing experience.

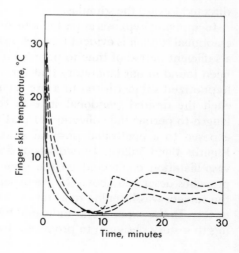

FIGURE 2.
Finger temperature data from a series of four separate cold-vasodilatation experiments conducted on one subject. At time 0, the fingers of the left hand were immersed in an ice water bath. The temperature curves were obtained by cementing a small thermocouple to the dorsum of the distal phalanx of the index finger.

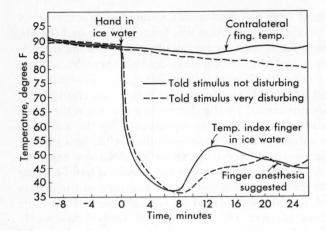

FIGURE 3.
Finger temperature data from two separate cold vasodilatation experiments conducted on one subject.

In the experiment graphed by a solid line in Fig. 3, the subject was told that the stimulus was not disturbing, the stimulus was not uncomfortable, and that nothing was bothering him. In the case where he was told the stimulus was disturbing, the contralateral finger temperature continued to fall, indicating a maintained vasoconstriction, and the rewarming that did occur in the experimental hand occurred comparatively slowly. On the occasion when the subject was told the stimulus was not disturbing, the rewarming phenomenon appeared promptly and to a rather marked degree. Furthermore, the contralateral finger temperature, after an initial drop lasting for about 12 minutes, started to rise and continued to do so throughout the remainder of the experiment. In the two experiments described here, hypnosis was used solely to direct the focus of attention of the subject. In one case his attention was being directed away from a painful stimulus. In the other case his attention was being directed toward the stimulus.

In applying hypnosis as part of a technique for manipulating an individual's emotional state, it is evident that the desired emotion has to be maintained for a sufficient period of time to permit the collection of physiologic data. It has been found in our laboratory that this could be accomplished by having the hypnotized subject listen to a pre-recorded story. The story is designed to elicit the desired emotional state in the subject. The story is of sufficient length to permit the collection of pertinent physiologic data. The subject is exposed to a controlled physical stress while he is listening to the story. Figures 4 and 5 illustrate two sets of data obtained from experiments on cold vasodilatation conducted on the same subject using the experimental approaches described above. In the experiments indicated by the dotted lines, the subject was listening to a story calculated to produce a feeling of anxiety or fear. In the experiments indicated by the solid lines, the subject was listening to a story designed to produce a feeling of extreme well-being. The two

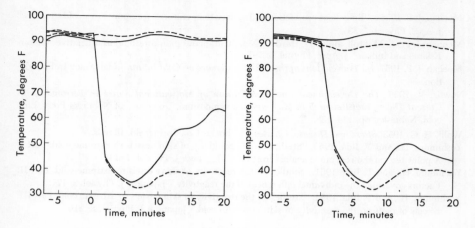

FIGURE 4 (*left*).

Data from two separate experiments on cold vasodilatation conducted on the same subject.

FIGURE 5 (*right*).

Data from two separate experiments on cold vasodilatation conducted on the same subject.

sets of data indicate that it is possible to obtain reproducible results with this technique.

An integral part of the type of experiment described above is the independent psychological assessment of the emotional state produced in the subject. One of the testing methods that has proved useful is a modified Adjective Check List as described by Nowlis (1953). At the conclusion of this type of experiment, possible correlations between the physiological and the psychological data are studied.

Observations such as those cited above indicate that there is a relationship between the emotional state of an individual and his cardiovascular reactions to acute physical stress. An interesting technique for shifting the emotional state of an individual through the use of hypnosis has been developed. The data discussed here represent the first attempt in our laboratory to conduct physiological experiments in which the emotional state of the subject is one of the controlled variables. Currently, an extensive program aimed at elucidating the relationships between emotional states and physiological responses to acute stress is underway.

REFERENCES

Hardy, J. D., H. G. Wolff, and H. Goodall. 1952. *Pain Sensation and Reactions,* Williams and Wilkins Co., Baltimore.

Lewis, T. 1929. "Observations upon the reactions of the vessels of the human skin to cold," Heart. *15:* 177.

Meehan, J. P. 1955. "Individual and racial variations in a vascular response to a cold stimulus," Military Med. *116:* 330.

Meehan, J. P. 1955a. "Body heat production and surface temperatures in response to a cold stimulus," J. Appl. Physiol. 7: 537.

Meehan, J. P., A. M. Stoll, and J. D. Hardy. 1954. "Cutaneous pain threshold in the native Alaskan Eskimo and Indian," J. Appl. Physiol. 6: 397.

Meehan, J. P. 1957. In: Transactions of the Fifth Conference on Cold Injury. Josiah Macy Jr. Foundation.

Nowlis, V. 1953. The Development and Modification of Motivational States in Personality: in Current Theory and Research in Motivation, a symposium, University of Nebraska Press, Lincoln, Nebraska, pp. 114–138.

Wolff, H. G. 1953. Stress and Disease, Charles C. Thomas Co., Springfield, Illinois.

Yoshimura, H., and T. Iida. 1950. "Studies on the reactivity of skin vessels to extreme cold. Part I. A point test on the resistance against frost bite," Japanese J. Physiol. 1: 147.

Yoshimura, H., and T. Iida. 1951. "Studies on the reactivity of skin vessels to extreme cold. Part II. Factors governing the individual differences of the reactivity," Japanese J. Physiol. 2: 177.

Yoshimura, H., and T. Iida. 1952. "Studies on the reactivity of skin vessels to extreme cold. Part III. Effects of diets on the reactivity of skin vessels to cold," Japanese J. Physiol. 2: 310.

DISCUSSION

Chairman Gauer: Let us start the discussion with Dr. Gregg's paper.

Dr. Bjurstedt: One thing that struck me was that when the apnea was on, and you gave a base at the time, the pCO_2 stayed constant for a certain time during that period. Is that right?

Dr. Gregg: Yes, I think that is correct.

Dr. Bjurstedt: I could not imagine that the pH stayed constant. The CO_2 stayed constant even if you gave a base at the same time?

Dr. Gregg: It comes out in the form of bicarbonate. I do not know about the urinary studies.

Dr. Bjurstedt: One more question I would venture to ask is, was that solution quite freshly prepared or had it been standing for some time.

Dr. Gregg: I think he prepares it fresh.

Dr. Lambertsen: Yesterday I raised a question about the separation of carbon dioxide from pH effect. Today, with all the discussion of circulatory changes, there has not been any mention along those lines. What I would like to know is whether any one can comment on whether there has been much consideration of the use of pharmacological agents to change some of the adaptive processes mentioned, particularly by Dr. Gregg. What I have in mind is whether we must consider reflexes in the normal sense or we can sensitize reflexes and thereby have increased resistance to forces.

Dr. Gregg: Dr. Nahas believes he is going to be able to do something of this sort by primary and secondary means, that he will separate the effects of pH and CO_2 themselves. I do not know whether this hits your question or not. He is very hopeful along these lines.[1]

Chairman Gauer: Experiments have been done on the effect of drugs and

[1] See symposium: "In Vitro and In Vivo Effects of Animal Buffers," New York Academy of Sciences, Dec., 1960.

CO_2 on G tolerance; when breathing 4% CO_2, for instance, G tolerance is up. This may be due to a sensitizing effect upon the carotid sinus reflex. In the horizontal posture CO_2 has no clearcut effect on the pressure volume relationship of the vascular bed of the hand, if one uses concentrations not higher than 4%.

Captain Behnke: I would like to ask Dr. Gregg what the buffer is he uses, and how long you can control the CO_2, I think it is a rather remarkable and spectacular finding. How long can this go on? In the apnea preparation I did not notice an asphyxial rise in blood pressure. Do you get that when the CO_2 builds up?

Dr. Gregg: Regarding the first question, I am just an errand boy in this particular part of the presentation. I think if you write Dr. Nahas at an address I will give you, he can give you the details on the material. He has been using a number of different compounds, and I am not up to date as to which one now. There is nothing secret about this. I am just not familiar with the compounds he has used. It seems to me some of these were used many years ago by Krebs. I think he was interested in certain types of buffer bases in tissue cultures, and I think some of these derived from that period. In this particular slide, it seems to me there was a fall in blood pressure but you can very well get a marked rise in blood pressure with arrhythmias and so on.

Captain Behnke: Were any experiments carried on longer than 60 minutes?

Dr. Gregg: With the buffer base, I believe he has been up to an hour and a half to two hours, but not longer. Probably it is only an hour and a half, but at least that much I know.

Chairman Gauer: Is this slide of Dr. Sarnoff's on the effect of vagus and sympathetic stimulation on the cardiac dynamics a private communication, or has it already been printed?

Dr. Gregg: No, he has not yet published it, and he was nice enough to give it to me for this meeting.

Chairman Gauer: I had the impression from recent publications by Kramer and others that in warm-blooded animals the vagus has no inotropic effect on the left ventricle, but only on heart rate.

Dr. Gregg: Well, I spent most of one day arguing about these particular experiments. I did not believe them. It was one Saturday two weeks ago; I spent almost a whole day over there, and he finally convinced me. I am convinced of the data. They are adequate. I have to believe it under the circumstances in his dogs. I would like to do those experiments myself.

Chairman Gauer: Kramer also found that the injection of adrenalin in the intact dog does not change the maximum pressure in the isometric contraction. However, adrenalin has a very marked effect when, as in a Starling preparation, the heart deteriorates.

Dr. Gregg: It is maybe just an accumulation of blood in the left ventricle cavity; whereas in the early stages, the heart is more nearly empty.

Chairman Gauer: Are there some more questions? I get a lot of satisfaction
by trying to separate the static from the dynamic component of homeostasis
of the circulation. Don't you think that these experiments of Roddie may
indicate that the two systems are tied together by a crossover effect from the
carotid sinus, in the arterial circulation on the capacitance vessels of the low-
pressure system—while a change of the filling of the atria in low-pressure
system seems to make a dilatation of the arteriols.

Dr. Bjurstedt: I wanted to ask a question about the patient who had changes
of pressure in the carotid sinus. I believe you had a catheter to take the pressure.

Dr. Gregg: I apologize. I forgot to mention these were done by someone
else. There were changes in carotid sinus pressure.

Dr. Bjurstedt: In humans it would be rather difficult to exclude the aortic
system, which would counteract.

Dr. Gregg: Much more work should be done to get the realization of what
is happening.

Chairman Gauer: Dr. Gregg is certainly correct when he says that we are
too placid in the assumption that we know everything about the homeostasis
of the arterial pressure. I remember experiments which I saw at the Mayo
Clinic some time ago. Arterial pressure was raised by inflating the G-suit. As
verified by catheterization, the pressures in the right atrium and in the pulmonary artery went up by the same amount. This experiment would then indicate, if there are not any flaws in it, that these regulations attempt to main-
tainanappropriate arterial-venous pressure differential rather than a homeostasis of the arterial pressure, *per se.*

Dr. Pulkrin: I was interested in Dr. Pappenheimer's statements about the
capillary circulation. I wonder if he can shed some light on some gross observations that I made some years back on the possible role of the intestinal
tract as a respiratory or excretory organ for gases. In the analysis of these
gases, I found that the concentration of these gases seemed to attain an equilibrium with that concentration that was in physical solution in the blood.
In injecting gases within the intestinal tract, I found the absorption rates of
the gases related to the concentration that was present in the physical solution in the blood. Apparently the state of the capillary network within the
walls of the intestine must have some influence in this tissue circulation.

I found that carbon monoxide has a high rate of diffusion; oxygen, less so,
and nitrogen, very little. As a matter of fact, carbon dioxide within the intestinal tract is absorbed rapidly enough to shift the Barcroft curve and liberate oxygen, which would be expelled in the expired air in higher concentrations.

Do you know of any quantitative work to elaborate a little bit on these observations?

Dr. Pappenheimer: I have not done any work in this field, but Dr. Rahn has
worked a great deal on gaseous exchanges in relation to air pockets.

Dr. Rahn: I think there are answers to your problems in analyzing gas pockets, and I think your specific observations have been repeated in other organs. I think it can be calculated that the gastrointestinal tract would be able to take care of a certain amount of oxygen uptake and CO_2 release, but I am afraid it is a low order of magnitude in terms of gas consumption of the total body.

Your specific observations about radical shifts in the oxygen and CO_2 curves can be, and have been, observed. I think it was at Randolph Air Field that someone has been able to inject carbon monoxide in the gas pocket. It is a very nice little organ, from which you can get very interesting observations. The practical aspects of it seem to me rather difficult to evaluate at the moment.

Chairman Gauer: I want to ask Dr. Pappenheimer a question. It is well known to the people who work in acceleration research that you can get edema in either end of the body when exposing a man to high accelerations; but it is much easier to get it in the face and in the upper region of the body than in the legs. Could one quantitate this effect and make predictions from tissue pressures or resiliency of the tissue or the like?

Dr. Pappenheimer: I do not know of any way apart from doing the experiments and finding out how much edema per unit there is and how much increase in capillary pressure. I know the figures you refer to, and I suppose this was worked on by Hyman and Henry. I know of no specific permeability difference between the capillaries of the upper part of the body as compared to the lower or of the tissue pressure counteracting.

Chairman Gauer: Now let us discuss the paper on "Homeostasis of the Extra-Arterial Circulation."

Dr. Adolph: Of course, there is a very nice correlation that Dr. Gauer has presented to us between central venous pressure and the volume changes that were produced experimentally. These central venous pressures are a measure of what happens in part in the region where there may be receptors. In the schematic diagram that Dr. Gauer presented, however, he emphasized the pulmonary part of the circuit. I was wondering whether anything has been done to indicate the relative importance of the pulmonary circuit and of the central venous system circuit in pressure changes, in volume changes, and in the resultant homeostasis.

Chairman Gauer: The experiments in dogs (Fig. 2) showed that during hemorrhage and transfusion, the central venous pressure, the pulmonary arterial pressure, and the left atrial pressure changed in parallel. In experiments in man, recording central venous pressure, pulmonary arterial pressure and wedge pressure, the same relationship was found. It seems therefore permissible to predict from the behavior of the central venous pressure the behavior of the other pressures. It is particularly interesting that the pressure gradient in the left atrium is appreciably steeper than in the right atrium and in the pulmonary—that is, when bleeding or transfusing a man, the pressures change most in the left atrium. When producing diuresis by inflation of a balloon in the left atrium, the right atrial pressure does not change. Thus, an increase in central venous pressure and a distention of the right atrium is not necessary to produce the diuretic reflex.

Dr. Forster: I wonder if Dr. Gauer would go on. You gave us a hint that the diuretic reflex was not mediated through the circulation, but probably through one of the endocrines, and you gave us a hint. Would you give us any more on that?

Chairman Gauer: Well, we cannot be absolutely sure, but the pattern of the diuresis, with a very slow onset and perseverance after cessation of the stimulus, looks exactly like a water diuresis. This indicates that there is a hormonal factor involved. On inflation of a balloon in the left atrium, cardiac output falls. So the diuresis can certainly not be induced by an improvement of the hemodynamic condition of the kidney. Dr. Surtshin and Dr. White in St. Louis did negative-pressure breathing experiments on dogs with one denervated and one normal kidney. They got diuresis in both kidneys at the same time. Thus, an intact nerve supply of the kidney is not essential.

Dr. Pappenheimer: I wonder if it's being too practical to ask what the order of magnitude of pressures is likely to be in a natural take-off and acceleration in a proposed rocket, in order to give us a sort of framework within which to get an order of magnitude, at least, of the pressures with which we will have to deal.

Chairman Gauer: Let's say we have during take-off an acceleration of 6 Gs. Then if you sit upright (which you would not do) you would have a hydrostatic pressure in the legs of about 80 cm times six. This is 500 cm of water in the legs. This pressure should squeeze plasma fluid out into the interstitial spaces very fast.

Dr. Bjurstedt: How long does the diuresis last, if the stimulus, e.g., balloon inflation, is kept constant for a period of time? Would this go on for a length of time, or would it decrease by itself?

Chairman Gauer: We continued negative pressure breathing in dogs for about one hour, and as a rule the diuresis keeps on going for one hour, but in some instances we found that there is a slight decline after three-quarters of an hour.

Dr. Bjurstedt: So that it would seem to be the slowly adaptive type?

Chairman Gauer: Yes.

Dr. DuBois: Dr. Gauer, as I understood, this reflex from the carotid sinus constricts all the veins; and yet with acceleration you want to constrict the ones in the lower body. What's the current status of adaptation of venous tone? Could you bring us up to date on that?

Chairman Gauer: I do not know of any experiments which were specifically designed to clarify this problem and I have a hunch that the veins do not just show an over-all constriction but that the body knows what is up and down and where the constriction has to take place to be most efficient. There are suggestions from Burton's and our own work that it might be so.

Chairman Gauer: Let us turn now to Dr. Lambertsen's paper on cerebral circulation with reference to the oxygen and acid base environment.

Dr. H. Rahn (Buffalo): Dr. Lambertsen, do your data indicate that the oxygen consumption of the brain in the physiological range that you have used is dependent upon the pO_2 of the blood?

Dr. Lambertsen: That's obviously a loaded question. Do you mind telling me what your real question is?

Dr. Rahn: It seems to me that this apparently happens in invertebrate organisms. However, down to the oxygen ranges that you have used, I would not expect this in the mammal—the warm-blooded animals.

Dr. Lambertsen: I think I understand your question now. You are relating this to the mention of the very low pO_2 which would result in decreased oxygen consumption. We can not determine the oxygen tension of an individual capillary. I tried to emphasize that we are dealing with a mean calculated capillary pO_2.

Dr. Rahn: Even forgetting about that, you have normal oxygen and low oxygen, and you are essentially saying that, in the brain, oxygen consumption is reduced by 25%, is that right?

Dr. Lambertsen: Yes. I am sure we could reduce it to zero if we went low enough. The tensions of oxygen indicated in the capillary diagram, of course, are those tensions which are required to push oxygen through some distance of tissue, and we have not the slightest idea what the actual tensions are at the cellular level at different parts of the brain. I do not know whether I have answered your question.

Dr. Pappenheimer: May I just make one point for the record? There's very little information on the number of open capillaries and the capillary density of the brain. This is something that is much needed. We always think of the brain as having a good blood supply, but the number of open capillaries is about equivalent to resting muscles, and the only measurement of blood volume in the brain indicates a very low blood volume—of the order of 1 to 2% of the blood flow in the brain as a whole. Perhaps you would care to comment on that. I have made this remark for the record, because more work needs to be done on that.

Dr. Lambertsen: If there is any comment, it would be merely to relate Dr. Pappenheimer's statement to the very short period of time one has to stay conscious, and perhaps alive, after the circulation stops.

Dr. Goetz: I would like to ask Dr. Stroud what pressure he used when he injected the catheter. I ask this question because of an incident which happened to us when we were doing arteriography. When we used as little as 3 kg per square centimeter of pressure in one of our experiments with the catheter in the subclavian artery, we found to our amazement that the dye appeared and disappeared in the vena cava via the subclavian vein. We had produced a fistula. I know of one other case where the dye went through the walls.

Dr. Stroud: If you are referring to the second diagram, the injection was made rapidly but the pressure was not measured. The injection was by means of a syringe. However, Dr. Tobin examined the lungs anatomically and found that there was a true communication.

Chairman Gauer: To turn now to Dr. Meehan's paper, there are two things which we cannot eliminate in space. One is weightlessness—the other our own soul—fears, emotions, and the like. Enclosing a man in a sealed chamber with the understanding that he will be taken out if he gets virus pneumonia or appendicitis is not the same thing as exposure to a deadly hostile environment in a capsule. So Dr. Meehan tried to impose such emotional stresses by hypnosis and studied the effects on the circulation.

Dr. Aschoff: Did you make your experiment always at the same time of the day? Surely you know that you can have 100 phenomena in the same person in the afternoon and not in the morning. It depends on the state of the reception centers. And did you do your experiments on the same subject with the same history of temperature reaction?

Dr. Meehan: Yes. I'm quite mindful of the problems when doing these particular experiments. I have done quite a lot of them, controlling heat balance, observing relationship to meals, and so on. As a matter of fact, we established our usual laboratory response of the individual in this type of experiment.

Dr. Aschoff: What was the history of temperature reaction? In other words, the subject, after being overheated during the examination, might have had a tendency to constrict after the examination.

Dr. Meehan: I see what you mean. Here, again, we are sure only that the individual is in the same state of heat balance.

Dr. Aschoff: Room temperature is not different?

Dr. Meehan: Room temperature and his body temperature are not different.

Dr. Aschoff. Body temperature, yes, but was the basic change of heat regulation given due regard?

Dr. Meehan: We have done these experiments with thermocouple suits on the individual, and have actually controlled the matter of body heat content as well as it can be done by this technique. I grant you, there is a chance for error in that method.

Dr. Büttner: Dr. Kramer some time ago told me a story. I don't know whether it has been published. He recorded on himself a full-fledged Lewis reaction during the war. When he tried to repeat it in the lean years, immediately after the war, he found no action on the fingers at all. Afterward, he got it again at Randolph Field. My question to Dr. Meehan is, might this have been psychological in terms of psychological stress, because of the war, or was it purely physiological because of malnutrition?

Dr. Meehan: I would presume that an individual's physical condition can alter it considerably. A group of Japanese investigators, I believe, have pretty well defined the variables of that type. I might say that our studies were not confined to the Lewis reaction at all. We happen to be collecting fairly complete cardiovascular data; the time of preparation of this paper was so short that I had to pull what I had off the shelf.

Dr. DuBois: We have this closed chamber body plethysmograph. The question came up whether the airways might be affected as an emotional response to closing up people in this chamber which they cannot get out of. We evaluated airway resistance, but found no change in it. The subjects were interviewed by the psychiatrist, and they showed verbal responses to particular things, such as a sign on the door, a sign on the window that said "Break Glass in Case of Emergency." They asked, "Well, how do you know when there is an emergency?" They worried about things such as: would the doctor be all right, and let them out? They did not seem to worry about the actual confinement. It was more about specific things such as the wires running through the box. The fact that the airway resistance did not respond at all in the face of various degrees of hostility or resentment, or whatever you want, seemed to indicate that, although the cardiovascular system may be somewhat reactive, the bronchial system seemed to be somewhat unreactive.

PART FOUR

Effects of Acute and Chronic Atmospheric Changes on Respiratory Mechanisms

Chairman

DR. RODOLFO MARGARIA

Physiological Institute, University of Milan
Milan, Italy

Effects of Atmospheric Factors on the Mechanics of Breathing

JAMES L. WHITTENBERGER

Professor of Physiology, Harvard School of Public Health,
Boston, Massachusetts

One of the purposes of this symposium is to review the present state of knowledge of certain aspects of environmental medicine. The respiratory system comes to attention as the principal physiological contact between the organism and the gaseous environment. The interactions of the biologic and environmental systems may be categorized in two principal ways: barometrically and chemically. Barometrically, changes in the environment may affect the organism by the effects of high and low pressures *per se* and by alteration of specific partial pressures such as those of oxygen and nitrogen. A special case of barometric effect is that produced by a difference in pressure between the lungs and the surface of the body, as induced by a pressure-breathing apparatus or anti-G suit. Chemically, the gaseous environment affects the organism when physiologically active agents are present in sufficient concentration; these include carbon dioxide, carbon monoxide, and a host of toxic compounds. The lungs provide a large area in fairly direct contact between the air and the blood stream.

The "mechanics of breathing" are those aspects of the respiratory system which have to do with the physical movements of the lungs and thorax—ventilatory movements which serve to dilute the alveolar gases with environmental gas. Physical characteristics of the tissues and airways are included, along with the forces and energy exchange involved in ventilation of the lungs.

It should be stressed that the mechanics of breathing are only a part of the system, and that the limiting effects of environmental changes are rarely due to specific actions on the mechanical system. However, the mechanics of breathing have been generally ignored until recent years, and better understanding of total respiratory responses depends on recognition of the role of

257

mechanical factors. Further, the mechanics of breathing have particular relevance to problems of individual oxygen supply, underwater breathing apparatus, free escape from submarines, responses to noxious agents in the environment, and the effects of rapid acceleration and deceleration.

HIGH CARBON DIOXIDE ENVIRONMENTS

One of the classic problems in the habitability of enclosed spaces is the acute and chronic effects of exposure to low concentrations of carbon dioxide. Such an agent may affect respiratory mechanics directly or indirectly in a number of ways, involving not only respiration but circulatory and other systems. Separation of direct and indirect effects is usually difficult and is seldom done experimentally. Carbon dioxide has been said to affect directly the resistance to gas flow into and out of the lungs (Nisell, 1951). Pulmonary resistance, or its reciprocal, conductance, is largely a function of the caliber of the air passages. It also includes frictional energy losses in the tissue and is influenced by the density and viscosity of the respired gases. Changes of resistance are occurring continuously throughout the respiratory cycle as the caliber of the tracheobronchial tree is influenced by the level of lung volume and by changes of intrapleural pressure. If carbon dioxide lowers resistance, it may therefore do so by increasing the mean level of lung volume as well as by a possible direct effect on the tone of smooth muscle in the tracheobronchial tree.

Increase of inspired carbon dioxide by 3 or 5% at sea level may also affect the compliance or elastic behavior of the lungs, although it is very doubtful that it would do so in healthy young adults. Hyperventilation would be expected to produce an apparent slight increase in compliance, since deep breathing tends to keep all alveolar units open and therefore participating in dynamic compliance measurements (Mead et al., 1957). Excessive inhalation of carbon dioxide could produce a reduction of compliance through the development of pulmonary edema, but this would occur only with very toxic levels of carbon dioxide sufficient to impair the function of the heart. Carbon dioxide-enriched environments increase the mechanical work of respiration in proportion to the increase of pulmonary ventilation. Since the work of breathing accounts for only a small fraction of total metabolism under sedentary conditions, the increased work would not be significant in healthy young adults until the carbon dioxide concentration reached 5% or more. However, the additive effect of exercise, particularly under conditions of high pressure, greatly aggravates the effects of increased respiratory work, and the metabolic cost of breathing becomes of high significance (Mead, 1956; Otis, 1954).

Although the multiple factors which cause dyspnea or subjective respiratory distress are not fully understood, it is almost certain that the increased respiratory work due to carbon dioxide breathing is a cause of respiratory muscle fatigue and breathlessness. When other fatigue-inducing factors are present it is especially important to avoid rebreathing, as in a face mask or breathing apparatus.

Acute increases of inspired carbon dioxide, therefore, produce measurable but slight effects on the mechanics of breathing in normal people, in the concentrations likely to be encountered in submarine and space medicine. Most, if not all, of these effects are the indirect result of stimulation of ventilation. Chronic effects from such concentrations are unlikely, and if they do occur would be in proportion to changes of ventilation.

LOW OXYGEN ENVIRONMENTS

As with environmental changes of carbon dioxide, the effects of low oxygen environments on respiratory mechanics are mostly secondary to the nonspecific mechanical effects of respiratory stimulation. It has been postulated that low oxygen produces an increase in the size of the lungs and better "aeration" of the blood (Peyser et al., 1950). Measurements of respiratory mechanics at high altitude have not been made, but it seems likely that the increase of thoracic size is due to hyperventilation rather than to intrinsic changes of respiratory tissue (Gaensler et al., 1952).

Hypoxia may cause pulmonary vasoconstriction and increase of pulmonary blood volume, but as an acute effect this is not sufficient to alter pulmonary mechanical attributes (Borst et al., 1957). On the other hand, if hypoxia is severe enough to impair the heart and left atrial pressure rises, lung distensibility may be significantly reduced. Pulmonary compliance is greatly reduced if high capillary pressures persist long enough to cause pulmonary edema (Cook et al., 1959).

HIGH PRESSURE ENVIRONMENTS

Apart from specific effects of oxygen, carbon dioxide, nitrogen, and other gases, high pressure produces a number of effects on respiratory mechanics. At sea level the acceleration of tissues and gases in the respiratory system during cyclic changes of flow has a usually negligible role as a force in breathing. At several atmospheres of pressure, however, the density of gases makes their inertia appreciable. For example, pulmonary resistance at 4 atmospheres pressure is approximately doubled from its sea level value (Mead, 1956). Such an increase by itself might not be physiologically significant but it can be important in association with other factors which increase respiratory work.

The problems of skin diving and the respiratory characteristics of trained divers are hardly relevant at this point, although of great interest from a respiratory mechanics point of view. The same can be said of the effects of anti-G suits. Some research has been done on these problems but much remains to be done.

ATMOSPHERIC CONTAMINANTS

Recent work has shown the value of using respiratory mechanical characteristics as a quantitative estimate of physiologic responses to low concentrations of contaminants in the air. Most helpful is the precise measurement of resistance, by one of a number of methods which can be used in both experimental animals and man (Amdur and Mead, 1958; Dubois and Dautrebande, 1958). An asthmatic type of response can be quantified before a change of resistance becomes apparent to the human subject.

One striking result of studies with the new technique is the demonstration of a marked potentiating effect of inert particulates when the air contains low concentrations of certain gases such as sulfur dioxide and formaldehyde. For example, sulfur dioxide at two parts per million has a barely measurable effect on the guinea pig's pulmonary resistance; when given with an aerosol of small particles of sodium chloride the same concentration had an effect equal to that of 70 parts per million when given alone (Amdur, 1959).

SUMMARY

For purposes of analysis, the mechanical qualities and behavior of the lungs and thorax are considered separately from the remainder of the respiratory system, although functional interrelationships are very important between the mechanical properties, gas exchange, and distribution of the pulmonary circulation. Specific mechanical attributes include elastic behavior, resistance to volume changes in the respiratory cycle, inertia, and the muscular forces and pressure changes associated with the volume changes. While inertia of the gases in the respiratory passages is normally negligible, this factor increases in significance when gases are breathed at high barometric pressures. Inertia of blood and abdominal organs may also affect respiration when the body is exposed to changes in gravitational stress.

Possible atmospheric changes in enclosed spaces are usually indirect in their effects on the mechanics of breathing. High carbon dioxide concentrations increase respiratory work, especially during exercise; there is probably no significant effect on resistive or elastic properties. Low oxygen environments stimulate respiratory movements to a lesser extent than carbon dioxide, and respiratory work increase is mitigated by the decrease of gas density. Irritant gases in the environment often cause an increase of respiratory work by increasing resistance to air flow, due largely to bronchospasm. In sensitive experimental animals, the rise of resistance may be enhanced by the presence of fine aerosols.

REFERENCES

Amdur, M. O., and J. Mead. 1958. "Mechanics of Respiration in Unanesthetized Guinea Pigs," Am. J. Physiol. *192:* 364–368.

Amdur, M. O. 1959. "The Physiologic Response of Guinea Pigs to Atmospheric Pollutants," Int. J. Air Poll. *1:* 170–183.

Borst, H. G., E. Berglund, J. L. Whittenberger, J. Mead, M. McGregor, and C. Collier. 1957. "The Effect of Pulmonary Vascular Pressures on the Mechanical Properties of the Lungs of Anesthetized Dogs," J. Clin. Invest. *36:* 1708–1714.

Cook, C. D., J. Mead, G. L. Schreiner, N. R. Frank, and J. M. Craig. 1959. "Pulmonary Mechanics During Induced Pulmonary Edema in Anesthetized Dogs," J. Appl. Physiol. *14:* 177–186.

Dubois, A. B., and L. Dautrebande. 1958. "Acute Effects of Breathing Inert Dust Particles and of Carbochol Aerosol on the Mechanical Characteristics of the Lungs in Man. Changes in Response After Inhaling Sympathomimetic Aerosols," J. Clin. Invest. *37:* 1746–1755.

Gaensler, E. A., J. V. Maloney, Jr., and V. O. Björk. 1952. "Bronchospirometry. II. Experimental Observations and Theoretical Considerations of Resistance Breathing," J. Lab. Clin. Med. *39:* 935–953.

Mead, J. 1956. "Measurement of Inertia of the Lungs at Increased Ambient Pressure," J. Appl. Physiol. *9:* 208–212.

Mead, J., J. L. Whittenberger, and E. P. Radford, Jr. 1957. "Surface Tension as a Factor in Pulmonary Volume Pressure Hysteresis," J. Appl. Physiol. *10:* 191–196.

Nisell, O. 1951. "The Influence of CO_2 on the Respiratory Movements of Isolated Perfused Lungs," Acta physiol. scand. *23:* (4), 352–360.

Otis, A. B. 1954. "The Work of Breathing," Physiol. Rev. *34:* 449–458.

Peyser, E., A. Sass-Kortsak, and F. Verzar. 1950. "Influence of O_2 Content of Inspired Air on Total Lung Volume," Am. J. Physiol. *163:* 111–117.

The Effects of Changes in the Partial Pressures of Inspired Gases on the Ventilation of Respiratory Dead Space and Gas Diffusion in the Lungs

ROBERT E. FORSTER

Department of Physiology and Pharmacology, Graduate School of Medicine, University of Pennsylvania, Philadelphia, Pennsylvania

In the interest of clarity, let us discuss first the ventilation of the respiratory dead space—particularly with an eye to defining terms—and then go on to consideration of gas diffusion in the lungs.

VENTILATION OF THE RESPIRATORY DEAD SPACE [1]

Dead space ventilation equals respiratory dead space volume multiplied by respiratory frequency. The discussion of dead space ventilation therefore evolves immediately into a discussion of dead space volume, or at least its relationship to tidal volume. One cannot discuss "respiratory dead space" in man without some preliminary statements as to the meaning attached to the term. Originally it presumably referred to the volume of the lung conducting airways which are filled with fresh gas on inspiration and yet in which there is no exchange with the blood, thus representing a wasted effort on the part of the bellows action of the lungs. The measured volume corresponding most closely to this definition is that made by the single breath technique, described

[1] Unfortunately for the subject of this symposium, data concerning the effects, both acute and chronic, of changes in inspired CO_2, O_2 and N_2 tensions on respiratory dead space ventilation and diffusion of gases in the lung, have turned out to be for the most part unavailable for the conditions desired. Under these circumstances I have been forced to extrapolate existing information. The following discussion is divided into two parts, the first dealing with the effects of changes in the partial pressures of CO_2, O_2 and N_2 in the inspired gas upon the respiratory dead space, the second with the effects upon diffusion within the lungs.

by Fowler (1948) and DuBois *et al.* (1952), in which a continuous measurement of expired gas concentration is plotted against the simultaneously measured expired volume. I shall designate this as "anatomic dead space." In this technique, the value obtained is actually the volume of the airways down to the first sudden change in concentration of the gas studied, from the value in the inspired gas to that in "alveolar" gas. The average value in 45 normal men breathing naturally at a normal end expiratory level is 156 ml (Fowler, 1948). Anatomical dead space increases with increasing lung volume (DuBois *et al.*, 1952; Sevringhaus and Stupfel, 1957; Folkow and Pappenheimer, 1955; Young, 1955), and with increasing esophageal-mouth pressure differences (Shepard *et al.*, 1957), the latter being a measure of the pressure difference across the lung. It is relatively independent of tidal volume (Folkow and Pappenheimer, 1955; Shepard *et al.*, 1957). It also is larger the greater the body size (Fowler, 1948).

As respiratory physiologists have become more sophisticated the term "dead space" has also been applied to include that volume of the fresh inspired gas which is wasted as far as aeration of the arterial blood is concerned, not only because of the actual volume of the conducting airways, but also because of right to left shunts across the pulmonary fields and uneven distribution of alveolar ventilation in relation to capillary blood flow. While the term "dead space" might with reason be applied to the entire volume of inspired gas which was wasted insofar as the aeration of any particular gas in the arterial blood was concerned, it is general practice to do so only for CO_2 (Sevringhaus and Stupfel, 1957; Riley *et al.*, 1946). The respiratory dead space volume calculated on this basis is usually called the "physiological dead space." In resting man, Filley and co-workers report physiological dead space tidal volume equal to 26.6% (Filley *et al.*, 1954). At a tidal volume of 600 ml, this would give a physiological dead space volume of 159 ml. Physiological dead space in dogs increases with tidal volume but is almost independent of total lung volume (Sevringhaus and Stupfel, 1957; Williams and Rayford, 1956; Gray *et al.*, 1956).

Although Pappenheimer and associates (1955), using the isosaturation method of measuring dead space, and Margaria *et al.* (1957), using an indirect method of calculating dead space, found no increase with increasing tidal volume (or presumably with total lung volume) in man, this is possibly because of the limits of precision of the extrapolation technique both used, as has been pointed out by Folkow and Pappenheimer (1955). Thus while physiological dead space and anatomical dead space are not theoretically the same thing, in normal males at rest the two are numerically similar, and for present purposes will be considered the same. As a matter of fact, the difference between physiological dead space and anatomical dead space in a given individual can be used as an index of the extent of uneven distribution of alveolar ventilation/alveolar blood flow (Sevringhaus and Stupfel, 1957).

The effect of increased inspired CO_2 partial pressure
on respiratory dead space

Cooper *et al* (1953), have reported that breathing concentrations of CO_2 up to 5.48% leads to increases of physiological dead space from a value of 142 ml breathing air to 385 ml; but the alveolar-arterial PO_2 difference increased at the same time, suggesting that at least part of this increase in physiological dead space was due to an increase in uneven alveolar ventilation/alveolar blood flow. I have been unable to find any report of measurements of dead space in normal subjects by the single breath technique following inhalation of increased concentrations of CO_2 or any reports of measurements after chronic exposure. Inspiring 7% CO_2 for 10 min in 6 normal subjects led either to no change in the airway resistance as measured in the body plethysmograph or to slight and variable changes (10%) (personal communication from A. B. DuBois). This suggests that inspiring this concentration of CO_2 has no striking effect on the caliber of the airways, and therefore an anatomical dead space. However, one might expect an increase in anatomical dead space because of the increase in average lung volume accompanying the hypercapnia or possibly because of increased liberation of adrenaline (Sevringhaus and Stupfel, 1957).

Effect of decreased inspired O_2 partial pressure
on respiratory dead space

I have not come across any report of measurements of single breath dead space in man during or after exposure to an hypoxic atmosphere. However, Sevringhaus and Stupfel (1957) found that breathing 7 to 10% O_2 led to a decrease of 8 to 54% in anatomical dead space in anesthetized dogs, possibly from airway constriction. Breathing gas mixtures with an O_2 concentration of 10% or less will lead to an increase in minute ventilation, largely because of an increase in tidal volume (Dripps *et al.*, 1947) which of itself would produce an increase in dead space as mentioned earlier. Riley *et al.* (1951) found no significant difference in physiological dead space in 46 individuals after at least 15 minutes breathing with an alveolar PO_2 of about 100 mm Hg as compared with an alveolar PO_2 of about 55 mm Hg. Hurtado *et al.* (1956) reported resting data on residents at 14,900 ft, equivalent to an inspired PO_2 of 83 mm Hg, which give a physiological dead space of 141 ml, certainly in the normal range.

The effect of increased inspired O_2 partial pressure
on respiratory dead space

I have not been able to find any reports of measurements of the effect of breathing enriched O_2 mixtures on the anatomic dead space in man. However, since the single breath dead space volume for N_2, measured after taking a breath of 100 per cent O_2, is not significantly different from that for CO_2 or O_2, measured while breathing air, it seems unlikely that inspiring an O_2 tension up to 700 mm Hg for several seconds has any remarkable effect on anatomic dead space (Bartels *et al.*, 1954). R. L. Burdick, working in our laboratory (unpublished data) failed to find any change in airway resistance as measured in the body plethysmograph after breathing about 100% O_2 for 6 hrs, again suggesting that cross-sectional area of the airways, and therefore the size of the anatomic dead space was not affected. Sevringhaus and Stupfel (1957) found that breathing approximately 100% O_2 in anesthetized dogs led to an initial increase in anatomic dead space, followed by a fall to or below control values in 5 to 10 min.

The effect of variations in inspired N_2 partial pressure and in total ambient pressure on respiratory dead space

Although there are no obvious reasons why one would expect a change in respiratory dead space because of exposure to abnormal N_2 or total atmospheric pressures, except possibly as a secondary result of another condition such as multiple gas emboli in the lungs, I have not found any reports on this subject. When the alveolar partial pressure of N_2 is reduced, the probability of atelectasis occurring is increased because the effective solubilities in blood of the remaining gases, O_2 and CO_2, are much greater than that of N_2, so that if an occlusion of an airway occurs, the gas behind the block is more likely to be reabsorbed by the blood. Such areas of atalectasis in the lung would act to increase the physiological dead space.

In considering the difficulties attendant upon living in a sealed space cabin, the possibility of changes in the composition of the local atmosphere should certainly be considered. Although very few experiments have been reported which give direct answers to the question of the effects of acute and chronic exposure of healthy young men to air containing increased CO_2, increased or decreased O_2, and increased or decreased total atmospheric pressure upon their respiratory dead space, the predictions given in Table 1 might be extrapolated from existing data. It can be seen from this table that no striking effects upon the volume of the respiratory dead space appear likely to result from short periods of exposure to air altered as indicated. In addition I would like to point out that the effect of an increase in anatomical dead space (and in normals, approximately the same is true of physiological dead space) upon aeration of the arterial blood can be largely canceled out simply by an increase in minute ventilation (Clappison and Hamilton, 1956), for which there is ample reserve in normal individuals. While this may be uncomfortable in extreme cases, it would appear unlikely that the changes in respiratory dead space predicted would be a critical factor in pulmonary gas exchange.

TABLE 1

Predicted changes in respiratory dead space in man when the inspired gas composition is varied.

Changes in inspired gas mixture	Effect upon respiratory dead space
$\uparrow P_{CO_2}$	Slight $\uparrow$, probably proportional to $\uparrow$ mean lung volume
$\downarrow P_{O_2}$	No important change or slight $\uparrow$ because of $\uparrow$ mean lung volume
$\uparrow P_{O_2}$	No important change
$\uparrow \downarrow P_{N_2}$ ($\uparrow \downarrow$ total pressure)	No important change

DIFFUSION OF GASES IN THE LUNG

Diffusion within the alveolar gas

The diffusion of gases within an alveolus or slightly larger respiratory unit is not considered to be a limiting process in the exchange of gases between alveolar air and pulmonary capillary blood for a number of rather indirect reasons (Forster, 1957) primarily because of the difficulty of obtaining direct measurements over such small distances and over such short time periods. However, the diffusion coefficient of a gas in a gas phase is approximately inversely proportional to the pressure. Thus, as Haldane suggested a number of years ago (1928), the rate of diffusion within the alveolar air would be increased at high altitudes and decreased under conditions of high atmospheric pressure. If this rate is slow enough to exert any influence on gas exchange in the lungs it should be possible to detect it by measuring pulmonary diffusing capacity at the same inspired alveolar PO_2, but over a wide range of ambient pressures, an experiment which has not been carried out to my knowledge. While one would not expect to find any changes, the experiment would be well worth trying.

There are no apparent reasons why increased or decreased O_2 concentrations or increased CO_2 concentrations in the alveolar gas would significantly alter the rate of gas diffusion within the alveolus at normal atmospheric pressures.

Diffusion across the pulmonary membrane and within the pulmonary capillaries

The most generally used index of the efficiency of diffusion between alveolar gas and the pulmonary capillary blood is the pulmonary diffusing capacity (D) which equals the rate of movement of gas across the membrane in ml per minute per mm Hg of pressure difference. D can only be measured with O_2 and low concentrations of CO, because all the other available gases equilibrate so rapidly that their uptake in the lung is not limited by diffusion at all. It is only by virtue of their combination with hemoglobin in the red cell that O_2

and CO do not equilibrate completely between the blood and the alveolar gas in one passage through the lung and are, at least partially in the case of O_2, limited by their ease of diffusion. As customarily measured, D includes the entire diffusion path from alveolar air to the intracellular hemoglobin molecule, and has therefore been called (D_L), the subscript L indicating that it applies to the lung as a whole. D_L depends on two separate "diffusing capacities," that of the pulmonary membrane (D_M) and that of the capillary blood. The latter depends upon the volume in the pulmonary capillary bed (V_c) at any instant which can combine with the gas once it passes through the membrane into the blood itself and upon the rate of the reaction of O_2 or CO with intracellular hemoglobin per ml of blood (Forster, 1957). The only method available at present to separate the parts of D_L and obtain D_M and V_c is by calculation from measurements of $D_{L_{CO}}$ at several different alveolar P_{O_2} (Roughton and Forster, 1957).

There are actually three groups of methods (Forster, 1957) for the measurement of D_L: (a) the O_2 method of Lilienthal *et al.* (1946) in which the measurements are carried out under steady state conditions; (b) CO methods in which measurements are carried out under steady state conditions; and (c) breathholding and rebreathing methods using CO. Most of the measurements of D_L pertinent to this discussion have been carried out by the O_2 method or the CO breathholding method for which the normal values at rest are 21 ml per minute per mm Hg (Lilienthal, *et al.* 1946) and 30 ml per minute per mm Hg, respectively (Forster, 1957). Ideally, D_{O_2} should equal $1.23 \times D_{CO}$ (Krogh, 1914).

The pulmonary diffusing capacity of CO_2 is about twenty fold that for O_2 (Forster, 1957) so that CO_2 exchange in the alveoli will never be limited by diffusion. Even in the case of O_2, equilibration between the alveolar gas and end-capillary blood is complete to within 1 mm Hg when breathing air. $D_{L_{CO}}$ is of importance primarily because an estimate of $D_{L_{O_2}}$ can be derived from it.

Effect of increased inspired CO_2 partial pressure on D

Because of its ubiquitous physiological properties, CO_2 would be expected to exert an important influence on the pulmonary capillary bed and therefore on D_L. For example, Nisell has reported that an increase in alveolar P_{CO_2} leads to a constriction on the venous side of the capillary bed in the lungs of the cat (Nisell, 1951) which would presumably dilate the capillaries and increase D_L. Drs. Fowler, Bates, Van Lingen, and myself investigated the effect of including 6% CO_2 in the inspired mixture during measurements of the rate of disappearance of CO from the alveolar gas during breathholding (1954), and found that it increases this rate, at least after the first sec of breathholding. Drs. Rankin, McNeill, and myself have extended these findings (Rankin, McNeill, and Forster, to be published) and found that the 10 sec breathholding $D_{L_{CO}}$ increased an average of 5.3% (probability 0.05) in 7

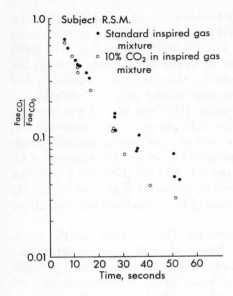

FIGURE 1.

This is a graph of expired alveolar CO concentration obtained after different times of breathholding, expressed as a fraction of the expired alveolar CO concentration that would have been present if no CO had disappeared into the blood ($F_{EA_{CO_0}}$). This last is obtained from the dilution of the inspired helium in the expired alveolar gas sample. The solid circles were obtained after inspiring a single breath of gas mixture containing approximately 0.4% CO, 10% helium, 20% O_2, and the remainder N_2. For the observations indicated with an open circle, the inspired gas mixture contained approximately 0.4% CO, 10% helium, 20% O_2, 10% CO_2, and the remainder N_2.

normal subjects when 10% CO_2 is included in the inspired gas mixture. Detailed alveolar CO disappearance curves were obtained in 2 subjects; the data from one of these are presented in Fig. 1. The solid circles are data obtained using an inspired mixture of approximately 0.4% CO, 10% helium, 20% O_2, and the remainder N_2. The open circles are data obtained when the inspired mixture was approximately 0.4% CO, 10% helium, 20% O_2, 10% CO_2, and the remainder N_2. Up until about 10 seconds of breathholding there is only a slight difference between the relative alveolar CO concentrations in the two cases, but thereafter it becomes more obvious that the CO disappears more rapidly in the presence of the higher alveolar P_{CO_2}. This effect of CO_2 represents either an increase in the effective diffusing surface of the pulmonary vascular bed or an increase in the rate of the reaction of CO with intracorpuscular hemoglobin.

We also measured breathholding $D_{L_{CO}}$ in 9 subjects before and after breathing air containing approximately 7.5% CO_2 for 5 to 10 minutes and found an average increase of 24.5%, which was significant (probability less than 0.01). In 5 out of these 9 subjects we followed $D_{L_{CO}}$ during exposure and in all it rapidly increased and remained above control values throughout the entire period, returning thereto at the end of the period. Figure 2 is a graph of minute ventilation, respiratory rate, $D_{L_{CO}}$, blood pressure, pulse and pulmonary blood flow [measured with a breathholding technique using C_2H_2 (Cander and Forster, to be published)] against time during the subject's breathing a gas mixture containing 7.8% CO_2. The most interesting observation is that although minute ventilation, respiratory rate, blood pressure, and pulse continued to rise during the period of exposure, D_L actually rose and then fell. While all other subjects did not show this phenomenon as well as it is seen in Fig. 2, there was a general lack of correlation between the magnitude of the increase in D_L at any time and the magnitude of the increases in the various indices of ventilatory and circulatory activity. The mechanism by which breathing an increased CO_2 concentration increases $D_{L_{CO}}$ is not clear although these data suggest something other than a passive response to general changes in the cardiovascular system. The actions of CO_2 on the pulmonary capillary bed should be investigated further.

I am aware of no measurements of D_L during or after chronic exposure to increased CO_2 concentrations. Although D_L has been studied in many clinical conditions where arterial P_{CO_2} is chronically elevated, such as in chronic obstructive emphysema (Forster, 1957), a great many other factors have changed,

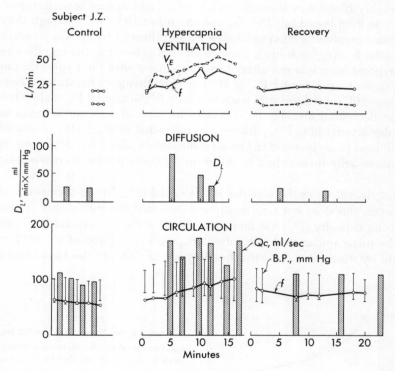

FIGURE 2.

A graph of indices of ventilatory and circulatory activity, and breathholding $D_{L_{CO}}$ before, during and after breathing 7.8% CO_2. Reading along the ordinate from the top down, V_E is minute ventilation in L/min, t is respiratory rate, D_L is breathholding $D_{L_{CO}}$, Q_c is pulmonary capillary blood flow in ml/second by the breathholding C_2H_2 technique, BP is brachial blood pressure in mm Hg, and f is pulse rate. Control values were obtained over a longer period than that of the other observations.

in addition, and we cannot come to any conclusion about the effect of increased P_{CO_2} alone. There is a possibility that increased alveolar P_{CO_2} may influence $D_{L_{CO}}$ by acting to modify the rate of combination of O_2 or CO with hemoglobin in the red cells, thereby altering the intracapillary uptake rate. Our present data are not adequate to assess this point.

Effect of decreased partial pressure of inspired O_2 on D

Acute conditions

Although it is generally assumed that the relative hypoxia employed in the measurement of $D_{L_{O_2}}$ (arterial saturation of 82%) does not alter its value (Riley *et al.*, 1951), anoxia does increase $D_{L_{O_2}}$ at the same O_2 consumption (Riley *et al.*, 1954) possibly secondary to an increase in pulmonary blood flow. On the other hand, Fishman and associates (Fishman *et al.*, 1955) estimated pulmonary blood flow through each lung in man during bronchospirometry with one lung breathing 25% O_2 and the other 10% O_2. Although their calculations involved some reasonable assumptions as to the O_2 saturation of the blood leaving each lung, their results indicated that the capillary bed of the hypoxic lung was not altered in comparison with the hyperoxic lung, at least down to an alveolar P_{O_2} of 50 mm Hg. Obviously breathing gases with a reduced O_2 partial pressure leads to a drop in the arterial P_{O_2} mainly because of the decreased alveolar P_{O_2} but also because of any net increase in the alveolar-arterial blood P_{O_2} difference (Lilienthal *et al.*, 1946). These effects which lead to an increase in the alveolar end-capillary P_{O_2} difference should not necessarily be ascribed to diffusion difficulty at the decreased inspired P_{O_2}.

$D_{L_{CO}}$ increases as the alveolar P_{O_2} is raised (Fig. 3) (Forster *et al.*, 1954); however, this does not necessarily indicate that the pulmonary membrane diffusing capacity (D_M) has increased, because the *in vitro* rate of uptake of CO by intracapillary red cells falls as P_{O_2} rises (Roughton *et al.*, 1957) which would by itself interfere with the diffusion of CO into the blood and lower

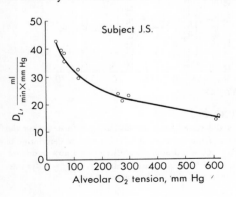

FIGURE 3.
A graph of the 10-second breathholding $D_{L_{CO}}$ against expired alveolar O_2 tension in subject J.S. In each observation, the alveolar P_{O_2} for approximately 10 minutes prior to the measurement ("conditioning" P_{O_2}) was the same as that during the measurement.

FIGURE 4.

A graph of 10-second breathholding $D_{L_{CO}}$ *against the expired alveolar O_2 at which the measurement was made in subject J.S. The solid curve is the same as that in Fig. 3 and represents the 10-second breathholding $D_{L_{CO}}$ when the alveolar P_{O_2} for approximately 10 minutes prior to the measurement ("conditioning" period) was the same as that during the measurement. The open triangles represent values of $D_{L_{CO}}$ obtained at the expired alveolar P_{O_2} indicated on the abscissa but when the conditioning P_{O_2} was not the same. The figures connected to the open triangles by a short straight line give the P_{O_2} during the conditioning period.*

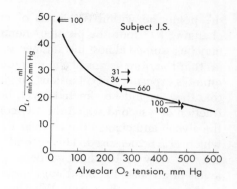

$D_{L_{CO}}$. In order to determine whether the changes found in $D_{L_{CO}}$ represented changes in D_M or changes in hemoglobin reaction rates, we took advantage of the fact that in performing the breathholding $D_{L_{CO}}$ alveolar P_{O_2} can suddenly be altered at the moment of inspiration by choosing a suitable inspired O_2 concentration. For this reason the alveolar P_{O_2} for the 10 minutes prior to the measurement of $D_{L_{CO}}$, the "conditioning" P_{O_2}, need not be the same as that during the actual measurement of $D_{L_{CO}}$. This enabled us to make measurements of $D_{L_{CO}}$ at the same alveolar P_{O_2} and yet have the capillary bed exposed to a variety of O_2 tensions during the conditioning period up until a mere second before the measurement. We hypothesized that any changes in D_M would represent changes in the dimensions of the pulmonary capillary bed which presumably would take a number of seconds to occur and which therefore would be primarily dependent on the conditioning P_{O_2}, whereas changes in the reaction rates for the combination of CO with hemoglobin would occur practically instantaneously with the changes in blood P_{O_2}, and would depend mainly on the alveolar P_{O_2} at which $D_{L_{CO}}$ was measured.

Figure 3 is a graph of 10-second $D_{L_{CO}}$ on the ordinate against expired alveolar P_{O_2} during the measurement on the abscissa, for subject J.S. In these data the "conditioning" alveolar P_{O_2} and the P_{O_2} at which $D_{L_{CO}}$ was measured were the same. $D_{L_{CO}}$ falls from a maximum value of 42.8 ml per minute per mm Hg at a P_{O_2} of about 40 mm Hg to a minimum value of about 15 ml per minute per mm Hg at an alveolar P_{O_2} of 610 mm Hg. In the next figure, Fig. 4 with similar coordinates, the smooth curve drawn through the data in Fig. 3 is reproduced for comparison. The open triangles represent measurements of $D_{L_{CO}}$ made at the expired alveolar P_{O_2} indicated on the abscissa, and at the conditioning P_{O_2} in mm Hg indicated by the numbers connected to each triangle by a short line. The data were obtained on one subject, but are typical of results obtained from 4 subjects. It can be seen that when the alveolar P_{O_2} during the 10-minute conditioning period was greater than about 60 mm Hg, the points lie within the limits of error of the curve. Since the effect of changing P_{O_2} upon the physico-chemical rate of CO uptake by the red cells may be assumed almost instantaneous, we interpret this finding to mean either (a) that the dimensions of the pulmonary capillary bed are unaltered by ten minutes exposure to O_2 tensions ranging from about 60 to 600 mm Hg, or (b) that they are indeed affected by O_2 tension in this range, but can alter in the fraction of a second which the CO containing inspired mixture takes to enter the alveoli and change the alveolar P_{O_2} from the conditioning value to that at which D_{CO} is measured. This second possibility seems very unlikely, particularly in view of the finding, demonstrated in Fig. 4, that at conditioning levels of alveolar P_{O_2} less than about 40 mm Hg, D_{CO} is increased compared to the values on the curve. Whether this is a direct action of hypoxia upon the capillaries or a passive one dependent upon hemodynamic changes elsewhere in the cardiovascular system is difficult to assess at present. It is in this range of hypoxia that cardiac output begins to rise (Fishman et al., 1952).

While these experiments on the breathholding D_{LCO} separate the effect of altering alveolar P_{O_2} upon D_M from that upon the red cell reaction rates, the measurements of D_{LO_2} (Riley et al., 1954; Fishman et al., 1955) do not. This requires, among other things, detailed knowledge of the rate of uptake of O_2 by human red cells at $37°C$. which is not available. It is possible, however, to assume from present information on the reaction rates of O_2 with intra-corpuscular hemoglobin (including some unpublished data of Bishop, Staub, and Forster), that changes in D_{LO_2}, which is the important physiological variable, will in general parallel changes in D_M derived from measurements of D_{LCO}.

Chronic conditions

Hurtado and co-workers (1956) using the techniques of Lilienthal and his co-workers (1946) found practically no difference in the O_2 tension of arterial blood and alveolar gas in natives living at 14,900 ft at rest when alveolar O_2 tension was 45 mm Hg, although residents at sea level at similar alveolar O_2 tensions generally have an alveolar-arterial O_2 tension difference of about 9 mm Hg (Riley et al., 1951); Houston and Riley (1947) found that the alveolar-arterial O_2 tension difference was less than control values in 4 normal men exposed to altitudes up to 22,000 ft (corresponding to an alveolar O_2 tension of about 38 mm Hg) for approximately one month in a pressure chamber, although there were some technical questions about the results. Velasquez (1956) measured D_{LO_2} in 12 residents at 14,900 ft, having them inspire air and a gas mixture containing 35% O_2 for the requisite low and high levels of O_2. He found that the values of D_{LO_2} so obtained, which fulfilled the requirements for "maximal" diffusing capacity, were considerably greater than comparable values obtained on other normal subjects at sea level (Riley et al., 1954). All these results, to which can be added the original and cruder observations of Barcroft and his group (1921), indicate that there is little or no alveolar-arterial O_2 tension difference in acclimatized subjects or natives at high altitudes, suggesting that chronic exposure to hypoxia increases $D_{L_{O_2}}$.

The next question is whether this increase in $D_{L_{O_2}}$ represents (a) an increase in the effective diffusing surface of the pulmonary capillary bed (D_M), or (b) an increase in the rate at which the total amount of hemoglobin in the capillary bed can take up O_2. The latter, b, could result from an increase in the pulmonary capillary blood volume (V_c), an increase in the hemoglobin concentration of the blood in the capillary bed, or an increase in the rate of O_2 uptake per red cell. The reaction kinetics of the combination of O_2 with intracellular hemoglobin have not been adequately studied at the proper physiological conditions to permit us to separate these various factors. However, the reaction rates of CO with intracellular hemoglobin for similar conditions are known well enough to be used in conjunction with measurements of $D_{L_{CO}}$ to estimate the diffusing capacity of the pulmonary membrane (D_M) and the pulmonary capillary blood volume (V_c). Unfortunately I know of no measurements of $D_{L_{CO}}$ which might help to unravel these questions. While Barcroft et $al.$ (1921) did measure D_{CO} by Krogh's original breathholding technique in 13 subjects at rest at high altitude and found no significant difference from normal data obtained at sea level, there were no control measurements on these same subjects. It is to be hoped that measurements of D_{CO} can be made using any of the modern techniques, and preferably using the subjects as their own controls.

Effects of increased inspired O_2 partial pressure on D

Breathing high concentrations of O_2 for several days will produce pulmonary damage resulting in anoxemia and the post mortem histological changes of capillary damage and hemorrhagic edema in the lungs of various laboratory animals (Bean, 1945) and it might reasonably be expected that the same would occur in man. Some of the pathological changes, particularly the thickening of the diffusion path between alveolar air and capillary blood, are of the kind that classically would be expected to lead to a decrease in D_L. In 1945 Comroe, Dripps and coworkers (1945) exposed 55 human volunteers to 100% O_2 for 24 hours. A majority of these subjects showed a decrease in vital capacity and reported substernal pain which disappeared in the following 24 hours. In 1947 Ohlsson had 6 volunteers breathe 100% O_2 for 55 hours. These subjects also showed a decrease in their vital capacity and substernal distress and, in addition, reported dyspnea on exertion for several days. Although man does not appear to be as susceptible to breathing high concentrations of O_2 as test animals, these reports suggest that some damage may be produced in the lungs of man following exposure, and that D_L might be an important index of this damage. On these grounds, Commander R. L. Burdick exposed 11 normal subjects in our laboratory at sea level to 100% O_2 administered by a mask for 6

TABLE 2
Approximate changes in pulmonary diffusing capacity, when the inspired gas composition is varied.

Changes in inspired gas mixture	Effect upon pulmonary diffusing capacity
$\uparrow P_{CO_2}$	$\uparrow D_L$, increase in alveolar P_{CO2} of 15 mm Hg for 10 seconds leads to a 5% increase in D_{LCO}
$\downarrow P_{O_2}$	No change in D_M unless alveolar P_{O2} drops below about 40 mm Hg
$\uparrow P_{O_2}$	No change in D_M after 6 hours breathing approximately 100% O_2
$\uparrow \downarrow P_{N_2}$ (total pressure)	No data: no change predicted

hours. Each subject was at liberty at the end of a pressure hose. He measured (a) airway resistance in the body plethysmograph by the method of DuBois *et al.* (1956) in all 11 subjects, (b) vital capacity in all subjects, and (c) D_{LCO} by the breathholding method in 3 subjects. Airway resistance averaged 1.61 cm H_2O per L per second before exposure and 1.62 cm H_2O per L per second after. This difference was not significant, thus there was no significant constriction of the airways. However, vital capacity was not significantly altered by the procedure, which suggests that the exposure was not carried out long enough, in view of the previous reports of changes in this lung volume. D_{LCO} measured breathing air did not change, indicating that there was no significant effect on the pulmonary capillary bed.

Although these studies are very helpful in assessing the importance of brief exposures to high concentrations of inspired O_2, further investigations of longer duration should be carried out in man, and D_L should be measured in animals under analogous conditions.

The effect of variations in inspired N_2 partial pressure and in total ambient pressure on D

There are no data available on this subject but there are no obvious reasons why such changes should alter D.

A brief summary of approximate or predicted changes in pulmonary diffusing capacity is given in Table 2. Although the data available do not give detailed answers to all the questions that might be raised in this connection, it seems reasonable to assume for the moment that no remarkable alterations in D_L are produced in normal man by changing inspired CO_2, O_2, or N_2 partial pressures that would cause diffusion to be a limiting factor in gas respiratory exchange at rest or during moderate exercise.

REFERENCES

Barcroft, J., C. A. Binger, A. V. Bock, J. H. Doggart, W. S. Forbes, G. Harrop, J. C. Meakins, and A. C. Redfield. 1921. "Effect of high altitude on physiological processes of the human body," Phil. Trans. Roy. Soc. London. *B211*: 351.

Bartels, J., J. W. Sevringhaus, R. E. Forster, W. A. Briscoe, and D. V. Bates. 1954. "The respiratory dead space measured by single breath analysis of oxygen, carbon dioxide, nitrogen, or helium," J. Clin. Invest. *33:* 41.

Bean, J. W. 1945. "Effects of oxygen at increased pressure," Physiol. Rev. *25:* 1.

Clappison, G. B., and W. K. Hamilton. 1956. "Respiratory adjustments to increase in external dead space," Anesthesiology. *17:* 643.

Comroe, J. H., Jr., R. D. Dripps, P. R. Dumpke, and M. Deming. 1945. "The effect of inhalation of high concentrations of oxygen for twenty-four hours on normal men at sea level and at a simulated altitude of 18,00 feet," J. Am. Med. Assoc. *128:* 710.

Cooper, D. Y., G. L. Emmel, R. H. Kough, and C. J. Lambertsen. 1953. "Effects of CO_2 induced hyperventilation upon the alveolar-arterial P_{O2} difference and the functional respiratory dead space in normal man," Fed. Proc. *12:* 28.

Dripps, R. D., and J. H. Comroe, Jr. 1947. "The effect of inhalation of high and low oxygen concentrations on respiration, pulse rate, ballistocardiogram and arterial oxygen saturation (oximeter) of normal individuals," Am. J. Physiol. *149:* 277.

DuBois, A. B., R. C. Fowler, A. Soffer, and W. O. Fenn. 1952. "Alveolar CO_2 measured by expiration into the rapid infrared gas analyzer," J. Appl. Physiol. *4:* 526.

DuBois, A. B., S. Y. Botelho, and J. H. Comroe, Jr. 1956. "A new method for measuring airway resistance in man using a body plethysmograph," J. Clin. Invest. *35:* 327.

Filley, G. F., F. Gregoire, and G. W. Wright. 1954. "Alveolar and arterial oxygen tensions and the significance of the alveolar-arterial oxygen tension difference in normal men," J. Clin. Invest. *33:* 517.

Fishman, A. P., J. McClement, A. Himmelstein, and A. Cournand. 1952. "Effects of acute anoxia on the circulation and respiration in patients with chronic pulmonary disease studied during the steady state," J. Clin. Invest. *31:* 770.

Fishman, A. P., A. Himmelstein, H. W. Fritts, Jr., and A. Cournand. 1955. "Blood flow through each lung in man during unilateral hypoxia," J. Clin. Invest. *43:* 637.

Folkow, B., and J. R. Pappenheimer. 1955. "Components of the respiratory dead space and their variation with pressure breathing and with bronchoactive drugs," J. Appl. Physiol. *8:* 102.

Forster, R. E., W. S. Fowler, D. V. Bates, and B. van Lingen. 1954. "Absorption of CO by lungs during breathholding," J. Clin. Invest. *33:* 1135.

Forster, R. E. 1957. "The exchange of gases between alveolar air and pulmonary capillary blood," Physiol. Rev. *37:* 391.

Fowler, W. S. 1948. "Lung function studies. II. The respiratory dead space," Am. J. Physiol. *154:* 405.

Gray, J. S., F. S. Grodins, and E. T. Carter. 1956. "Alveolar and total ventilation and the dead space problem," J. Appl. Physiol. *9:* 307.

Haldane, J. S. 1928. *Respiration,* Yale University Press, New Haven, p. 362.

Houston, C. S., and R. L. Riley. 1947. "Respiratory and circulatory changes during acclimatization to high altitude," Am. J. Physiol. *149:* 565.

Hurtado, A., T. Velasquez, C. Reynafarje, R. Lozano, R. Chavez, H. A. Salazar, B. Reynafarje, C. Sanchez, and J. Munoz. 1956. "Mechanisms of Natural Acclimatization," School of Aviation Med., USAF Report No. 56–1.

Krogh, M. 1914. "Diffusion of gases through lungs of man," J. Physiol. *49:* 271.

Lilienthal, J. L., Jr., R. L. Riley, D. D. Proemmel, and R. E. Franke. 1946. "An experimental analysis in man of the O_2 pressure gradient from alveolar air to arterial blood during rest and exercise at sea level and at altitude," Am. J. Physiol. *147:* 199.

Margaria, R., A. Taglietti, and E. Agostoni. 1957. "Indirect determination of respiratory dead space and mean alveolar air composition," J. Appl. Physiol. *11:* 235.

Nisell, O. 1951. "The influence of blood gases on the pulmonary vessels of the cat," Acta physiol. scand. *23:* 85.

Ohlsson, W. T. L. 1947. "A study on oxygen toxicity at atmospheric pressure," Acta. Med. Scand. Suppl. *190.*

Riley, R. L., J. L. Lilienthal, Jr., D. D. Proemmel, and R. E. Franke. 1946. "Determination of physiologically effective pressures of O_2 and CO_2 in alveolar air," Am. J. Physiol. *147:* 191.

Riley, R. L., A. Cournand, and K. W. Donald. 1951. "Analysis of factors affecting partial pressures of oxygen and carbon dioxide in gas and blood of lungs: methods," J. Appl. Physiol. *4:* 102.

Riley, R. L., R. H. Shepard, J. E. Cohn, D. G. Carroll, and B. W. Armstrong. 1954. "Maximal diffusing capacity of lungs," J. Appl. Physiol. *6:* 573.

Roughton, F. J. W., and R. E. Forster. 1957. "Relative importance of diffusion and chemical reaction rates in determining the rate of exchange of gases in the human lung," J. Appl. Physiol. *11:* 290.

Roughton, F. J. W., R. E. Forster, and L. Cander. 1957. "Rate at which CO replaces O_2 from combination with human hemoglobin in solution and in the red cell," J. Appl. Physiol. *11:* 269.

Sevringhaus, J. W., and M. Stupfel. 1957. "Alveolar dead space as an index of distribution of blood flow in pulmonary capillaries," J. Appl. Physiol. *10:* 335.

Shepard, R. H., E. J. M. Campbell, H. B. Martin, and T. Enns. 1957. "Factors affecting the pulmonary dead space as determined by a single breath analysis," J. Appl. Physiol. *11:* 241.

Velasquez, T. 1956. "Maximal Diffusing Capacity of the Lungs at High Altitudes," School of Aviation Med., USAF Report No. 56–108.

Williams, M. H., Jr., and C. M. Rayford. 1956. "Effect of variation of tidal volume on size of physiological dead space in dogs," J. Appl. Physiol. *9:* 30.

Young, A. C. 1955. "Dead Space at rest and during exercise," J. Appl. Physiol. *8:* 91.

Recent Research on Oxygen-Carbon Dioxide Transport in Blood

RODOLFO MARGARIA

Physiological Institute, University of Milan, Italy

The interference between oxygen and CO_2 in their affinity with blood as first described by Bohr (1909) and later by Haldane, Barcroft, Henderson, Van Slyke, and others, is a well-known fact. The original Bohr hypothesis that CO_2 made a chemical complex with hemoglobin lacked evidence and it seemed to be disproved by subsequent work, particularly that of Van Slyke.

Such interference, also well known as the "Bohr effect," can be described either as a shift to the right of the oxygen dissociation curve for blood by adding CO_2, or as a displacement to lower values of the CO_2 dissociation curve for blood by adding oxygen.

For many years the Bohr effect seemed to be completely accounted for by a characteristic behavior of the Hb molecule, which merged out of the classical work by Haldane (1927), Barcroft (1925), Henderson (1928), and Van Slyke and Peters (1946): these authors gave evidence of a peculiar change of the acidic properties of hemoglobin with oxygenation, which can be summarized by the following relation:

$$Hb + O_2 \underset{T}{\overset{L}{\rightleftharpoons}} HbO_2^- + H^+ \tag{1}$$

(reaction L taking place in the lungs, T in the tissues)

The effect of CO_2 could then be described as due to its acidic properties as shown from the relation:

$$CO_2 + H_2O \underset{L}{\overset{T}{\rightleftharpoons}} H^+ + HCO_3^- \tag{2}$$

CO_2 then, by increasing the hydrogen ion concentration causes equilibrium (1) to shift from the right to the left (reaction T): the affinity of Hb to O_2 is thus decreased, and this is visualized as a shift to the right of the O_2 dissociation curve of Hb. The hydrogen ion given off by oxygenation probably comes from a ionized free amino group of the Hb molecule:

$$-NH_3^+ \rightleftarrows H^+ + -NH_2 \qquad (3)$$

This hypothesis, however, fails to explain some peculiar phenomena, and particularly the low value of pK_1 for carbonic acid as found in bicarbonate solutions containing hemoglobin.

Some evidence of a direct binding of the CO_2 with Hb was given in 1928 by Henriques, who tried to explain with this mechanism the rapid taking up of CO_2 by hemoglobin solutions and by blood. While this latter phenomenon was later shown to be of a catalytic nature (Brinkman and Margaria, 1931; Brinkman et al., 1932), the formation of a CO_2Hb compound was made evident by osmotic determinations of hemoglobin solutions to which CO_2 was added (Margaria, 1931). It is evident that combined CO_2 will increase the osmotic pressure of a solution only if it combines with water to form HCO_3^-, while it will not appear osmotically if it combines directly with Hb in a CO_2Hb complex.

On the other hand, on the experimental ground that hemoglobin does not affect the osmotic coefficient of electrolytes (Margaria, 1931; Margaria et al., 1933), the hypothesis that the low pK_1 value for carbonic acid could be due to a decrease of the activity coefficient caused by hemoglobin in solution (Stadie and Hawes, 1928) was disproved; such an effect could then only be interpreted as the result of a binding of CO_2 to hemoglobin and from its magnitude the quantitative determination of the CO_2Hb complex could be made as shown by Margaria and Green in 1933.

These authors also observed that the dissociation curve of Hb in $NaHCO_3$–CO_2 is more displaced to the right than the curve of a similar Hb solution without $NaHCO_3$–CO_2, at the same pH and at the same ionic strength, the electrolytes being replaced by NaCl. Evidently this effect cannot be explained on the basis of reactions (1) and (2), as a change in hydrogen ion concentration is not involved, and new support to the hypothesis of the formation of a CO_2Hb complex was thus given.

The nature of this compound may be of a carbamate type. First described by Siegfried (1909), and later extensively studied quantitatively by Faurholt (1925), was the fact that many organic compounds containing an undissociated $-NH_2$ group can bind CO_2 with the formation of a carbamine compound, whose acidic properties are fairly high:

$$-NH_2 + CO_2 \rightleftarrows H^+ + -NHCOO^- \qquad (4)$$

The pK for the dissociation of the amino groups of the amino acid (reaction 3) is generally near 10, and this value is not changed appreciably when the amino acids are linked together in the protein molecule. It is for this reason that most amino acids such as glycine make carbamino compounds only at a very alkaline range ($pH > 9$), while at physiological pH (< 8) the formation of carbamino compounds for most amino acids and for most proteins, such as serum proteins, casein, etc., is nil. In fact the sum of the equilibria (2) and (4) gives

$$-NH_2 + HCO_3^- \rightleftarrows -NHCOO^- + H_2O \qquad (5)$$

from which it is evident that for the formation of the carbamino compound both $-NH_2 + HCO_3^-$ must be present in a sufficient concentration. At $pH > 10$, $-NH_2$ is abundant, but HCO_3^- is progressively decreasing owing to its transformation to $CO_3^=$ ($pK_{HCO_3^-} = 10$ ab.); at $pH < 10$, HCO_3^- is abundant, but $-NH_2$ is progressively decreasing owing to "dissociation" to $-NH_3^+$ (Margaria, 1952) (Fig. 1).

The peculiarity of hemoglobin of binding CO_2 even at $pH < 7$ could be due either to the presence on the hemoglobin molecule of an $-NH_2$ group having a particularly low pK, such as are found in some diamino acids, e.g., histidine, ornitine, or in other amines such as phenilhydrazine, or to a binding of a different nature, as Margaria stated in 1932.

The CO_{2carb} can be differentiated from all other known forms of combined CO_2, i.e., with water, because it does not precipitate with Ba salts in a very alkaline medium (Faurholt, 1925) and it can thus be tested chemically in the clear solution. Ferguson and Roughton (1935) estimated with this method the amount of CO_2 bound with Hb and this turned out to be less than the amount found by Margaria and Green in 1933, when, using a different, "thermodynamic," method; this consists in measuring the total combined CO_2 with Van Slyke's manometric method, HCO_3^- and $CO_3^=$ being known:

$$HbCO_2 = CO_2tot. - HCO_3^- - CO_3^=$$

the amounts of HCO_3^- and $CO_3^=$ were calculated from Henderson's formula or from the second dissociation of the carbonic acid equation, the pH being measured, and the pKs calculated as from Hastings and Sendroy (1925), the ionic

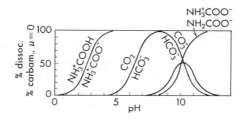

FIGURE 1.

Dissociation curves for carbonic acid [as from equilibrium (2)] for HCO_3^- and glycine (1st and 2nd dissociation). The heavy marked curves on the right indicate the formation of glycine-carbamino compound. At plot 7.4 the CO_2 is mainly in the form of HCO_3^-, little as CO_2, and practically nothing as $CO_3^=$; glycine is all as amphion, $+H_3N - CH_2 - COO^-$, and no carbamino glycine is present.

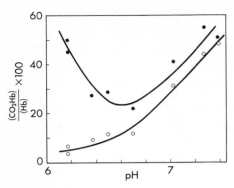

FIGURE 2.
CO₂ bound with reduced hemoglobin as a function of pH at 37° plus = total (found with Margaria and Green's method). Open circles represent carbamino-bound CO₂ (Faurholt's method). Similar data are obtained with HbO₂, only the CO₂ bound with hemoglobin is lower. (From Milla, Giustina, and Margaria, 1953)

strength of the solution being known. This method detects any possible form of CO₂ combined in a different form than with water.

Roughton (1935) explained this discrepancy assuming that only some of the CO₂ was in the form of a carbamino compound with hemoglobin, the remainder being a compound of a different nature. This hypothesis, however, could only be accepted with reluctance since it was based on results from different authors working under different experimental conditions.

Experiments made in this laboratory in Milan, however, confirmed such a hypothesis (Giustina, Milla, and Margaria, 1952–1953). These experiments were carried on at the same time and on the same solutions with the same chemical method and with Margaria and Green's procedure on both oxygenated and reduced hemoglobin, over a pH range from 6 to 12. Figure 2 shows the relative amount of the CO₂Hb found with the two different methods for reduced Hb. This appears to be mainly carbamino hemoglobin, or carbhemoglobin, at $pH > 7$, and a different, unknown compound at $pH < 7.5$. Figure 2 shows how much of the total CO₂Hb is in this unknown form.

Direct evidence of the noncarbamino fraction was given by Milla and Margaria (1954), who showed that when the $-NH_2$ groups of Hb are blocked by means of acetylation with ketene, Hb binds CO₂ at low pH in a compound that can be detected with the thermodynamic method, but that cannot be detected by the chemical method; at $pH > 7.5$ no CO₂Hb can be detected any more when ketene-treated Hb is used.

The formation of a noncarbamino compound is peculiar to Hb: none of the proteins tested (casein, seroprotein, salmin), not even myoglobin (Giustina, Temelcou, De Fusco, and Margaria, 1954), binds CO₂ into such a compound. This binding presumably involves the protein fraction of the molecule, as hematin solutions do not bind CO₂ at pH values between 6.56 and 7.54, as Margaria and Green showed in 1933.

Carbamino compounds on the other hand may be formed by all the proteins tested—some only in the very alkaline range of pH (> 9), such as seroprotein, casein, some also in the physiologic range of pH (< 8), such as salmin; this is in accordance with the particular value of the pK of free $-NH_2$ groups of the protein molecule, as explained before.

Certainly the existence of a CO_2Hb compound at $pH < 7.0$ is somewhat distressing; nevertheless, there can be no doubt of its existence, unless a more plausible explanation is found for the low pK_1 values for carbonic acid in this pH range, found by Van Slyke *et al.* (1925), Stadie and Hawes (1928), Dill in 1937, and for the results, calculated on similar experiments obtained by Margaria (1931), Margaria and Green in 1933, and Milla, Giustina, and Margaria (1953).

It may be of interest to evaluate the amounts of the two different fractions of CO_2Hb in the blood. To that end it is necessary to measure the total CO_2Hb by the thermodynamic method, and to subtract from this value the amount of one of the fractions. The direct determination in whole blood of the carbamino compound (CO_2Hb carb) is technically difficult. This fraction, however, can be calculated if the K_{NH_2}, i.e., the dissociation constant of the $-NH_2$ group [as from reaction (3)] which is responsible for the binding of CO_2 on a carbamino compound, and the K_c, which is defined [as from the equilibrium reaction (4)] by

$$K_c = \frac{[-NHCOO^-] \cdot [H^+]^2}{[-HN_2] \qquad \cdot [CO_2]} \tag{6}$$

are known (Giustina, 1955). By such an analysis the following relation has been worked out:

$$\frac{[CO_2Hb_{carb}]}{[Hb]} = \frac{K_{NH_2} \cdot K_c \cdot [CO_2]}{[H^+]^2} \tag{7}$$

K_{NH_2} and K_c have been calculated from the data obtained by Ferguson (1936) in 1937, on solutions of human Hb $\cdot$ [Hb] is the molar fraction of Hb (mol. weight $= 17.000$) and $[CO_2]$ the molar fraction of CO_2 dissolved. From Equ. (7) the fraction of carbhemoglobin in the blood can be easily calculated when $[CO_2]$ or pCO_2 and $[H^+]$ are known. A change of CO_2Hb_{carb}, as from formula (7), is much more dependent on $[H^+]$ than on CO_2, these two factors acting in opposition. The addition of CO_2 however, makes $[H^+]$ change in the same direction, and this involves only small changes of CO_2Hb_{carb}, depending on the buffer power of the blood toward CO_2.

From a quantitative analysis of the equilibria of the noncarbamino CO_2Hb compound by Giustina in 1954, it appears that the amount of this compound in the blood at equilibrium can be considered directly related to pCO_2 and to $[H^+]$.

In 1954 Giustina applied relation (7) to the data of Henderson (1928) on

TABLE 1

Concentration of the compounds CO_2Hb_{tot}, CO_2Hb_{carb}, and $CO_2Hb_{noncarb}$ in 1 liter of human blood *at rest* as calculated by Giustina in 1954 from the data of Henderson (1928).

		Arterial blood		Venous blood		Venous-arterial		
		serum	cells	serum	cells	serum	cells	blood
pH		7.431	7.169	7.406	7.124			
pCO_2	mm HG	40		45.4				
CO_2 diss.	mM	0.71	0.34	0.8	0.39	0.09	0.05	0.14
CO_2 comb.	mM	15.23	5.25	16.19	5.83	0.96	0.58	1.54
HCO_3^-	mM	15.23	3.98	16.19	4.13	0.96	0.15	1.11
$CO_2Hb_{tot.}$	mM		1.27		1.70		0.43	0.43
CO_2Hb_{carb}	mM		0.97		1.21		0.24	0.24
$CO_2Hb_{noncarb}$			0.30		0.49		0.19	0.19
$\dfrac{CO_2Hb_{noncarb}}{CO_2Hb_{tot.}} \times 100$			23.6		28.8		44.2	

TABLE 2

Concentrations of compounds during exercise.

		Arterial blood		Venous blood		Venous-arterial		
		serum	cells	serum	cells	serum	cells	blood
pH		7.33	7.131	7.262	7.05			
pCO_2	mm Hg	38		54.8				
CO_2 diss.	mM	0.65	0.38	0.92	0.56	0.27	0.18	0.45
CO_2 comb.	mM	11.02	5.38	13.36	7.06	2.38	1.68	4.02
HCO_3^-	mM	11.02	4.08	13.36	4.99	2.34	0.86	3.20
$CO_2Hb_{tot.}$	mM		1.30		2.07		0.77	0.77
$CO_2Hb_{chim.}$	mM		0.85		1.15		0.30	0.30
$CO_2Hb_{noncarb}$	mM		0.45		.92		0.47	0.47
$\dfrac{CO_2Hb_{noncarb}}{CO_2Hb_{tot.}} \times 100$			34.6		44.5 ———————	61.0		

human blood at rest, and at work. The carbamino and the noncarbamino fractions of the CO_2Hb complex for arterial and venous blood are given in Tables 1 and 2.

The noncarbamino CO_2Hb is only a small fraction of the total CO_2 bound with hemoglobin, about ¼ at rest for arterial blood, and increasing up to ⅓ during exercise because of the increase of the hydrogen ion concentration in the red cells. In venous blood these amounts are correspondingly higher, because of the greater affinity of the reduced hemoglobin for CO_2. This fraction, however, being more labile chemically, contributes more than other combined CO_2 to the respiratory exchanges of CO_2 at the tissue or lung level, as evidenced in the Tables 1 and 2.

In conclusion, of the total CO_2 combined in blood only less than 10% is in combination with Hb, and of this about ⅔ is in the form of carbhemoglobin. Of the CO_2 which is given off through the lungs, however, about 20 to 25% comes from the CO_2Hb complex, about ½ of which was in form of carbhemoglobin.

Though the two forms of CO_2Hb are only a small fraction of the total CO_2 combined in blood, the part taken by these complexes in blood CO_2 transport is considerable, particularly for the noncarbamino fraction of CO_2Hb.

Oxygenation of hemoglobin, besides increasing its dissociation from reaction (1), and decreasing therefore the affinity of its solutions, or of blood, for CO_2 (reaction 2), interferes also with the direct binding of CO_2 with hemoglobin both as carbamino or noncarbamino compound. The over-all effect of oxygenation on the formation of the CO_2Hb complex was shown by Margaria and Green in 1933, as this compound was found by them in higher proportion in solution of reduced Hb than in HbO_2 solutions. Giustina, in 1954, found that reduced horse Hb binds more CO_2 as carbamino compound than HbO_2. That the amount of noncarbamino compound also decreases with the oxygenation of Hb, was supported by the data of Margaria and Green in 1933 when they found in horse Hb that, at $pH = 7$, when about all CO_2 is bound with Hb only in a noncarbamino form, HbO_2 binds only one tenth as much CO_2 as reduced Hb. These data have been confirmed by Sidwell et al. (1938) who also found that at $pH = 6.8$ the affinity of Hb for O_2 in human Hb solutions is decreased by CO_2.

The discovery was made that CO_2 binds with hemoglobin, and that in blood there are, therefore, two kinds of this protein capable of binding with O_2, i.e., Hb and CO_2Hb. No attempt had been made to investigate quantitatively the different acidic properties of these two substances; even the effect of CO_2 on the dissociation curve of Hb for O_2, independent from pH, was determined by Margaria and Green in 1933, only at a single pH value, 7.37, at which it was shown later that both CO_2Hb compounds are present in appreciable amounts.

FIGURE 3.

Oxygen dissociation curves of the same horse Hb preparation in $NaHCO_3CO_2$ (continuous line) or in the absence of CO_2 (dotted line) at pH values as indicated. For all experiments (Hb) = 10 mM/ (on the asumption that its m.w. = 17,000) and ionic strength = 0.1. The different pH values were obtained by adding to the original NaHb solutions either CO_2 or lactic acid (a weak acid was preferred to HCl, to prevent alteration of Hb in solution).

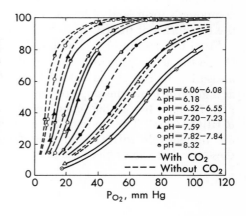

pH = 6.06–6.08
pH = 6.18
pH = 6.52–6.55
pH = 7.20–7.23
pH = 7.59
pH = 7.82–7.84
pH = 8.32
—— With CO_2
---- Without CO_2

P_{O_2}, mm Hg

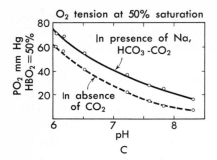

FIGURE 4.

Data from Fig. 3 (pO₂ for 50% saturation) are plotted against pH. Continuous line refers to Hb in the presence of NaHCO₃CO₂, dotted line to Hb in the presence of NaCl of same ionic strength. (From Margaria and Milla, 1955)

A revision of the effect of CO_2 on the O_2 dissociation curve of Hb in solution, and reciprocally of the effect of O_2 on the acidic properties of Hb and of its compounds with CO_2, was needed over the whole range of pH 6 to 8. A possible additional bit of information on the two mechanisms of the combination of CO_2 with Hb could have been given by this analysis.

A set of dissociation curves for O_2 of the same Hb solution both in $NaHCO_3^-$ CO_2 and in absence of CO_2, the ionic strength being kept constant, has been worked out experimentally over the greatest possible range of pH (Margaria and Milla, 1955). This shows that the effect demonstrated by Margaria and Green, in 1933, on the shift to the right of the O_2 dissociation curve caused by CO_2 and independent from pH, is evident over the whole range of pH experimented.

The Bohr effect, i.e., the effect of acidity on the affinity of hemoglobin for oxygen, can best be expressed by the value of pO_2 at a given saturation value, e.g., 50%, as a function of pH; for the two $NaHCO_3^-$ CO_2 and the CO_2-free solutions two different curves for the Bohr effect have been obtained (Fig. 4), the vertical distance between the two curves being the CO_2 effect independent from pH. The pO_2 values are higher in presence of CO_2, in the whole range of pH experimented. Nor is it possible to detect an appreciable difference in behavior between the range of high pH values (>7.5) where carbamino compounds form, and of lower pH values (< 7). This seems to indicate that the two forms of the CO_2Hb compound have very similar acidic properties.

From the data in Figs. 3 and 4, the effect of the change of oxygenation of Hb on the acidic properties of its molecule can be calculated. This is done by measuring in Fig. 3 the value of the slope of the curve at 50% dissociation at a given pH and the slope of the corresponding curve of Fig. 4 at the same pH. In fact the acidic effect of Hb oxygenation can be described by $d[HbO_2]/d$pH. The slope of the two curves of Figs. 3 and 4 as described, are respectively $[dHbO_2]/d$pO$_2$ and dpO_2/dpH, and the multiplication of these two last values gives the first

$$\frac{d[\text{HbO}_2]}{d\text{pH}} = \frac{d[\text{HbO}_2]}{d\text{pO}_2} \cdot \frac{d\text{pO}_2}{d\text{pH}}$$

The $d\text{HbO}_2/d\text{pH}$ values for Hb at 50% oxygenation and for all experimented pH values are given in Fig. 5 for both sets of curves, in the presence and in the absence of CO_2.

The two curves run parallel, again not showing any substantially different pattern at pH about 7.0–7.5, where the CO_2 combination with Hb changes from the carbamino mechanism to the other. The curve for CO_2, however, is always at a lower level than the curve without CO_2, which shows that lesser oxygenation of $CO_2\text{Hb}$ is required to give the same effect on the pH of the solution than the oxygenation of CO_2-free Hb. Furthermore, for both Hb and $CO_2\text{Hb}$ the increase in acidity due to oxygenation is maximum at low pH (6.0); it decreases moderately and steadily up to pH 7.5, and drops to a minimum at pH 8.0.

The effect of oxygenation on pH depends not only on the change of the acidic properties of hemoglobin, but also on the buffer value of the solution. This is defined by $d\text{B}/d\text{pH}$, calculated from titration curve values of a hemoglobin solution. By dividing the values $d\text{B}/d\text{pH}$ by the buffer value referred to the oxygenation of Hb, $d\text{HbO}_2/d\text{pH}$, the value $d\text{B}/d\text{HbO}_2$ is obtained. This defines the amount of base (or acid) in moles corresponding to the subtraction (or addition) of 1 mole of O_2, and the acidifying properties of oxygen are described in terms of addition or subtraction of acid or base.

Titration curves of hemoglobin, oxyhemoglobin, and carboxyhemoglobin solutions are numerous in the literature (Van Slyke, Wu, McLean, 1923; Hastings et al., 1924–1925; German and Wyman, 1937; Wyman in 1939; Cohn, Green, and Blanchard, 1937), but particularly interesting for the present argument are those by Hastings, Van Slyke et al. (1924) and of Hastings et al. (1925), in which the titration was made using both HCl and CO_2 as acids. It is well

FIGURE 5.
Acidic effect of oxygenation of hemoglobin in $NaHCO_3CO_2$ solution (continuous line) and NaCl (dotted line). (From Margaria and Milla, 1955)

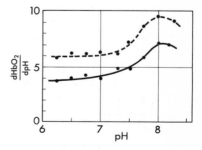

known that these authors could not find any difference using these two acids. Though not being necessarily in conflict with the hypothesis of the formation of a CO_2Hb complex, it makes it a little less probable.

Titration curves of hemoglobin have been made on the same hemoglobin preparations on which the other experiments were performed, and over a pH range 6.0 to 8.5; and the results confirm substantially the previous findings by Hastings, Van Slyke, and their collaborators (1924–1925) in the sense that within the limits of experimental error the titration curve with CO_2 is the same as with HCl.

No indication is given in the titration curve of the existence of a compound of CO_2 with Hb, either at $pH > 7.5$ or < 7.0, where different compounds have been evidenced. Evidently the acidity due to hydration of CO_2 and dissociation of carbonic acid equals the increase of acidity of hemoglobin when a combination of this protein with CO_2 takes place; this increase in acidity is represented, for the carbamino compound, by reaction (4).

The data $dB/dHbO_2$, calculated as described, are given in Fig. 6 as a function of pH for a 50% saturation with O_2. These data, referred to in the CO_2 experiments, are of the same order of magnitude as the data given by Hastings, Van Slyke *et al.* (1924). The only difference is that the maximum values are not found at pH 7.4, but are displaced toward the acid side, at pH 7.0

The values referring to the experiments made without CO_2 are appreciably lower than those obtained with CO_2, the maximum of $dB/dHbO_2$ being 0.5 instead of 0.7; these are not to be compared with Hastings and Van Slyke's data (1924), as the latter were obtained experimenting on solutions of Hb with $NaHCO_3^-CO_2$.

Data such as those in Fig. 6 can be obtained not only for 50%, but also for all values of saturation of Hb with O_2. Each set of such data $dB/dHbO_2$ then can be plotted as a function of oxygenation at a given pH, as described in Fig. 7 for pH values 7.2, 7.4, and 7.6

The data $dB–dHbO_2$ as given by Van Slyke in 1924 had been calculated on the difference between the base binding power of Hb relative to HbO_2, and no effect of a change of the acidic properties of Hb has been found for intermediate values of oxygenation (1923). The data in Fig. 7 seem to show, however, that the base equivalent of O_2 binding to Hb is lowest at about 60% oxygenation, having a value about $= 0.5$, increasing to about 1.0 at saturation with O_2; at low oxygenation it increases also up to about 1.0 without CO_2, and up to as much as about 2.0 with $NaHCO_3^-CO_2$. Though the values at the extreme conditions of oxygenation may not be too reliable, owing to the difficulty of exact measurement of the tangent of the dissociation curves for O_2 for very low or very high saturation values, nevertheless a change in the direction described in Fig. 7 seems certain.

This would imply that, in the CO_2-free solutions, the oxygenation of Hb has a different effect on the dissociation of the neighboring acidic group in re-

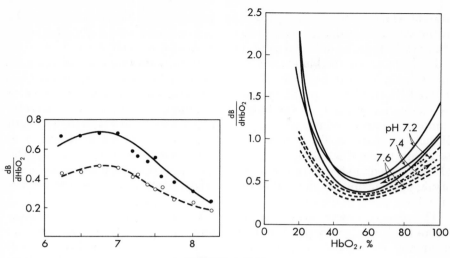

FIGURE 6 (*left*).

Acidic equivalents of oxygenation of Hb as a function of *p*H, in the presence of $NaHCO_3$-CO_2 (continuous line) or of NaCl (dotted line). (From Margaria and Milla, 1956)

FIGURE 7 (*right*).

Acidic equivalents of oxygenation of Hb as a function of O_2 saturation. The three continuous lines refer to the effect on Hb in the presence of $NaHCO_3CO_2$ at the *p*H indicated. The three dotted lines refer to analogous experiments in the absence of CO_2. v = normal venous point (rest conditions); a = normal arterial point. (From Margaria and Milla, 1956)

lation with the number of O_2 molecules already taken up by Hb. Such an event is not too unlikely in view of the fact that only the polymerization products of elementary Hb (molecular weight 17,000) seem to present the Bohr effect. Myoglobin, not differing appreciably from hemoglobin in amino acid composition, particularly in histamine, has no Bohr effect, i.e., its oxygenation does not affect the neighboring $-NH_2$ group acidity. If only the polymerized product of elementary Hb offers such change in its acidic properties as a result of oxygenation, it is not surprising that the change may not be the same for all four reacting groups of the natural hemoglobin.

Under ordinary resting conditions the base equivalent of O_2 for O_2 saturated arterial blood Hb is approximately 0.7, the same value as given by Hastings, Van Slyke *et al.* (1924). It implies that with a R.Q. of 0.7 no difference in *p*H could be detected between arterial and venous blood.

In Fig. 7, the approximate arterial and venous points are indicated. It appears from this diagram that the first molecules of O_2, which are being taken up along the course of the lung capillaries by venous blood, increase the acidity very little—only about 0.5 acid equivalents. Only at the end of the oxygenation process does the uptake of oxygen result in greater acidic changes.

The venous blood entering the pulmonary capillary vessels, the characteristics of which are defined by point v on the diagram of Fig. 7, first loses CO_2, as the diffusion of this gas takes place at a very rapid rate. Only later is the Hb oxygenated, the diffusion of O_2 taking place at a much slower rate.

Loss of CO_2 by the blood causes a shift from point v to a lower value on the diagram, toward the broken line representing the acidic properties of Hb without $HCO_3^-CO_2$; a contribution to a shift in the same direction is given also by the higher alkalinity of the blood due to the CO_2 loss, as can be seen by comparing corresponding curves at different pH values. Only later in the length of the pulmonary capillary, when O_2 is admitted to the Hb molecule, will there be a shift to the right along the curves of the base-binding effect of O_2. The pH of the medium is thus restored toward the original value, the bigger change taking place mainly by the end of the oxygenation process. A reverse mechanism takes place in the tissues.

The process shows a somewhat different behavior if the venous blood coming to the lungs is very much reduced and rich in CO_2. In this last case the beginning of oxygenation of Hb may imply a strong acidification corresponding to the absorption of 1 to 2 moles of CO_2 per mole of O_2 absorbed. This would immediately compensate for the high alkalinization due to the CO_2 loss; only later, toward the 60% oxygenation, would the acidification go to a lower pace, to increase again towards 90–100% oxygenation.

The conditions illustrated in Fig. 7 for the path followed by blood during its passage in the lung or in the tissue capillaries has no strict quantitative meaning; the curves drawn for CO_2-free Hb solutions or for Hb solutions in which CO_2^- $NaHCO_3$ is the only electrolyte are extremes that are not met in living conditions. In this last case pCO_2 shows little change from venous to arterial blood, and the changes of pH are appreciable only in conditions of very strenuous anaerobic work. For all curves, nevertheless, the $dB/d[HbO_2]$ value is about 0.3 higher, near complete oxygenation, than at 50% HbO_2 saturation.

These changes in the acidic properties of Hb during its oxygenation process along the course of the lung or tissue capillary may not have an important physiologic effect. What is certainly important is the over-all change in acidity of Hb from venous to arterial blood, for this property influences the uptake of CO_2 at the tissue level, or the liberation of CO_2 at the lung level.

The average value of the acidic effect of oxygenation of Hb may not be necessarily constant at 0.7, its normal resting value, but may change appreciably, not so much as an effect of a change of pH or of the CO_2 content of the blood, but mainly of the average oxygenation of blood Hb (Margaria, 1957).

From Figure 7 it appears clear that:

(1) Breathing CO_2, or respiratory acidosis, tends to increase this value because it involves both an increase of CO_2 and a decrease of the pH of the blood.

(2) Anoxia tends to decrease this value because of the involved acapnia and

consequent alkalosis. If, however, the anoxia is very pronounced, and leads to very low average O_2 saturation of the blood, which factor tends to increase such a value, the actual value will be a compromise between the two factors involved.

(3) Strenuous muscular exercise will tend to increase the acidic effect of oxygenation of Hb, for the changes in CO_2 content, pH of the blood, and HbO_2 saturation act in the same direction. In this case the average value of $dB/dHbO_2$ may well approach 0.9 or 1.0

SUMMARY

1. Hb may bind CO_2 with two different mechanisms, making a carbamino compound at $pH > 7$, and a chemically different compound at $pH < 7.5$.

2. Both forms of CO_2Hb retain the Bohr effect.

3. The amounts of carbamino and noncarbamino CO_2Hb in blood at rest and during exercise are given, and the part played by CO_2HB in the elimination of CO_2 by the lungs is described.

4. The Bohr effect, i.e., the increased acidic properties of Hb as a consequence of oxygenation, seems to be bound with the polymerization of the Hb molecule, as it is not shown by the chemically similar myoglobin. The same can be stated also for the capacity of binding CO_2.

5. The acidic change of the hemoglobin molecule due to oxygenation, $dB/dHbO_2$, is given for a pH range from 6 to 8.5 and for both Hb and CO_2Hb. This seems to change with the degree of oxygenation.

6. A description of the acidic properties of hemoglobin in conditions of anoxia, CO_2 breathing, acapnia, muscular exercise, and acidosis is given.

REFERENCES

Barcroft, J. 1925. *The Respiratory Function of the Blood*, Part I, "Lessons from high altitudes," Cambridge University Press, London.

Bohr, C. 1909. *In:* Nagel, Handbuch. d. Physiol. *I:* 54.

Brinkman, R., and R. Margaria. 1931. J. Physiol. (Brit.) 72: 6.

Brinkman, R., R. Margaria, N. H. Meldrum, and F. J. W. Roughton. 1932. J. Physiol. (Brit.) 75: Proc. 3.

Cohn, E. Y., A. A. Green, and M. H. Blanchard. 1937. J. Am. Chem. Soc. 33: 780.

Faurholt, C. 1925. J. Chim. Physiol. 22: 1.

Ferguson, J. K. W. 1936. J. Physiol. 88: 40.

Ferguson, J. K. W., and F. J. W. Roughton. 1935. J. Physiol. (Brit.) 80: 143.

German, B., and J. Wyman. 1937. J. Biol. Chem. 117: 533.

Giustina, G. 1955. Arch. Fisiol. Suppl. 95.

Giustina, G., E. Milla, and R. Margaria. 1952. Giorn. Biochim. I: 475.

Giustina, G., E. Milla, and R. Margaria. 1953. Giorn. Biochim. II: 357.

Giustina, G., O. Temelcou, F. De Fusco, and R. Margaria. 1954. Giorn. Biochim. Italo-Franco-Elvetiche, Napoli.

Haldane, J. S. 1927. *Respiration*, Yale University Press, New Haven, Connecticut.

Hastings, A. B., D. D. Van Slyke, G. M. O'Neill, M. Heidelberger, and C. R. Harrington. 1924. J. Biol. Chem. *60:* 89.

Hastings, A. B., and J. Sendroy, Jr. 1925. J. Biol. Chem. *65:* 445.

Hastings, A. B., J. Sendroy, Jr., C. D. Murray, and M. Heidelberger. 1925. J. Biol. Chem. *61:* 317.

Henderson, L. J. 1928. *Blood,* Yale University Press, New Haven.

Henriques, O. M. 1928. Biochem. Z. *200:* 1, 5, 10, 18, 22.

Margaria, R. 1931. J. Physiol. (Brit.) *72:* Proc. 7.

Margaria, R. 1952. Schweiz. Med. Woch. *82:* 990.

Margaria, R., and E. Milla. 1955. Boll. Soc. Biol. Sper. *31:* 1250.

Margaria, R. 1957. Clin. Chem. *3:* 306.

Margaria, R., P. Rowinski, and S. Goldberger. 1933. Arch. Sci. Biol. *18:* 481.

Milla, E., G. Giustina, and R. Margaria. 1953. Giorn. Biochim. *II:* 153, 434.

Milla, E., and R. Margaria. 1954. Boll. Soc. It. Biol. Sper. *30:* 475.

Roughton, F. J. W. 1935. Physiol. Rev. *15:* 241.

Sidwell, A. E., R. H. Munch, E. S. G. Barron, and T. R. Hongney. 1938. J. Biol. Chem. *123:* 335.

Siegfried, M. e coll. 1909. Z. Physiol. Chem. *59:* 376.

Stadie, W. C., and E. R. Hawes. 1928. J. Biol. Chem. *77:* 265.

Van Slyke, D. D., Wu, and E. C. McLean. 1923. J. Biol. Chem. *56:* 765.

Van Slyke, D. D., A. B. Hastings, C. Murray, and J. Sendroy, Jr. 1925. J. Biol. Chem. *65:* 701.

Van Slyke, D. D., and J. Peters. 1946. *Quantitative Clinical Chemistry,* Vol. I, Williams and Wilkins Co., Baltimore.

Effects of Acute and Chronic Atmospheric Changes on Chemogenic and Centrogenic Drives: Chemoreflexogenic and Centrogenic Ventilatory Drives

PIERRE DEJOURS

Faculté de Médecine, Paris, France

Our knowledge of chemoreflexogenic and centrogenic ventilatory drives comes essentially from studies on animals and can be summarized thus. The ventilatory stimuli of the arterial blood can increase ventilation through two mechanisms: (1) the centrogenic mechanism (also called central), by direct action upon the respiratory centers, whatever the true local mechanism may be (action of the blood on the cells of the respiratory center, or through the cerebrospinal fluid) (Loeschcke *et al.*, 1958; Winterstein, 1955); (2) the chemoreflexogenic mechanism (also called chemoreflex, glomerogenic, or chemogenic), by indirect action through the chemoreceptors of the carotid and aortic bodies, the afferent fibers of the ninth and tenth pairs of nerves conducting messages to the respiratory center. Whatever the agent stimulating the chemoreceptors, local formation of acetylcholine (Liljestrand, 1954) or a local change of pH (Winterstein, 1955) would be involved in the initiation of the afferent impulse.

That decrease of arterial P_{O_2} and increase of arterial P_{CO_2} and $[H^+]$ can stimulate the chemoreceptors was proved directly, since action potentials of the chemoreceptor fibers were found to be increased under such chemical stimulation. Hypoxia increases ventilation only through chemoreceptor stimulation; after destruction of the chemoreceptors, acute hypoxia does not provoke any hyperventilation, but rather depresses ventilation. Hypercapnia and acidosis still increase ventilation after interruption of the chemoreceptor mechanism; thus, these factors can act directly on the respiratory center. (Heymans and Neil, 1958; Schmidt, 1956.)

291

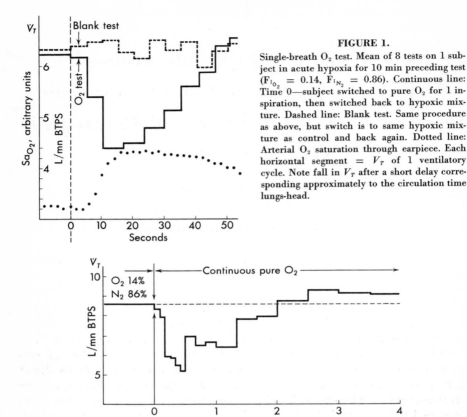

FIGURE 1.

Single-breath O_2 test. Mean of 8 tests on 1 subject in acute hypoxia for 10 min preceding test ($F_{I_{O_2}} = 0.14$, $F_{I_{N_2}} = 0.86$). Continuous line: Time 0—subject switched to pure O_2 for 1 inspiration, then switched back to hypoxic mixture. Dashed line: Blank test. Same procedure as above, but switch is to same hypoxic mixture as control and back again. Dotted line: Arterial O_2 saturation through earpiece. Each horizontal segment = V_T of 1 ventilatory cycle. Note fall in V_T after a short delay corresponding approximately to the circulation time lungs-head.

FIGURE 2.

Continuous O_2 test. Mean of 6 tests on 1 subject in acute hypoxia as in Fig. 1. At time 0: subject switched to pure O_2. From 0–30 sec: V_T measured on each ventilatory cycle. After 30 sec: V_T measured over several cycles. Just on the basis of the observation that there is no hypoventilation after the 3rd minute, it would be tempting to conclude in the absence of an O_2 stimulus when breathing a hypoxic mixture. However, as this figure shows, there is a transitory but considerable drop in V_T starting shortly after time 0. The breathing of pure O_2 has partially abolished a ventilatory O_2 stimulus. The subsequent hyperventilation is a complex phenomenon due to the appearance of secondary factors. (From Dejours *et al.*, 1958)

At sea level, what is the relative role played by the chemoreceptor mechanism and the central mechanism as far as a CO_2 stimulus is concerned? The opinions are conflicting. According to Heymans and Neil, 1958, the CO_2 drive is at least in part of chemoreceptor origin, the main reason in favor of this view being the fact that, in normocapnia, chemoreceptor action potentials are initiated. Schmidt (1956), on the other hand, considers that in normoxia and normocapnia there is no chemoreflexogenic stimulation of ventilation, but when severe hypoxia or hypercapnia are present, the chemoreflex drive becomes powerful. According to this view, the chemoreflexogenic mechanism would be involved only in cases of "emergency."

Since the general features of anatomical organization and functional responses are about the same in humans and in experimental animals, it is assumed that in human beings the part played by the chemoreflexogenic and centrogenic drives is the same as that in animals; there is, however, no definite proof that this is so. In effect, of the methods used on animals, (1) destruction of the chemoreceptors, (2) vascular isolation of the chemoreceptors permitting an independent variation of the composition of the blood flowing by them, (3) recording of action potentials of chemoreceptor fibers, none can be commonly applied to human beings.

If a ventilatory O_2 drive does exist in humans in a given condition, how can it be demonstrated? The inhalation of a high-O_2 mixture will suppress it, and it is expected that ventilation would decrease. In practice, most physiologists have studied the expected change of ventilation following a certain period, say a few minutes, of the inhalation of a high-O_2 mixture. This method is inadequate as far as studying an O_2 drive is concerned. A prolonged O_2 inhalation not only suppresses the O_2 drive, but can and does provoke changes in many other factors which also act on ventilation; for instance, decrease of arterial pH due to an increase of HbO_2, change of alveolar and arterial P_{CO_2} related to a variation in alveolar ventilation, increase of P_{CO_2} and $[H^+]$ in the respiratory center, through the Gesell effect and through the decrease of cerebral blood flow, and changes of metabolites carried by the blood due to variations in the conditions of cellular oxidations. For these reasons, the observed change in ventilation represents one component of a change in the oxygenation of the whole body, and therefore it cannot be interpreted simply in terms of oxygen drive. Thus, a decrease in ventilation observed during prolonged O_2 breathing does not demonstrate formally the disappearance of an O_2 drive which existed prior to the O_2 inhalation.

However, it is possible to obtain a change in the O_2 drive almost free of secondary reactions. If in a given condition there is a chemoreflex O_2 drive, the inhalation of a high-O_2 mixture increases $P_{A_{O_2}}$ at the first breath; after a few seconds, the blood with higher P_{O_2} flowing from the lungs perfuses the chemoreceptor bodies, the activity of which must then decrease. Just at this time, a decrease in ventilation must be observed. With such a method, all the secondary factors described above, except one, are avoided, because they are secondary in time. Only the change of pH of the blood related to a change of the Hb/HbO_2 ratio cannot be avoided. The inhalation of O_2 can be restricted to one single breath, or can be prolonged for any length of time; the first technique is referred to as the "single-breath O_2 test" (Fig. 1), the second as the "continuous O_2 test" (Fig. 2) (Dejours et al., 1958).

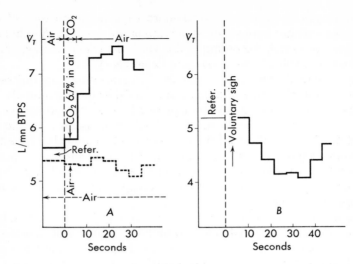

FIGURE 3.

CO_2 tests. *A. Single-breath CO_2 test.* Mean of 7 tests at sea level, at rest, breathing ambient air. Continuous line: 0 sec. subject switched to CO_2 6.7% in air for 1 inspiration (arrow), then back to ambient air. $P_{A_{CO_2}}$ rises by 3 to 4 mm Hg, thus remaining within transitory physiological limits. Note rise in V_T following the sudden rise in $P_{A_{CO_2}}$. Dashed line: Blank test. Same procedure, but subject switched to ambient air and back. *B. Single deep breath test.* Mean of 20 tests, same conditions as above. 0 sec. subject takes 1 deep breath of CO_2-free gas; $P_{A_{CO_2}}$ drops by 10 mm Hg; $P_{A_{O_2}}$ is kept constant by appropriate adjustment of $F_{I_{O_2}}$. A few seconds later, V_T goes down. (From Dajours *et al.*, 1958a)

The same line of reasoning can be held and the same type of method developed for the study of the CO_2 drive (Dejours *et al.*, 1958a). In fact, the increase of ventilation observed when breathing a mixture containing several per cent of CO_2 does not prove that a CO_2 stimulus controls ventilation in normocapnia when breathing air; it shows only that hypercapnia provokes hyperventilation. In turn, the ratio of change of ventilation over change of $P_{A_{CO_2}}$ does not measure with certainty the ventilatory CO_2 sensitivity at the level of normocapnia. Methods have been developed which permit the study of the CO_2 drive in a qualitative, and with some difficulty a quantitative manner (Fig. 3).

These methodological difficulties and the restriction of the techniques available for the study of ventilatory regulation in humans explain why our knowledge about the CO_2 and O_2 drives is relatively incomplete.

At sea level (Dejours *et al.*, 1958), breathing normal air, at rest and during muscular exercise, it was shown using the O_2 test that an O_2 drive does exist. Although the O_2 test is not an adequate quantitative measure of the O_2 drive, it is probable that at sea level and breathing normal air this drive controls only a small part of ventilation. That there is no O_2 drive when $P_{A_{O_2}}$ is 170 mm Hg shows that the threshold for this drive lies somewhere between 170 and 100 mm Hg for $P_{A_{O_2}}$.

In acute hypoxia, the balance between the O_2 drive and the CO_2–H drive is changed. Bjurstedt (1946), using the technique of cold block of the afferent chemoreceptor fibers, showed on dogs that during an acute hypoxia the O_2 chemoreflex drive is increased and that the centrogenic drive, related to arterial P_{CO_2} and pH, is decreased; under conditions of extreme acute hypoxia, the ventilation is entirely under the control of the chemoreflex stimulus. Rahn and Otis (1949) extended this concept to include human beings, and the concept was partially demonstrated by means of the O_2 test mentioned above (Dejours *et al.*, 1958) (Figs. 1 and 2). Even though in a mild hypoxia ($P_{A_{O_2}}$ greater than 60 mm Hg) the O_2 drive is increased, ventilation and $P_{A_{CO_2}}$ remain unchanged because of a decrease in the other stimulus, probably a rise in pH related to a drop in the amount of relatively acid HbO_2 (Rahn and Otis, 1949).

In chronic hypoxia, opinions concerning ventilatory control are conflicting. According to Bjurstedt (1946) and Rahn and Otis (1949), after the first period of hypoxia, during which the O_2 drive is increased, the progressive compensation through a renal mechanism of the initial alkalosis results, after completion of the acclimatization, in a state in which the O_2 drive is small, but the CO_2 drive "supernormal" because of an increased CO_2 sensitivity of the centers. At this time, ventilation is increased above the value observed at the beginning of the hypoxic condition. This concept is schematically illustrated in the middle of Fig. 5. Other workers (Åstrand, 1954; Kellogg *et al.*, 1957) have, however, concluded that an oxygen stimulus persists throughout the whole period spent at altitude.

The question of ventilatory control in short-term altitude-acclimatized subjects was reinvestigated using the O_2 test method (Dejours *et al.*, 1957). It appears that in such subjects there exists a powerful ventilatory O_2 stimulus (Fig. 4) which does not show any trend toward diminution over a period of more than two weeks. This observation is taken into account in the provisional scheme of the evolution of the balance between the O_2 and other stimuli in altitude, as illustrated at the bottom of Fig. 5. The "central drives" in this figure

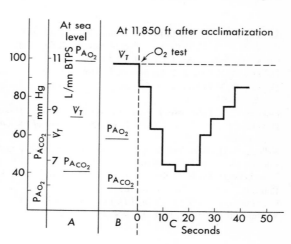

FIGURE 4.
Single-Breath O_2 tests in chronic hypoxia. Three subjects at rest. A: Mean $P_{A_{O_2}}$, V_T, $P_{A_{CO_2}}$ at sea level. B: Mean $P_{A_{O_2}}$, V_T, $P_{A_{CO_2}}$, 6 to 19th days at 11,850 ft (480 mm Hg). C: Mean of 90 single-breath O_2 tests; procedure and measurement as in Fig. 1. The increase in $P_{A_{O_2}}$ provokes, after a short delay, an important fall in V_T. (From Dejours *et al.*, 1957)

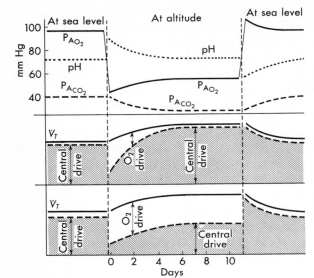

FIGURE 5.

Top: Changes of arterial pH, P_{AO_2}, and P_{ACO_2} during altitude acclimatization and following return to sea level, as classically described. Bottom: schematic representation of concepts concerning ventilatory drives in chronic hypoxia. Above: concept of a *transitory* O_2 drive followed by a supernormal "non-O_2 drive." Below: concept of a *permanent* and important O_2 drive concurrent with an undefined "non-O_2 drive."

can be more prudently defined as "drives other than the O_2 drive," and they would include the CO_2–H^+ drive whose existence and magnitude must be investigated using appropriate methods. The ventilatory characteristics of long-term residents in high altitudes may differ from those of short-term altitude-acclimatized subjects (Chiodi, 1957); it must therefore be pointed out that the balance between the O_2 drive and the non-O_2 drive in the two groups of subjects is not necessarily the same.

REFERENCES

Åstrand, P. O. 1954. Acta Physiol. Scand. *30:* 335–42, 343–68.
Bjurstedt, H. A. G. 1946. Acta Physiol. Scand. *12:* Suppl. 38.
Chiodi, H. 1957. J. Appl. Physiol. *10:* 81–7.
Dejours, P., F. Girard, Y. Labrousse, R. Molimard, and A. Teillac. 1957. Compt. rend. *245:* 2534–6.
Dejours, P., Y. Labrousse, J. Raynaud, F. Girard, and A. Teillac. 1958. Rev. Fran. Etud. Clin. Biol. *3:* 105–23.
Dejours, P., Y. Labrousse, J. Raynaud, and R. Flandrois. 1958a. J. Physiol. Paris. *50:* 239–43.
Heymans, C., and E. Neil. 1958. *Reflexogenic Areas of the Cardiovascular System,* Churchill, Ltd., London.
Kellogg, R. H., B. E. Vaughan, and D. W. Bagder. 1957. Fed. Proc. *16:* 70–1.
Liljestrand, G. 1954. Pharmacol. Rev. *6:* 73–8.
Loeschcke, H. H., H. P. Koepchen, and K. H. Gertz. 1958. Pflüg. Arch. *266:* 569–85.
Rahn, H., and A. B. Otis. 1949. Am. J. Physiol. *157:* 445–62.
Schmidt, C. F. 1956. *In: Medical Physiology,* 364–79. P. Bard, ed., C. V. Mosby Co., St. Louis.
Winterstein, H. 1955. Ergeb. Physiol. *48:* 328–528.

The Gas Stores of the Body, with Particular Reference to Carbon Dioxide

HERMANN RAHN

Department of Physiology, University of Buffalo, New York

All the gases which one finds in the tissues of the whole human body, whether in physical solution or chemically bound, constitute the gas stores of the body. Thus we carry so many liters of O_2, CO_2, and N_2 in all of our tissues at any time and under special circumstances these can either increase or decrease independently of each other. The factors which affect these gas stores have been discussed in detail elsewhere (Farhi and Rahn, 1955). For the problem of confined spaces the change in the inspired gas composition and consequently the changes in the alveolar gas concentration are probably the most important factors. At the alveolar level the arterial blood gas tensions are determined, which in turn equilibrate with the tissues.

There are two problems of general interest, namely, how large is the store for a particular gas, and at what rate will it increase or decrease. The N_2 store and O_2 store are fairly well established by measurement and calculation. It is surprising, on the other hand, how little we know about the magnitude and behavior of the CO_2 store, particularly since it is rather large and CO_2 is easily measured.

Before we consider the complexities of the CO_2 stores let us briefly survey the magnitude of all the gas stores in the human body. These are shown in Fig. 1 and have been calculated for a 70 kg man. The total amount of N_2 in the tissues is approximately 1 liter. The absolute magnitude and its depletion upon breathing oxygen are now well established (Jones, 1951). The oxygen store is of similar size and resides principally in the blood. Its change can be readily calculated with the help of the oxygen dissociation curve for hemoglobin. The CO_2 store, by comparison, is enormous. Even when we neglect the bone with its 110-liter capacity, we still have 20 liters in the soft tissues. Furthermore, we find in contrast to the O_2 stores, that most of the soft tissue CO_2 lies not in the blood but in the other tissues, particularly the muscles.

297

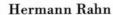

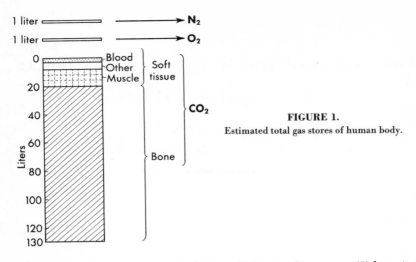

FIGURE 1.
Estimated total gas stores of human body.

The particular problems which I would like to discuss are (1) how is the CO_2 distributed within the body; (2) how will it vary with changes in CO_2 tension; and (3) how good is man as a CO_2 absorber when confined to a small space.

THE DISTRIBUTION OF CO_2

Almost all of our detailed information concerning the CO_2 content of various tissues and their CO_2 dissociation curves is based upon experiments of Freeman and Fenn (1953), and Thompson and Brown. The recent studies of Nichols (1958) could not be incorporated at this time but furnish excellent additional data. I have assumed that the tissues of man and rat are similar in their content and capacity changes and have tried in Fig. 2 to establish the over-all behavior of CO_2 in various tissues of man. I should like to point out that even in the rat our information is fragmentary and that many of the values indicated in Fig. 2 are "guesstimates." The least it can do is to furnish us with a basis for discussion.

In column 2 we have an indication of the normal CO_2 content of the tissues. The various soft tissues are quite similar in content but bone has 3 to 4 times as much CO_2. By allowing for the weight of the organs we have in column 3 the total store in each organ. This information was used to construct Fig. 1.

THE CO_2 STORAGE CAPACITY OF TISSUES

More difficult to answer is the question of how much CO_2 each tissue is able to store as the CO_2 tensions change. Column 4 expresses the CO_2 dissociation curve slope above 40 mm P_{CO_2} and is based upon fully equilibriated ani-

	1	2	3	4	5	6	7
				CO$_2$			
		Weight	Content at 40 mm	Total at 40 mm (column 1x2)	Dissoc. slope above 40 mm	Total/mm (column 1x4)	Production	Blood flow
Organ	Kg	L/Kg	L	cc/Kg/mm	cc/mm	cc/min	cc/min/Kg
Heart	0.3	0.42	0.13	2.4	0.7	26	660
Brain	1.5	0.34	0.5	2.9	4.3	68	560
Blood	6.0	0.48	2.9	4.5	27.0	–	–
"Other"	13.2	0.34	4.5	3.0	40.0	50	170*
Muscle	40.0	0.30	12.0	4.2	168.0	40	25
Bone	9.2	12.00	110.0	30.0	275.0	26	55
TOTAL or mean/ 70 Kg man	70.0	1.86	130.0	7.4	515.0	210	86

*If blood flow to kidney is omitted

FIGURE 2.

"Estimation" of various CO$_2$ functions in a resting 70 kg man. Columns 2 and 4 have been adapted from the rat tissue data of Freeman and Fenn (1953) and Thompson and Brown. The blood values are derived from standard dissociation curves of man. Columns 1, 6, and 7 have been taken and modified from the data of Rahn and Fenn (1955).

mal tissues. We notice that blood and muscle appear to store considerably more of this gas than the other soft tissues. The bony tissue will not be considered henceforth since it does not respond readily to changes in blood CO$_2$ (Freeman and Fenn, 1953) or may actually be dependent on other factors as far as its CO$_2$ content is concerned (Nichols, 1958). In column 5 we have finally an expression of the total amount of CO$_2$ which all the organs will absorb for each mm change in P_{CO_2}. Excluding the bone we would, therefore, expect to accommodate 240 cc of CO$_2$/70 kg man/mm CO$_2$ or the slope of man's body dissociation curve would be equal to 3.4 cc CO$_2$/kg/mm. These figures are all based upon the analysis of individual tissues (Freeman and Fenn, 1953; Thomp-

	Equilibration Time	Slope of dissoc. Curve cc CO$_2$/kg/mm	Reference
Man	1–5 min	.46	Mithoefer (5)
	3–8 min	.40	Klocke and Rahn (1958)
Dogs	30–45 min	1.5	Farhi and Rahn (1955)
Cats	30–90 min	1.6	Shaw (1928)
Rats	1–4 wk.	6.5	Freeman and Fenn (1953)

FIGURE 3

Equilibrating compartment	Blood flow cc/kg/min	Organ	CO_2 capacity cc/mm
Fast	> 500	Kidney, heart, and brain	6 ⎱
		Blood	27 ⎰ 34
Intermediate	170	"Other tissues"	40
Slow	25	Muscle	168

FIGURE 4

son and Brown). How do these compare with studies of CO_2 equilibration made on whole man or animals?

WHOLE BODY STORAGE CAPACITY

In Fig. 3 a few data are given for the observed storage capacity and equilibration time when animals or men were subjected to higher than normal CO_2 tensions. These figures are to be compared with the value of 3.4 cc/kg/mm estimated above on the basis of fully equilibrated tissue where animals had been exposed for several hours or days. It is apparent that even in 1 hour of increased CO_2 tension exposure the total amount of CO_2 retained was far from the value predicted. The highest CO_2 storages reported so far in man are the data of Schaefer and Alvis (Schaefer and Alvis, 1951) where the values yield 2.1 cc/kg/mm after a 33-minute exposure. The 1–4 week equilibration of the rat includes the bone CO_2 and is therefore not comparable with the other data. The most striking differences between predicted and observed values are the breathholding data for man (Mithoefer; Klocke and Rahn, 1958). Although the CO_2 tensions rose rapidly only ⅛ the predicted amount of CO_2 accumulated for each mm change in arterial CO_2.

These observations suggest that CO_2 does not distribute itself equally as rapid among the various tissues and that we must think in terms of various body compartments each with its own rate of CO_2 accumulation which in turn depends upon the compartment perfusion rate. If we consult Fig. 4 we have a crude estimate of three compartments of the human body with their relative perfusion rate and absolute CO_2 storage capacity. We see that of the total 242 cc CO_2 which would accumulate for each mm change, 168 cc or 70% must go to the muscles which at rest represent the slowest equilibrating compartment. It is possible that this is the reason that the whole body experiments do not yield the expected values for CO_2 storage capacity since not enough time was allowed to fully equilibrate the muscle mass. The rate of CO_2 accumulation, therefore, would not be expected to yield a simple exponential curve as had previously been described (Fahri and Rahn, 1955). It is possible that under the conditions of these experiments (Fahri and Rahn, 1955) with anesthetized dogs only the filling of the more rapidly equilibrating compartments was seen and the slow compartments could not be differentiated during the 30–45 minute exposure. The recent observations of Nichols (1958) further suggest that more than 1 hour is needed to saturate the muscle tissues of rats.

THE CO_2 DISSOCIATION CURVE OF WHOLE MAN

In Fig. 5 an estimate of the CO_2 dissociation curve of the soft tissue for a 70 kg man is indicated. The heavy line (ABD) represents the best estimate of the dissociation of CO_2 (expressed in liters) when the equilibration is carried on for a period of 30–60 minutes. Line BD is based upon CO_2 breathing experiments of cat (Shaw, 1928), dog (Farhi and Rahn, 1955) and man (Schaefer and Alvis, 1951). Point A is based upon values reported by Lillehie and Balke (1955) who hyperventilated their subjects until they reached a state of tetany. They made the interesting observations that whenever 3.5 liters of stored CO_2 per square meter of body surface were lost, tetany resulted regardless of the time taken to reach this state. On the basis of their data we might say that in the average man a 6 liter loss of the CO_2 stores will bring on tetany. If we assume, furthermore, that at a P_{CO_2} of 70 mm narcosis sets in, we can estimate from the dissociation curve that this state is reached when 3 liters of CO_2 have been added to the store. Thus man is able to perform with soft tissue CO_2 stores ranging from 14 to 23 liters of CO_2. This means that he can

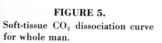

FIGURE 5.
Soft-tissue CO_2 dissociation curve for whole man.

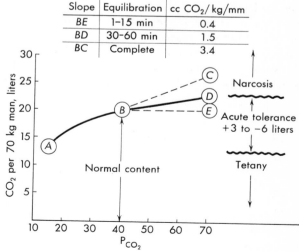

Slope	Equilibration	cc CO_2/ kg/mm
BE	1–15 min	0.4
BD	30–60 min	1.5
BC	Complete	3.4

afford to lose twice as much CO_2 as he can afford to gain before becoming incapacitated.

Line BE indicates the amount of CO_2 retained during acute breathholding experiments (Mithoefer; Klocke and Rahn, 1958), while line BC indicates the retention if we have perfect equilibration predicted from the values in Fig. 2.

MAN CONFINED TO SPACE

When man is confined to space, such as a submarine or a space vehicle, the problem of CO_2 contamination can become a very real problem (Schaefer, 1951). However man is not only a source of this contamination but will also act as a CO_2 absorber at the same time. In comparatively large confined spaces man as a CO_2 absorber is not important and the predicted changes in the atmosphere with time have been calculated (Rahn and Fenn, 1955). In small confined spaces, on the other hand, the presence of man can have a considerable influence upon the rate of CO_2 accumulation.

The question is then how good is man as an absorber of CO_2? If all the metabolically produced CO_2 is not exhaled but is partially stored in the tissues, then it is obvious that the CO_2 concentration of the confined space will rise more slowly. Figure 6 shows the rate of CO_2 rise when man is confined to very small spaces from 10 to 80 liters. These data were supplied through the courtesy of Dr. J. C. Mithoefer. After a forced expiration the subject was connected to a gas bag and then breathed at constant tidal volumes (3.83 l) at a rate of 18/minute until the continuously monitored alveolar CO_2 reached values of 55 mm. This procedure kept the gas volume well mixed and the work of breathing constant.

It will be seen that after the initial periods of acapnia these observations yield linear relationships of CO_2 with time while the slope is a function of the confined space volume. If we now extrapolate these lines to a P_{CO_2} of 60 and plot the time it takes to reach this value against the volume of the space (rebreathing volume) we have the relationship as shown in Fig. 7. The slope of this line is of some practical interest since it tells us that under the conditions of this experiment for every 3 liters of volume added it will take the subject 1 minute

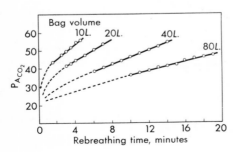

FIGURE 6.

Alveolar CO_2 during rebreathing O_2 into a bag of varying volume. The ventilation was maintained at a rate of 18/min L and a tidal volume of 3.83 liters throughout the experiment. Rebreathing was started after a complete expiration. The initial total gas volume was, therefore, the residual volume plus the bag volume indicated. (Data supplied by Dr. J. C. Mithoefer)

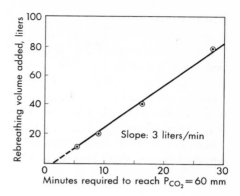

FIGURE 7.

Relationship of rebreathing time and rebreathing volume calculated from Fig. 6. The slope of this line indicates that each additional 3 liters added to the rebreathing volume will extend the time by 1 minute.

longer to reach a P_{CO_2} of 60. If we accept arbitrarily 60 mm P_{CO_2} as a narcosis level we can predict how long man will retain consciousness when confined to small spaces provided he does not alter his metabolic rate. Every additional 3 liters of space will extend his time 1 minute and a 1 cubic meter volume will allow him to remain conscious 1000/3 or 333 minutes.

The rate of change of CO_2 in Fig. 6 is a function of the CO_2 production, the rebreathing volume, and the over-all CO_2 storage capacity of the body. The metabolically produced CO_2 must distribute itself between the tissues and the external gas volume. Thus V_{CO_2} = (gas volume × F_{CO_2}) + (70 kg × 0.4 cc/kg/mm × P_{CO_2}).

If the rebreathing gas volume is 20 liters and after 9 minutes the F_{CO_2} is 60/B-47 or 8.4% and the change in alveolar CO_2 rises from 40–60 mm, then

$$V_{CO_2} = (20,000 \times 0.084) + (70 \times 0.4 \times 20)$$
$$= 1680 + 560 = 2240 \text{ cc or } 250 \text{ cc/minute.}$$

It can be seen that 560/2240 or 25% of the metabolically produced CO_2 was retained in the body. Had this not occurred the CO_2 fraction in the bag would have been 2240/20,000 or 11.1% instead of 8.4 at the end of 9 minutes.

MAN'S "EQUIVALENT VOLUME FOR CO_2"

In Fig. 5 we expressed the CO_2 storage capacity of man above 40 mm P_{CO_2} by 3 different slopes each depending upon the equilibration time (given in the table above the figure). For example, in short equilibration periods we have a value of 0.4 cc/kg/mm or 28 cc/average man/mm. This can be compared with the amount of CO_2 added to 1 liter of air which will just change the P_{CO_2} by 1 mm. This value is 1.4 cc/liter/mm. Thus 28/1.4 or 20 liters of air volume will store the same amount of CO_2 as a 70 kg man for a 1 mm P_{CO_2} rise in each compartment. Thus 20 liters is man's "equivalent volume for CO_2" when the equilibration time is short. When the equilibration time is 30–60 minutes, then the "equivalent volume" becomes 75 liters and presumably for longer equilibration periods will reach values of 170 liters.

It should be pointed out in passing that for situations where the CO_2 accumulates in a confined gas volume the rate of change of P_{CO_2} in this volume is much greater than the rate of change in the alveolar or tissue space. In the example given above, for instance, the CO_2 rose from 0 to nearly 60 mm in the confined space but only from 40 to 60 mm in the man. It is for this reason that a man whose "equivalent volume for CO_2" is 20 liters when confined to a breathing volume of 20 liters will not share his metabolic CO_2 production equally between these two compartments.

ADDENDUM

An understanding of CO_2 storage and equilibration requires recognition of how CO_2 is distributed and stored within the body as the alveolar tensions are either lowered or increased. In a recent analysis the whole body of man has been described in terms of a multiple compartment system in which each compartment (organ) has its own capacitance (storage capacity) and resistance (inversely related to blood flow). An analog was programed using the specific values available for man. The computer results were found to duplicate existing physiological data and by varying parameters the most important factors in body CO_2 store equilibration were established. These are (1) time, (2) perfusion of muscle mass, and (3) alveolar ventilation. Time required for readjustment of stores always requires a duration of several hours. Details of the analysis will be found in L. E. Farhi and H. Rahn, "Dynamics of changes in CO_2 stores," Anesthesiology (in press).

REFERENCES

Farhi, L. E., and H. Rahn. 1955. J. Appl. Physiol. 7: 472.
Freeman, F. H., and W. O. Fenn. 1953. Am. J. Physiol. 174: 422.
Jones, H. B. 1951. In: Decompression Sickness, W. B. Saunders Co., Philadelphia.
Klocke, F. J., and H. Rahn. 1958. The Physiologist 1(4): 41.
Lillehie, J. P., and B. Balke. 1955. Report No. 55–62. USAF Sch. Aviation Med.
Mithoefer, J. C. Personal communication, Bassett Hospital, Cooperstown, New York
Nichols, G., Jr. 1958. J. Clin. Invest. 37: 1111.
Rahn, H., and W. O. Fenn. 1955. The O_2–CO_2 Diagram. Am. Physiol. Soc. Washington, D.C.
Schaefer, K. E., and H. J. Alvis 1951. Report No. 175, Med. Res. Lab. U.S. Navy 10: 76.
Schaefer, K. E. 1951. Report No. 181, Med. Res. Lab. U.S. Navy 10.
Shaw, L. A. 1928. Am. J. Physiol. 85: 158.
Thompson, A., and E. B. Brown, Jr. Report No. 58–11. USAF Sch. Aviation Med.

DISCUSSION

Dr. DuBois: Concerning these respiratory mechanics, it is true that I do not see any problems as far as the range of gas concentrations that have been discussed. On the other hand, we should emphasize the fact that in the full expiratory position there are a number of things about the lungs that are far from ideal. One is that the airways are small, and if the chest is cramped for some reason—by restricting garments or position—the smallness of the size of the airways is somewhat detrimental as to disturbances in the lungs reflecting blood flow. As Dr. Whittenberger pointed out, eventually you get some degree of impairment. I therefore think we should reemphasize that the lungs are not very efficient in their mechanical function at small volumes.

Dr. Verzar: I was very pleased to hear both Dr. Whittenberger and Dr. Forster emphasize the increase of lung volume during lack of oxygen, because I think this is an extremely important physiological reaction. This increase of lung volume means an increase of respiratory surface, because more or less closed—I would not say completely closed—alveoli are opened. If you measure the quantity of surface increase, you can make an experiment and you will find that the surface increases during hypoxia about 30% to 35%. Now, the velocity of oxygen exchange in the lung must be calculated with this surface increase. If the surface is a third larger, 3% more oxygen will diffuse—other conditions being equal. So I think these experiments which were shown to us are important to finally accept changes for which I have been responsible for some years and which nobody believed. Oxygen lack leads immediately to a compensatory increase of respiratory surface.

Dr. Whittenberger: I would like Dr. DuBois to discuss further the changes in the lung while breathing near its maximum expiratory position. I showed that the compliance of the dog's lung changes with recumbency. We assumed that the smaller alveoli were closed off completely. However, since the diffusion capacity has not changed significantly and since the amount of the difference in pressure between alveolar blood and oxygen with respect to oxygen has not changed, we assumed that the circulation also was closed off in these units, although we couldn't really explain it. I wonder to what extent alveoli are closed in man, and to what extent diffusion capacity changes in this condition.

Dr. DuBois: In the subjects with air trapping, the airway conductance did go to zero. We have been able to confirm your findings about this small volume effect on compliance in man by strapping the chest, thereby pushing the lungs down. It is very uncomfortable. Rubber bands placed around the chest constrict it and, after five or ten minutes, pain occurs in the chest muscles and there is dyspnea. Some of the subjects tend to faint. The compliance of the lungs diminishes to about a half or third, and there are these secondary changes. We had one subject who started with 1300 cc and went down to 700 cc, just from the effects of having been put in a cast, and got in severe difficulties during operation. These are the reasons I think that pushing the lungs down would be quite deleterious in its mechanical effects on the lungs.

Dr. Hesser: I would like to mention that we have made a few experiments during the last year, the results of which seem to confirm the prediction of Dr. Whittenberger that the increased air density may influence the ventilation not only during exercise but also during resting conditions.

Dr. Rahn: Dr. Bjurstedt has brought up the interesting problem of the increased lung volume surface area with low oxygen. I would like to ask Dr. Forster whether there is any evidence as to whether the diffusing capacity is concerned, because it would seem to me that in order to be beneficial the diffusing capacity or the capillary surface area should have to increase. Do you have any evidence along those lines?

Dr. Forster: This is a subject of considerable discussion at the moment. Marie Krogh originally determined that the pulmonary diffusing capacity was proportional to the lung volume above midcapacity, which would mean it would double—going from approximately midcapacity up to maximum. A few years ago, Dr. Fowler, Bates, and I found an increase which was only about 10%. Dr. Marshall found a range of an average of 15% or 16%. Dr. Gensler's group in Boston and Dr. Caddigan reported changes up to 30%, but I don't believe they have given the complete data yet, so that we would expect at least part of the way a decrease at very low volumes, when there is trapping with the closure of some of the alveoli. We would expect the increase at larger lung volumes; possibly at extremely large volumes it may well decrease again from pressures on the capillaries. If there is an increase, I would say it was probably less than 25% to 30% for doubling the volume.

Dr. Lambertsen: It seems that one of the biggest questions regarding the gaseous atmosphere within closed spaces is whether inert gas is necessary. I do not see another place in the program where this might be considered. A primary question is whether or not a sufficient degree of atelectasis occurs during oxygen breathing to make an inert gas necessary over prolonged periods if the oxygen tension is really low during pure oxygen breathing.

Dr. Rahn: I think it is a very good point to consider. I agree, particularly if the space capsule is going to be with a total pressure equivalent to 33,000 feet with 100% oxygen, which would be equivalent to PIO_2 of this room. In such a case any atelectasis or tendency to it would proceed with a rate four times faster than it would on the ground level.

Dr. Bjurstedt: I would like to speak about the possibility of using decreased pressure in the capsule for space flight and keeping the oxygen percentage at about 100%. This might cause atelectasis. On the other hand, I think that some Dutch physiologists have been looking into the possible reasons for atelectasis and trying to get rid of it by using low oxygen.

Captain Behnke: What is the best way to breathe? The most efficient ventilation is the normal breathing. By that I mean oxygen utilization per liter of air taken in. This came up during the war with reference to pressure breathing. I felt that we never did pressure breathing properly, that is in the field, because we did not train individuals to breathe to conserve the carbon dioxide. In pressure breathing one may breathe at a rate of four times a minute; this conserves carbon dioxide, and is the most efficient way. As to breathing air at 25,000 feet, we were very much concerned about the most efficient way to breathe: slowly, deeply, or rapidly and in a more shallow way. The idea that Dr. Whittenberger advanced of periodic inflation or deep breathing may certainly be important. It is necessary to train individuals to breathe in a different way, and is it not worthwhile to breathe in a different way from the standpoint of general body economy?

Dr. Verzar: I would like to return to the problem of inert gases because I think that is an extremely important problem from a practical point of view. In the case where you decrease pressure—atmospheric pressure—and try to increase the oxygen to a higher pressure, you come to an important problem: When does the oxygen increase become dangerous, not from a physiological point of view, but from a technical point of view, from the fire hazards?

Col. Simons: We measured the burning rate of strips of paper and cloth at normal atmospheres and then at higher altitudes; decreasing the pressure and keeping the partial pressure the same. The burning rate increased about twofold. In other words, it took only half as long for the strip to burn under 100% oxygen at 33,000 feet as it did at ground level with 20% oxygen. Thus, the nitrogen, the inert gas present, apparently does exert some inhibiting effects in gross burning.

We also got in contact with Dr. Pace and Dr. Cook of the University of California to study the effect of helium as an inert gas in terms of the metabolic rate in animals as compared to nitrogen. There seemed to be no significant differences except the fact that helium increased conductivity of heat and caused increased heat loss. Therefore, the animals metabolized more to maintain the body temperature under similar conditions. This is a pure heat loss factor and not one due to the chemical effects of the inert gas. Except for that, there did not seem to be any detectable difference between the nitrogen and the helium. There is apparently some difference in gross burning, but we do not suspect that this burning effect applied metabolically.

Dr. Miles: I think we should give some consideration to the yogic patterns of breathing. For example, using the common Ujjoyi pattern, which is one respiration per minute with a respiration volume of about 3 liters, about 12% increase of oxygen consumption is observed. Transition from this Ujjoyi pattern to normal breathing is very quick, with no evidence of oxygen debt.

Dr. Hastings: Every time that we think we have the blood, as a physical chemical system, adequately described, something turns up to show that we have still got some more work to do. I think that Dr. Margaria's paper points out again one of the things that has been with us for some time. You can find it in the literature—differences in the effect of oxygen on the amount of CO_2 released whether the experiments are done with whole blood or with hemoglobin solution. There is a difference. When Van Slyke and I and the rest of the group were doing these original experiments at the Rockefeller Institute, we had the unfortunate experience of being so immersed in the fact that the Donnan equilibrium must prevail and that the Debye-Hückel theory accounted for all equivalents of CO_2, that instead of discovering carbamino we said that the activity coefficient of the ions in the cells was different from that of the chloride ion. The moral of this is that this very observation provides still a third way to calculate what I would call the nonbicarbonate-bound CO_2 in red cells. That is if you know the pH of the blood, the chloride distribution between the plasma and the red cells, and the bicarbonate concentration in the plasma, then you must—again for thermodynamic reasons, but different ones—be able to calculate the true bicarbonate ion concentration in the cells. Dr. Margaria's Van Slyke determination has given a very much bigger figure than this. The difference between his Van Slyke determination on bicarbonate of the cells and what you can be quite sure was the true bicarbonate concentration in those cells is the bound CO_2 in the cells. This hemoglobin-bound CO_2 consists of carbamino CO_2 and some more CO_2 that is bound in some unknown way. On the acid side or close to the acid side of the isoelectric point of the hemoglobin, we may have some undissociated hemoglobin bicarbonate.

Dr. Nichols: Since Dr. Hastings has so potent a feeling about Dr. Margaria's paper, I want to ask him if he has done any studies of this type on some of the proteins from muscle. It seems to me that he has opened the door to a way of explaining the quandary we have all been in about deciding what state and in what form CO_2 may exist inside tissue cells. In my discussion, I made the assumption that all of it was as H_2CO_3 or as bicarbonate ions. I did this because I had no other basis to go on. On the other hand, Dr. Conway a number of years ago pointed out that there was CO_2 inside cells that was probably neither H_2CO_3 nor bicarbonate, and left us there. I wonder if you have done any studies of this type on myoglobin, and, if so, what results you had.

Chairman Margaria: I did some work on myoglobin, and it did not show any pH effect (Bohr) or any CO_2 effect. I think this is also very interesting because it seems to show that both pH and CO_2 are due to the polymerization of the hemoglobin as this is in the blood cells. The amino-acid composition of hemoglobin does not fully account for the effects; its polymerized state seems also indispensable to this end.

We also tried this pH and CO_2 effect on proteins other than Hb. Most proteins, such as casein, plasma, proteins, or muscle as a whole, do not bind any appreciable CO_2 at pH < 8. Some alkali proteins, such as salmine, make carbamino compounds at pH's ranging from 7.4 to as low as 6.5. Peculiar to hemoglobin is the binding of CO_2 at the acid pH with a mechanism, which is certainly not carbamino. All other alkaline proteins bind at the acid pH, but with carbamino mechanism.

Dr. Bjurstedt: In reference to Dr. Dejours' paper on the interaction of "hypoxic" and "centrogenic" drives to respiration at altitude, the main interest was focused on the relative importance of these drives as hyperventilation is established, in the acute phase of hypoxia, and as it is continued and somewhat increased during the process of acclimatization. Dr. Dejours' method to find out about the relative importance of the two drives is an interesting one, in that he compares the immediate effects of administration of 100% oxygen on the respiratory minute volume at different times during the process of acclimatization. One can look at this method as a kind of "functional" blocking of the hypoxic drive, which brings out that share of the total respiratory activity that is taken care of by nonchemoreflex structures, i.e., chemosensitive cells in the medullary centers. In my view this amounts to something similar to cold-blocking of all known chemoreflex mechanisms, a method that was used for anesthetized dogs in our laboratory some years ago.

Our results agree completely as far as the effects of blocking in the acute hypoxic phase are concerned. The hyperventilation is abolished, and blocking may actually cause a sudden apnea. This of course points to the predominant role of the hypoxic (or chemoreflex) drive for the maintenance of acute hypoxic hyperventilation.

Now, as to the relative importance of the hypoxic and the centrogenic drives after acclimatization, our results differ somewhat in that Dr. Dejours observed that functional blocking of the hypoxic drive still caused a considerable decrease in the respiratory activity. This was interpreted as showing that there was still a considerable hypoxic drive in the hyperventilation observed after chronic exposure to low oxygen. We could find only a small decrease in the respiratory activity as a result of cold-blocking the chemoreflex drive in anesthetized dogs after prolonged exposure to low oxygen. This difference in our results may be due to influence of the anesthesia or to species differences. I am convinced that there is still a chemoreflex drive in the acclimatized state. Quite a few years ago, I demonstrated that the chemoreflex drive diminishes again after having first been responsible for the entire respiratory activity in the acute stage of hypoxia. This is, however, just one aspect of the control of respiration during low oxygen.

The other side of the matter is related to the centrogenic drive during the process of acclimatization. We both agree that it is practically nonexistent in the acute phase of hypoxia. One might say, therefore, that in this stage respiration is no longer controlled by any need for carbon dioxide removal. We actually have a situation of respiratory alkalosis caused by overventilation of chemoreflex origin. As the process of acclimatization goes on, however, the alkalosis tends to become compensated so that tissue and blood pH values return toward normal again, at least in the resting condition. Cold-blocking of the chemoreflex drive, or functional blocking of the hypoxic drive, now shows —and here our results agree again—that a substantial part of the hyperventilation is of centrogenic origin. That is to say, respiration is again largely controlled by the need for carbon dioxide removal.

I believe that our observations confirm each other rather than show any fundamental difference. In summing up, our results from anesthetized dogs and mice and Dr. Dejours' from human subjects *at rest* point to a changing interrelationship between the hypoxic and the centrogenic drives as acclimatization to low oxygen proceeds. The hypoxic drive is all-important for the development of the hyperventilation, while the centrogenic drive does not contribute at all in the first stage of hypoxic hyperventilation. As acclimatization is approached or completed, the hyperventilation is again of centrogenic origin to a substantial extent; i.e., the need for carbon dioxide removal is again an important factor in the control of respiration.

Turning to Dr. Rahn's paper, I would like to ask whether it would be possible to increase the tolerance to confinement in a cube of one meter size by giving bicarbonate. Would that change the situation to any appreciable degree? Would the survival be longer?

Dr. Hastings: I doubt that enough buffer could be added to affect materially the amount of CO_2 that the body could take care of. Some years ago when we were working on fatigue, we predicted that by giving animals bicarbonate we could increase the length of time that they could run or swim until exhaustion set in, and that by giving ammonium chloride (creating metabolic acidosis) the time would be shortened. The experimental results were exactly the opposite.

Dr. Schaefer: During the war, Dr. Pointner in the laboratory at Carnac, France, gave subjects alkaline salts to increase their tolerance to CO_2. The effects were the following. The subjects exposed to CO_2 reached compensation of the respiratory acidosis faster, and they did not have the symptoms to such an extent in the beginning as other people had. It had a certain value, but it did not help these subjects permanently, because as soon as they had reached the compensatory respiratory acidosis, they remained in a condition in which their performance was still not up to the normal level. These findings indicate that the increased CO_2 tension, which cannot be compensated, plays a decisive role in producing effects during chronic CO_2 exposure.

Dr. Rahn: I was interested in the observations regarding the 350 mm range, or thereabouts, of the oxygen tension, indicating that oxygen tensions between 300 and 100 still seem to have an effect upon breathholding. I gather that, switching to the other problem of nitrogen, you have no evidence that nitrogen *per se* does affect the breathholding time. Is that correct? I want to be absolutely sure.

Dr. Hesser: That is correct, at the pressures that we have studied, but at higher nitrogen pressures it might have some effect. However, we cannot say anything about that now.

Capt. Alvis: I would like to ask Dr. Hesser if he saw any signs of disorientation of his subjects when the alveolar CO_2 was so high.

Dr. Hesser: We observed none up to a certain point, but it is rather difficult to say exactly where the breaking point comes. For that purpose we also mention the time for the onset of the first train of diaphragmatic contractions, and if you calculate that as the breaking point, we also find that the breaking point curve increases with the CO_2.

Dr. Stroud: I would just like to say that we have also done complete breaking point curves similar to those of Dr. Hesser, and found the same effect, i.e., that it flattened out at about 300 mm of oxygen. We found that we could interpret this curve better by assuming that this effect was a change in the sensitivity to carbon dioxide below 300 mm of oxygen, down to a point of approximately 100 mm, where the oxygen effect *per se* was controlling.

Capt. Alvis: I feel we would be somewhat remiss if we left this subject without calling attention to a very practical and very dangerous implication here.

We attempted to do some of these tests, using instructors at the submarine escape training tank. All these men were instructors at the tank or they were deep-sea divers. My choice of an end point was a rather rigid one, and I insisted that they hold to it or we would not count the experiment. I had exactly the same experience that Dr. Forster has had. My subjects quit on me. The reason they quit was that, at the end point I chose, some of them were disoriented, so disoriented that they could not do any fine movements, such as sticking valves in their mouths. This happened at atmospheric pressure, incidentally. We had a man on hand who had just arrived to begin his indoctrination as an instructor in the tank. He was an experienced deep sea diver. I heard from him recently. He is still engaged in deep sea diving. This man became so disoriented he could not find which end of the valve to stick in his mouth. Another one of the subjects lost control of his bladder, and at this point walked out on me. We finally ended up with my own corpsmen and myself being the series.

While I was engaged in this series, I ran across an obscure note in a psychiatric journal calling attention to one confirmed suicide as a result of breath-holding. I did not mention this to the subjects. I kept this note in my desk drawer, and asked the doctor to confirm it. I had his letter of confirmation before we completed our series. My research partner and chief hospital corpsman, a deep sea diver, and a very phlegmatic sort of person, held his breath until he frightened me. He turned gray. The perspiration stood out in large bubbles; he began to weave around. The other hospital corpsman who was watching us through the port and controlling the pressure of the chamber thought something had gone wrong. He thought I was influenced so much by narcosis of nitrogen that I was not aware of the situation and called for help.

When we were through, I asked the corpsman how he felt. He said, "Well, I felt pretty good, but I was worried about you." I had felt pretty good, but I was worried about him. The point I am making is a very practical one. We meet people who are taking up sport scuba diving and also those who dive with masks. They just *will* hold their breath. They just will go deeper, because it is such a fascinating sport, and they just will kill themselves. I know this because I receive the reports of diving casualties treated at Navy installations.

Comdr. G. F. Bond: I, too, was involved in a breathholding experiment recently, along with my divers at the tank. We noted one thing. In the experienced divers at the tank the question of motivation seemed to be something which we could not pinpoint.

I have personally observed three of my boys, holding their breath in excess of four minutes coming out of a bell at 25 feet, which is less than one extra atmosphere. I noted with some alarm that, when they were faced with the breathholding procedure which Dr. Stroud conducted in the laboratory under other circumstances, without any urgency and with no water around, they held their breath less than three minutes. They had been breathing 100% oxygen. I challenged them about this on several occasions and I got varying responses, but the sum total response was "We had no essential motivation for doing this, other than we were told to do it as long as we could. Sure, when somebody is out in the water in trouble, I'll work until I drop." Some of them have been known to lose consciousness working with a struggling man in the water. These men simply would not exert themselves when sitting on a lab stool in a friendly atmosphere.

PART FIVE

The Effect of Specific Environmental Conditions on Respiratory Functions

Chairman

DR. RODOLFO MARGARIA

Physiological Institute, University of Milan
Milan, Italy

Recent Studies of Helium Exchange in Diving

GERALD J. DUFFNER

U. S. Navy, Bureau of Medicine and Surgery, Washington, D.C.

The diver using self-contained underwater breathing apparatus finds himself on the horns of a special dilemma. Unlike the conventional diver the depth and time of his exposure is unknown to anyone except himself, that is, presuming he has the capacity to pay attention to this detail in addition to more immediate problems. If he breathes compressed air under these conditions the swimmer is continually in danger of decompression sickness. If he were to use a closed-circuit apparatus with 100% oxygen he need not concern himself with decompression sickness, but the danger of oxygen poisoning handicaps him even more than the hazards of decompression sickness. One rather obvious compromise in this situation is to provide the swimmer with an oxygen-enriched inert gas mixture. Such devices known as mixed-gas scuba have been developed both in this country and abroad. The present mixed-gas scuba employ nitrogen-oxygen mixtures, the oxygen concentration being varied with planned depth of the dive. Most popular are 60%, 40%, and 32.5%.

A very definite cloud was placed into this seemingly happy picture by the work of Lanphier (1955; 1958). He demonstrated that the mechanisms which regulate respiration in man are altered when nitrogen-oxygen mixtures are breathed under increased atmospheric pressure. This alteration results in a marked retention of carbon dioxide by the body. The end results of this carbon dioxide retention are twofold. It produces toxic symptoms, *per se,* and also increases the hazard of oxygen toxicity, thereby limiting the depth and time duration of diving with these mixtures. These same studies indicate that the phenomena of carbon dioxide retention occur to much lesser extent when helium-oxygen mixtures are breathed under increased atmospheric pressure.

It was not considered feasible to employ helium-oxygen mixtures in scuba because of the experience with this gas in deep diving. It was commonly believed that due to its lesser solubility and greater diffusibility decompression

315

TABLE 1

Maximum depth of 12-hr exposures tolerated without symptoms of decompression sickness, while breathing air as compared to helium-oxygen mixture. Ascent (decompression) was at a rate of 25 ft/min.

Subject	Age (yr)	Air (depth ft)	Helium-Oxygen (depth ft)	Excess (He over air)
D.R.A.	28	33	36	3
B.T.L.	34	36	40	4
M.O.R.	28	34	40	6
R.O.B.	25	34	44	10
S.U.G.	21	36	50	14

sickness was more likely to occur in helium-oxygen diving than in air diving. However, helium-oxygen mixtures had a number of advantages in operational diving at depths greater than 150 ft. Principally it was less narcotic than nitrogen and, therefore, has been used successfully in U.S. Navy diving operations for over 20 years. The helium-oxygen decompression tables, however, are quite conservative. They were formulated by the Haldane method, assuming half-times of 5, 10, 20, 30, 40, 50, 60, and 70 min, and allowing a 1.7:1 ratio. Rates of ascent to the first stop vary with depth and the helium content of the mixture, being as slow as 20 ft/min at depths less than 100 feet when an 80% helium mixture is used. In addition the diver breathes 100% oxygen at depths of 50 and 40 ft during the decompression. With all these limitations it can readily be appreciated why this appeared to be an impossible situation to the advocates of scuba diving.

The author had in his possession data collected but not published some ten years previously (Duffner and Snider, 1958). Five enlisted Navy divers were exposed for 12 hours in a recompression chamber to increasingly greater pressure. The pressure in all cases was reduced at a rate of 25 ft per min. Each subject was exposed to compressed air at a depth of 34 ft and the experiment was repeated at weekly intervals increasing the depth by two ft until the subject developed decompression sickness. This same process was repeated with 80% He—20% O_2 as the breathing medium. Greater exposures were tolerated with the HeO_2 mixtures than with air; the difference amounting to pressure equivalent to 3, 4, 6, 10, and 14 ft of sea water (Table 1) (1 ft = 0.445 psi). Samples of expired gas were collected during various periods following the exposures to helium-oxygen, and analyzed to determine their helium content. Attempts to collect samples during decompression failed. In order to pool the data it was necessary to introduce an artificiality. Behnke and Willmon (1941) determined that the body is capable of absorbing 3.6 cc (±0.6 cc) of helium per pound of atmosphere. Using this figure, the helium elimination data was expressed as "fraction of computed helium content eliminated per minute." The data was then plotted on semilogarithmic paper and an equation devised to fit the data employing the method of Jones (1951). In order to check the method it was applied to helium elimination data contained in the Diving Unit files. It was concluded that a large fraction of the dissolved helium is contained in tissue components saturating and desaturating very rapidly. This data is compared in Table 2.

In view of Lanphier's findings concerning carbon dioxide retention it appeared that we had no choice but to explore the feasibility of utilizing helium-oxygen in mixed-gas scuba. Furthermore the data just reported lead one to conclude that helium-oxygen mixtures might be better tolerated than nitrogen-oxygen from the standpoint of decompression sickness.

At this point it was also decided to attempt to utilize a "single-component" hypothesis to describe the inert gas exchange. This is not a new idea, having been previously proposed by Hempleman (1952) and Rashbass (1955). The foremost reason for this decision in our case was the belief that it would facilitate the development of a computer. There also appeared to be reasonable hope, based on the results of analyzing the helium elimination data, that such a scheme might be successful. If most of the helium was contained in rapidly desaturating tissues most of this would be lost during the ascent. The single component hypothesis is also not inconsistent with the known facts concerning the oil-water solubility ratio of helium, which is 1.7 : 1, rather than 5 : 1 as in the case of nitrogen. One therefore might expect more homogeneity in the case of helium than nitrogen.

A study was next designed to answer the following questions: Is a 60 ft/min

TABLE 2

Comparison of two sets of data on helium elimination. ($T/2$ = half-time).

	NMRI data	EDU data
R_0'	0.25	0.085
R_0''	0.045	0.0095
R_0'''	0.0022	0.0015
R_0''''	0.0006	...
A_0'	0.5	0.283
A_0''	0.33	0.475
A_0'''	0.088	0.25
A_0''''	0.082	...
K_1	0.50	0.30
$T/2(1)$	1.387	2.31
K_2	0.135	0.02
$T/2(2)$	5.13	34.6
K_3	0.025	0.006
$T/2(3)$	27.7	115.5
K_4	0.0073	...
$T/2(4)$	95	...

rate of ascent acceptable when the body contains an excess quantity of helium? From what limiting depth-time combinations of exposures is a constant ascent at the rate of 60 ft/min possible without producing symptoms of decompression sickness? What is the limiting rate of ascent from any depth? Can a single-component method be utilized to predict the no-decompression dives and decompression stops?

Van der Aue (1951) has carefully defined the depth-time combinations from which it is possible to surface without decompressing with air diving (no-decompression curve). It was next decided to find the simplest single-component equation which would fit Van der Aue's data. An examination of this data disclosed that when the depth was multiplied by the square root of time an almost constant value was obtained between 10 and 100 min. It varied between 500 and 540 with a mean value of about 516. In view of this it was decided that Hill's (1928) equation for determining the amount of any substance which diffuses into or out of a semi-infinite solid bounded by a plane surface might apply. This equation is:

$$\text{amount} = 2\, y_0 \left[\frac{kt}{\pi} \right]^{\frac{1}{2}} \tag{1}$$

in which y_0 is the concentration of the diffusible substance; ($\pi = 3.1416$). Since the depth of a dive is a measure of the concentration of inert gas, the equation can be changed to the form:

$$Q = 2D \left[\frac{kt}{\pi} \right]^{\frac{1}{2}} \tag{2}$$

in which D is the depth of the dive in ft and Q is the quantity of inert gas which has diffused into the tissue.

Having determined that the inert gas uptake is proportional to the square root of time and having an equation which will probably apply, the next problem is to find a quantity in which to express Q. Fortunately Rashbass (1955) has devised such a unit which he calls a foot's worth, which is the amount of excess nitrogen a man would take during an infinitely long exposure at one ft.

The next step is to determine the value of the constant (k) which can be done by using this form of the equation:

$$k = \left[\frac{Q}{2D} \right]^2 \times \frac{\pi}{t} \tag{3}$$

However, before proceeding further it is necessary to assign a value to Q. The value of Q would be the number of ft's worth with which a diver could surface and yet remain free of symptoms of decompression sickness. A search of the Diving Unit files was made to find records of extremely long exposures. Van der Aue (1946) had exposed six divers at a depth of 33 ft for 36 hours and surfaced them without incident. It is admitted that 36 hours is not an in-finitely long exposure, but it is the nearest thing to infinity we had available. It was therefore decided to assume that a diver could surface with 33 ft's worth and remain free of decompression sickness.

At this point let us again refer to Van der Aue's work on the no-decompression curve (1951). For a few examples it was found that divers could be surfaced at a rate of 25 ft/min without developing symptoms after air dives of 26 min at 100 ft, 11 min at 150 ft, and 105 min at 50 ft. It is reasonable to assume that the bodies of these divers contained no more of an excess of nitrogen after any of these exposures than they did after the 36-hour exposure at 33 ft, because they did not manifest symptoms of decompression sickness after any of these dives. On the other hand after exposures of 28 min at 100 ft, 13 min at 150 ft, and 113 min at 50 ft the diver complained of symptoms; hence after these dives they must have contained more than 33 foot's worth. It now follows that we can determine the value of k by the equation:

$$k = \left[\frac{33}{2D} \right]^2 \times \frac{\pi}{t} \tag{4}$$

This was done and it was found that between 10 and 100 min the constant (k) varied from 0.00346 to 0.00308 with a mean value of 0.0032. It was decided for the purpose of convenience to round this value off to 0.003. To test the validity of this assumption the no-decompression curve predicted by the equation was calculated and plotted against Van der Aue's experimentally determined curve. The results can be seen in Fig. 1. It will be noted that the two curves coincide rather well out to 200 min. However, at about 180 min the computed curve crosses the experimental curve and becomes progressively inaccurate from that time on. A no-decompression curve was also constructed using the more complex equation of Rashbass (1955). It will be seen in Fig. 1 that the curve predicted by the Rashbass equation is slightly more conservative but follows the experimentally determined curve out to 350 min. However, it was decided that in scuba diving we were not interested in exposures longer than 180 min and therefore would employ the simpler square root equation.

That this square root equation should fit Van der Aue's data should not be surprising, in view of some of the recent applications of power functions. These are members of the special class of functions having the mathematical form

$$y = x^a \tag{5}$$

It is known that a sum of interrelated first-order exponential terms can often be closely approximated by a power over a large portion of the interval of quantitative significance. This method has been used for this purpose in radiobiology, for example, to describe the radioactive decay of mixed fission prod-

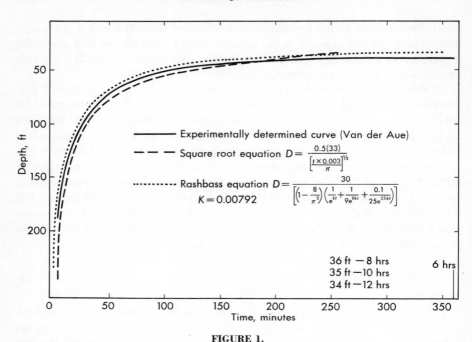

FIGURE 1.

Minimal decompression curves determined experimentally and by two computations.

ucts, and the retention of radioactive bone-seekers. Since the square root is the 0.5 power, we have here a form of power function describing the sum of the inert gas uptake by a large number of tissue components with varying half-times.

Referring again to Table 1, it will be seen that the divers tolerated a greater excess pressure of helium-oxygen than they did of air. If a diver can tolerate a long exposure to 33 ft in compressed air he should be able to tolerate a greater one with helium-oxygen. Taking the three lowest values for excess number of ft tolerated with helium-oxygen over air, we find a mean value of 4 ft. The mean of three highest values is 10 ft. Therefore the border-line no-decompression dive with an 80% helium-20% oxygen mixture should be one which results in the diver containing somewhere between 37 and 43 ft's worth. Using a middle value of 40 ft's worth, a predicted no-decompression curve was constructed using the equation:

$$D = \frac{0.5\,(40)}{\left[\dfrac{0.003 \times t}{\pi}\right]^{\frac{1}{2}}}$$

(6)

These values were plotted and a large number of depth-time combinations around the line were picked out to test the validity of the curve. (See Fig. 2.)

In all of these exposures it was planned to use a rate of ascent of 60 ft/min. Since these experiments were such a radical departure from previous concepts it was considered prudent to first perform a few exploratory experiments. These were conducted in a recompression chamber with the divers breathing an 80% helium-20% oxygen ($\pm0.5\%$) mixture. These experiments disclosed that men could tolerate decompression at the rate of 60 ft/min and that the projected experiments were not unduly hazardous.

The experimental dives between 10 and 100 minutes were conducted in a pressure diving tank. The ordered depth was simulated by placing compressed air over the top of the water. The helium-oxygen mixture was supplied from the surface through a demand valve. During the time on the bottom two subjects alternated between swimming at a speed of 0.8 kt on a swim ergometer, (1956) and weight lifting. Each dive was made by a pair of divers. The routine of the dive was as follows: (a) The dive was started when pressure was applied to the tank. (b) Descent was at the rate of 75 ft/min. (c) Five min were allowed for descending and getting set. (d) During the next ten min one

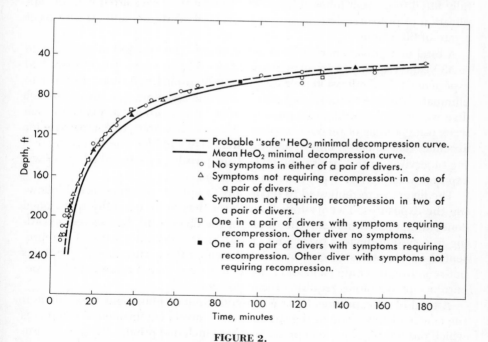

FIGURE 2.

Results of experimental dives with 80–20 HeO$_2$. Two divers were exposed to each depth-time combination.

diver swam on the ergometer and the other lifted a 70-lb-weight, up and down 24 in., 10 times a min. (e) At the end of this time they changed places, that is, the swimming diver now lifted the weight, and the lifting diver swam. (f) At the end of this ten-min period both divers rested for five min. (g)At the end of the rest period they repeated steps (d), (e), and (f) until the time of the dive was completed. (h) At the expiration of the ordered time of the dive, the subjects were brought to the surface at a rate of 60 ft/min.

Exposures which were less than 10 min and greater than 100 min were performed in a recompression chamber. The reason for this in the former case (less than 10 min) was because the time was too short to allow them to do much work and it was desired not to hazard the divers to submergence in addition to the high pressure and rapid decompression. The long dives (over 100 min) were carried out in the chamber for the following reasons: (a) The divers could not tolerate the mouthpiece for more than 100 min. (b) They could not work long at the prescribed rate. (c) It was believed that they would be so completely saturated at the end of these exposures that working would add little to the experiment. In these experiments the divers breathed the helium-oxygen mixture through a mask and demand valve. The mask was carefully fitted to prevent inboard leaks. The time of the dive started with the application of pressure; descent was at the rate of 75 ft/min and ascent was at a rate of 60 ft/min.

A total of 17 divers participated in the study. They ranged in age from 28 to 43 years. Experience in diving varied from 5 to 16 years. Ten of them had experienced decompression sickness previously, from 1 to 4 times. In order to eliminate bias due to individual differences, the assignment of divers to each dive was made according to a random order. A new order was made up each week using a table of random numbers. This was necessary to compensate for absences due to leave, illness, and transfers. Thus neither the diver, the diving supervisor, or the experimenters had any jurisdiction over which diver was exposed to any given depth-time combination.

The divers were requested to report any symptoms which occurred following the exposures. Twenty-four hours later they were carefully questioned concerning their condition. The results of the dives were then scored according to a system devised by Snyder (1958). In this system a score of 0 represented no symptoms, a score of 1–5 represented the occurrence of symptoms not requiring recompression and a score of greater than 5 represented the occurrence of symptoms requiring recompression.

A total of 84 exposures to various depth-time combinations were made in the course of this phase of the study. Sixteen divers complained of symptoms which did not require recompression. These included principally fatigue, pruritus, rash, and transient pain. Four divers presented symptoms of such severity as to require recompression. These data are presented in Fig. 2. The results of this study were interpreted to indicate that the no-decompression curve which was predicted by Eq. (6) setting Q at a value of 40 produced a situation which was borderline in safety. A "Q" value of 37 would probably produce a set of depth-time combinations which would be "safe" for no-decompression when an 80% helium mixture is used. The results also indicated that the equation was only accurate for exposures up to 100 min. When $t = 100$-180 min the depth or time of exposure which can be tolerated is greater than that predicted by the equation.

Scuba divers like to ascend as rapidly as possible. Therefore one of the principal objections to the use of helium-oxygen mixtures in scuba was the belief that fast rates of ascent could not be tolerated. To test this hypothesis the following experiments were performed. Four divers were exposed in a recompression chamber at a depth of 120 ft for 30 min while breathing a 67.5% helium-32.5% oxygen mixture ($\pm 0.5\%$), and then decompressed at a rate of 1 ft/sec. This produced no symptoms. The exposure was then repeated with the same number of subjects and they were decompressed at a rate of 1.25 ft/sec. Two subjects developed symptoms following this procedure and all complained of epigastric discomfort. This was due to the distention of the stomach and intestine caused by the sudden expansion of swallowed gas. At this point it was decided that 75 ft/min was the limiting rate of ascent from depth to the surface. It was believed, however, that more rapid rates might be tolerated if the ascent was terminated at 30 ft. The experiments were continued using the same exposure but introducing a stop at 30 ft. Four subjects were now decompressed from 120 to 30 ft at a rate of 1.5 ft/sec. There were no complaints. Two further experiments were performed in which the rate of ascent was further increased to 1.75 ft/sec and finally to 2 ft/sec. No further symptoms or complaints were noted.

In actual diving operations few dives are so short as to not require decompression. It was therefore necessary to determine whether or not the square root equation could be employed to compute decompression stops. This required making the following assumptions:

(a) If a diver can tolerate a "Q" of 37 foot's worth at the surface (1 atmosphere) then at any other depth he can tolerate:

$$37 \times \frac{D + 33}{33}. \tag{7}$$

This is simply an application of Boyle's law. The basic assumption being that little excess gas is held in supersaturation and that most of it is in bubbles of subcritical size (i.e., have a tendency to collapse rather than grow).

(b) If a diver ends a dive with a certain number of ft's worth this is equivalent to spending an infinitely long time at that depth. If, for example, a diver spends 47 min at 46.6 (say 47) ft's worth, this is the same as if he had spent an infinitely long time at 47 ft. He cannot ascend to the surface, since Q exceeds 37. He can however ascend to 10 ft because at this depth, according to Eq. (7), he can tolerate a Q of 48.

(c) If the diver were to spend an infinitely long time at 10 ft he would acquire 10 f.w. of excess gas. Since ascending to 10 ft from 110 ft after 47 min is the same as ascending to 10 ft after an infinitely long time, this ascent is equivalent to a minus 37-ft dive.

(d) The diver will then need to stay at a depth of minus 37 ft until Q reaches a value of 37, at which time he can ascend to the surface. This length of time (t) can be solved for by using the form of the equation:

$$t = \frac{\pi}{k} \times \left[\frac{Q - 37}{2(Q - D_s)} \right]^2 \tag{8}$$

Employing the above equation the foot stop was computed for the 110-ft 47-min dive. It was found to be 19.5 min. However, it was decided to test this figure. Dives were made in the diving tanks to 110 ft for 47 min employing the same procedure as described earlier in the test of the no-decompression dives. The difference was that at the end of 47 min the divers were decompressed to 10 ft at the rate of 75 ft/min. In the first experiments they remained at 10 ft for 22 min. In subsequent experiments this time was progressively shortened. When the time was shortened to 16 min two of the most susceptible subjects developed decompression sickness, one requiring recompression. When the time was reduced to 12 min two of the six divers developed mild symptoms. When the time was reduced to 10 min, four of the six divers developed mild to moderately severe symptoms; however, none required recompression. These findings would indicate that the equation which predicted the "safe" no-decompression exposure when employed to compute a decompression stop predicted a stop-time about 67% too long. This finding was tested on five other depth-time combinations 110 ft/34 min, 110 ft/40 · min, 130 ft/40 min, and 130 ft/50 min with about the same results. From a practical point of view this situation can be handled in one of three ways: A larger k value can be used to compute the decompression stops; a larger foot's worth value can be allowed in dives with stops; the proper length of the stop can be determined experimentally for each combination, which would not be too difficult if stops were prescribed in even five-min figures. Such a procedure would have definite value in scuba diving.

The data were also analyzed with a view to learning the significance of the observed differences in reaction scores following exposures resulting in higher or lower Q values. The reaction score of each subject following dives resulting in surfacing Q values of 32–33, 34–35, 36–37, and 38–39 foot's worth was subjected to a simple t test which made no assumption concerning the homogeneity of variance. This procedure permitted us to make certain predictions about the probable experience of this group of divers if they are exposed to decompression situations similar to those studied:

(a) Recording the scores after surfacing at any one Q level, the group could be subjected to a $Q + 2$ level with a significant increase in the average reaction-score less than 5% of the time.

(b) After surfacing at any one Q level, the group would, 95% of the time, show an increase in the average reaction-score if subjected to a $Q + 4$ level of exposure.

(c) At a $Q + 6$ level of exposure, the group will be virtually certain to show an increase in average reaction score.

Since 80% helium mixtures will rarely be used in mixed-gas scuba diving it is necessary to extrapolate these data to other gas mixtures. Behnke and Willmon (1941) have shown that the amount of helium dissolved in the body depends upon the number of atmospheres (absolute) to which the man is exposed and his body weight. Therefore the amount of helium Q_{He} in any component of the body after exposure can be stated as being:

$$Q_{He} = \frac{D + 33}{33} \times C_{He} \tag{9}$$

With an 80% mixture a diver can surface with 37 ft's worth. Since this by definition is the same as being exposed at 37 ft for an infinitely long time, Q_{He} can be said to be

$$Q_{He} = \frac{37 + 33}{33} \times 0.8 \tag{10}$$

Since the appearance of symptoms is a factor of the amount of excess gas present, they should not occur so long as Q_{He} is no greater with any other gas mixture than it is with an 80% mixture and a Q of 37. Putting this in the form of an equation we have

$$\frac{(37 + 33) \times 0.8}{33} = \frac{(Qx + 33) \times C_{He}}{33} \tag{11}$$

Solving this equation we have

$$Q = \frac{56}{C_{He}} - 33 \tag{12}$$

In the case of a 50% mixture this would be

$$\frac{56}{0.5} - 33 = 79 \text{ ft's worth} \tag{13}$$

As a result of this study we have concluded that helium-oxygen mixtures can be used in mixed-gas scuba diving and with some very definite advantages. However, the most important finding is that the inert gas exchange in diving can be described by a single mathematical expression and this has made it possible to design and carry out critical experiments. Moreover the data from these experiments can be subjected to statistical treatment. The Haldane method with multiple half-times and multiple ratios is too complex to control all of the variables in a single experiment. The limitations of the multiple tissue–partial pressure concept has contributed greatly to our lack of precise knowledge on the subject of decompression.

REFERENCES

Behnke, A. R., and T. H. Willmon. 1941. "Gaseous nitrogen and helium elimination from the body during rest and exercise," Am. J. Physiol. *131:* (3), 619–626.

Duffner, G. J., and H. H. Snider. 1958. "Effects of Exposing Men to Compressed Air and Helium-Oxygen Mixtures for 12 Hours at Pressures of 2–2.6 Atmospheres," USN Experimental Diving Unit Research Report 1–59.

Hill, A. V. 1928. "The diffusion of oxygen and lactic acid through tissues," Proc. Roy. Soc. Biol. *104:* 39–56.

Hempleman, H. V. *et al.* 1952. "Investigation into the Decompression Tables, Report III," Medical Research Council, Royal Naval Personnel Research Committee. R.N.P. 52/708.

Jones, Hardin. 1951 *Decompression Sickness,* W. B. Saunders Co., Philadelphia, Chap. IX, Part II, pp. 315–317.

Lanphier, E.H. 1955. "Nitrogen-Oxygen Mixture Physiology, Phases 1 and 2," USN Experimental Diving Unit Formal Report 7–55.

Lanphier, E. H. *et al.* 1958. "Nitrogen-Oxygen Mixture Physiology, Phases 4 and 6," USN Experimental Diving Unit Research Report 7–58.

Norris, W. P., S. A. Tyler, and A. M. Brues. 1958. "Retention of radioactive bone-seekers," Science *128:* (3322), 456–462.

Rashbass, C.1955. "Investigation into the Decompression Tables, Report VI, New Tables," Medical Research Council, Royal Naval Personnel Research Comm. R.N.P. 55/847, U.P.S. 151, D.P. 14, R.N.P.L. 9/55.

Snyder, J. F. 1958. "Dive Reaction Scale Study," USN Experimental Diving Unit Research Report 5–58; Tables, "Report III, Medical Research Council." Royal Naval Personnel Research Committee. R.N.P. S2/708 U.P.S. 131, D.P. 7, R.N.L. 4/52.

U.S. Navy. 1956. Bureau of Medicine and Surgery, *Submarine Medicine Practice,* NAVMED–P5054, U.S. Government Printing Office, Washington.

Van der Aue, O. E., 1946. Unpublished Data. Oct. 29 to Nov. 1. Experimental Unit Files.

Van der Aue, O. E. *et al.* 1951. "Calculation and Testing of Decompression Tables for Air Dives Employing the Procedure of Surface Decompression and the Use of Oxygen," USN Experimental Diving Unit Report, MN 002 007, Report No. 1.

The Role of Nitrogen in Breathholding at Increased Pressures

CARL MAGNUS HESSER

Laboratory of Aviation and Naval Medicine, Karolinska Institute,
Stockholm, Sweden

The problems associated with underwater swimming and escape from submarines are closely related to the physiology of breathholding at increased pressures. Though there are in the literature numerous studies of breathholding at normal or at reduced barometric pressures (Ferris *et al.*, 1946; Otis *et al.*, 1948; Rahn *et al.*, 1953; Fowler, 1954), only a few reports are available on breathholding under high atmospheric pressures (Shilling *et al.*, 1935; Alvis, 1951; Du Bois, 1955). These studies suggest that under normal resting conditions there is a combination of at least three interrelated stimuli to breathing that causes termination of voluntary apnea, i.e., (1) high alveolar (arterial) CO_2 tension, (2) low alveolar (arterial) O_2 tension, and (3) a decreased absolute lung volume. By assuming that at the breaking point the total stimulus to respiration is equal to the maximum voluntary inhibition of breathing, and by applying the chemical ventilation equation of Gray (1946) to estimate the stimulus strength existing at the breaking point, Otis, Rahn, and Fenn (1948) found evidence indicating that the breaking point of breathholding occurs when the sum of the separate partial stimuli from low P_{O_2} and from high P_{CO_2} gives a total stimulus sufficient to produce an alveolar ventilation about eight times the normal. This hypothesis would imply that as long as the arterial oxygen tension exceeds a certain level beyond which an increase in P_{O_2} causes no stimulation of breathing, the breaking point of breathholding should always occur at the same P_{CO_2}, *viz.*, 58 mm Hg on an average at resting lung volume. According to the general opinion "low oxygen" stimulates respiration only at arterial or alveolar tensions below 100–120 mm Hg.

In 1935, Shilling, Hansen, and Hawkins reported that the maximum breathholding time for 25 experienced divers increased from an average of 91 seconds at atmospheric pressure to 216.5 seconds at 6 atmospheres. Alvis (1951)

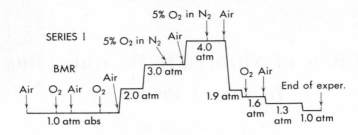

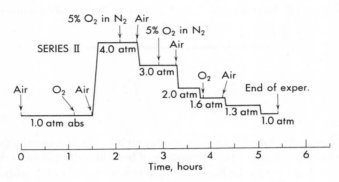

FIGURE 1.

Ambient pressures, exposure times, and gas mixtures used in experiments denoted "Series I" and "Series II." (This and following figures are from Hesser, Holmgren, and Beskow, unpublished.)

found that 3 subjects were able to hold their breath for longer periods and to higher alveolar P_{CO_2} as ambient pressure was increased (tested up to 4.0 atmospheres absolute, equivalent to 99 feet of sea water), although the alveolar P_{O_2} exceeded 100 mm Hg and, therefore, was presumed to play no important role in limiting breathholding at ambient pressures over 2 atmospheres.

Since nitrogen is known to exert a narcotic action at high pressures (Behnke *et al.*, 1935; Marshall, 1951; Carpenter, 1955; Bennett and Glass, 1957), the hypothesis was put forward that the increased ability to hold the breath at increased ambient pressures is due not only to the concomitant increase in oxygen tension but also to the increase in nitrogen pressure.

To test this hypothesis a series of experiments has been performed in collaboration with Drs. B. Holmgren and D. Beskow in the Laboratory of Aviation and Naval Medicine at the Karolinska Institute in Stockholm. Eight experienced subjects in a resting, standardized condition were exposed to air, 100% oxygen, or 5% oxygen in nitrogen in a dry recompression chamber at pressures ranging from 1.0 to 4.0 atmospheres absolute. The various gas mixtures were breathed from large polyethylene bags for 15 minutes before the breath was held. Two series of experiments, "Series I" and "Series II," were performed on each subject with an interval of 3 to 12 days. The ambient pressures, exposure times and gas mixtures used in the two series are shown in Fig. 1. Samples of alveolar gas were taken at the onset and at the end of maximum voluntary breathholding, and analyzed for oxygen, carbon dioxide, and nitrogen. To minimize any possible effects of variations in lung volume, the lung volume at the beginning of a breathholding test was adjusted for each subject in such a way that approximately the same lung volume existed at the breaking point, regardless of the time of apnea. The average expiratory reserve volume at the breaking point ranged from 1.02 to 1.34 liters.

In Fig. 2 the data obtained have been plotted on a CO_2–O_2 diagram. The inspired O_2 tensions in the various experiments are indicated by open circles on the axis of abscissa, whereas the alveolar O_2 and CO_2 tensions at the onset of breathholding are indicated by the appropriate values on the resting alveolar air curve, which was constructed from our own data (solid part of the curve) as well as from those of Otis *et al.* (broken part) (1948). The open circles on the breaking point curve denote the average alveolar gas tensions at the end of the breathholding periods, and form the basis for constructing the curve (broken part of the curve obtained from Otis *et al,* 1948. The broken lines leading from the resting alveolar points to the breaking points indicate the calculated

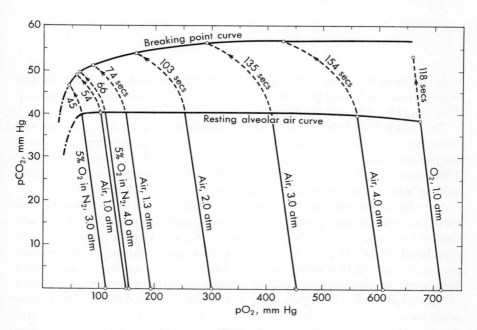

FIGURE 2.

Alveolar gas tensions in breathholding at increased pressures. Averages of 8 subjects.

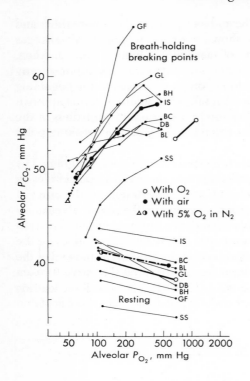

FIGURE 3.
Semi-logarithmic plot of same data shown in Fig. 2.

time course of the alveolar gas changes during the breathholding periods. The average maximum time that the breath could be held under the various conditions are also shown in the figure.

The data in Fig. 2 show that in air the maximum breathholding time as well as the breaking point P_{CO_2} increases with the atmospheric pressure, thus also in the pressure range where the breaking point P_{O_2} greatly exceeds 120 mm Hg. This confirms earlier findings of Alvis (1951). At 4.0 atmospheres the breathholding time was on an average 2.8 times longer than at 1.0 atmosphere.

As to the hypothesis that high pressures of nitrogen might contribute to the increased breathholding ability at increased ambient pressures, the results depicted in Fig. 2 seem to be somewhat conflicting. That the breaking points after breathing 5% O_2 in N_2 at 3.0 and 4.0 atmospheres fall on the same breaking point curve as that obtained after breathing air at normal or at reduced barometric pressures suggests that an increase in nitrogen pressure of the order of 3 atmospheres has no significant effect on the breathholding ability. On the other hand, after air breathing at 4.0 atmospheres the breathholding time was significantly longer, and the breaking point P_{CO_2} significantly higher, than after oxygen breathing at 1.0 atmosphere, despite a higher O_2 tension in the latter situation. This observation seems to speak in favor of an influence of high P_{N_2}.

In Fig. 3 the same data as in Fig. 2 have been replotted on a semi-logarithmic paper with the oxygen tensions represented on the logarithmic x axis. The upper group of filled circles connected by heavy lines indicates average breaking points following air breathing at 1.0, 1.3, 2.0, 3.0, and 4.0 atmospheres, respectively. The two open circles connected by a heavy line indicate the average breaking points following oxygen breathing at 1.0 and 1.6 atmospheres, whereas the triangle and the cross connected by a broken line denote the average breaking points after breathing 5% oxygen in nitrogen at 3.0 and 4.0 atmospheres, respectively.

Alvis (1951) states that at the breathholding breaking points P_{ACO_2} appears to have a linear relationship to $\log_{10} P_{AO_2}$. Our results confirm this to be valid when the breath is held at increased atmospheric pressures and the breaking point P_{O_2} ranges from about 60 to 300 mm Hg. Fig. 3 also shows the individual breaking points of the 8 subjects as well as the average and individual alveolar gas composition at the onset of breathholding tests. The great interindividual variations in alveolar gas composition at the breaking point in experiments under a given environmental condition are clearly demonstrated. It is also of interest to note that, at ground level, the breaking point P_{CO_2} of subject SS was less than the normal alveolar P_{CO_2} of subject IS.

As shown in Fig. 4A the average breaking point curve of the experiments per-

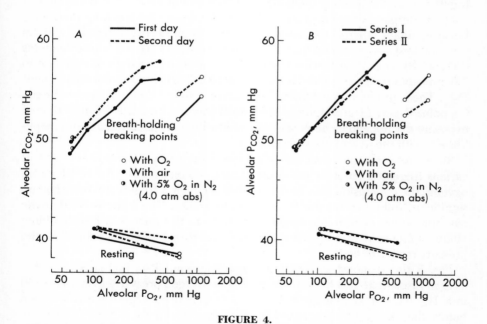

FIGURE 4.

a (*left*). Semi-logarithmic plot of average breaking-point curves from first and second experimental days. b (*right*). Semi-logarithmic plot of average breaking-point curves from Series I and Series II.

formed on the second experimental day rests above that of the first day's experiments, indicating that a "training" effect may have affected the results. The differences between each set of breaking-point values are small, however, and in no instance significant ($P > 0.05$). The average breaking points of Series I and of Series II are depicted in Fig. 4B. To minimize the influence of any possible training effect Series I and II were performed in the reverse order in 3 subjects. In Series II, in which the ambient pressure was raised directly to 4.0 atmospheres (Fig. 1), the breaking point P_{CO_2} at this pressure is not only significantly less than in Series I but also less than in the subsequent experiments at 3.0 atmospheres. On the other hand, when the ambient pressure was gradually increased to 4.0 atmospheres during the course of about 90 minutes (Series I), the breaking point P_{CO_2} also increased gradually. It may thus be argued that in the experiments where the ambient pressure was rapidly increased to 4.0 atmospheres, the exposure time of 15 minutes at this pressure was not long enough for chemosensitive structures involved in the control of respiration to come into gas equilibrium with the new O_2 tension.

To test this hypothesis a third series of experiments was performed, in which 4 of the subjects were exposed to 100% of oxygen throughout the experimental period of about 5 hours at pressures ranging from 0.3 to 2.5 atmospheres. The average breaking point curve of this series is shown in Fig. 5 (upper dotted line), together with the average breaking point curve of Series I + II on the same 4 subjects (upper heavy lines). As shown in the figure the breaking point P_{CO_2} became higher when the time of exposure to high O_2 pressures (1.0 and 1.6 atmospheres) was increased from 15 minutes (Series I + II) to about 45 minutes (Series "100% O_2"). A further increase to 4 hours of the time of exposure to 1.0 atmosphere of oxygen did not cause any further increase in breaking point P_{CO_2}. These results support the aforementioned suggestion that the low breaking point P_{CO_2} at 4.0 atmospheres in Series II occurred because the short time of exposure did not allow chemosensitive control mechanisms to come into equilibrium with the new oxygen tension.

Since the breaking point curve obtained from the experiments on air at various increased ambient pressures almost coincides with that obtained on oxygen, the conclusion may be drawn that the high nitrogen pressures had no significant influence on the breathholding ability. The hypothesis that the narcotic action of nitrogen might contribute to the increased breathholding ability at increased atmospheric pressures must therefore be abandoned for the pressure range studied.

Fig. 5 also demonstrates that the breaking point P_{CO_2} increased with the oxygen pressure to reach a plateau at alveolar oxygen pressures over about 350 mm Hg. To our knowledge it has actually not been experimentally shown before that, as might be expected from a theoretical point of view (Otis et al., 1948), there exists an oxygen threshold above which the breaking point becomes entirely dependent upon the CO_2 pressure, or, in other words, that, as

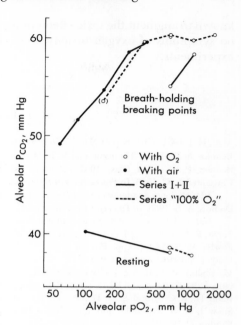

FIGURE 5.

Semi-logarithmic plot of alveolar gas tensions in breathholding at various ambient pressures after breathing air and oxygen. Average of 4 subjects.

P_{O_2} increases, the breaking point curve may flatten out to reach a final, maximum CO_2 value which will not permit breathholding even for the shortest period. In our experiments on oxygen the average O_2 threshold was found to lie at an alveolar O_2 tension of approximately 350 mm Hg, whereas the final CO_2 plateau had, on an average, a value of about 60 mm Hg. Whether the same holds for breathholding on air at increased pressures cannot be settled, since the data obtained so far do not include the critical O_2 and CO_2 pressure ranges. To reach these ranges experiments should be performed at ambient pressures in excess of 4.0 atmospheres.

It seems somewhat surprising that the O_2 threshold may have such a high value as 350 mm Hg since oxygen is considered to stimulate the chemoreceptors of the carotid and aortic bodies only at oxygen tensions below 100–120 mm Hg. One explanation may be that during the breathholding tests the *arterial* O_2 tension became less than 120 mm Hg as soon as the *alveolar* O_2 tension fell below 350 mm Hg. Such a state may be caused by pulmonary shunts including partial atelectasis and/or impaired O_2 diffusion due to lung oedema from high oxygen tensions. Another possibility could be that high arterial O_2 tensions might facilitate tissue oxidations and thus diminish the formation of such metabolites as may stimulate respiration. The existence of special chemo-sensitive control mechanisms which may respond to arterial O_2 tensions already below 300–400 mm Hg cannot, however, be ruled out.

Finally it should be mentioned that though high alveolar CO_2 tensions are known to augment the toxic effects of high O_2 (Shaw *et al.*, 1934; Taylor, 1949), no symptoms of oxygen toxicity were observed in any of the breathholding experiments.

REFERENCES

Alvis, H. J. 1951. MRL Report No. 177, Vol. 10, pp. 110–120.

Behnke, A. R., R. M. Thomson, and E. P. Motley. 1935. Am. J. Physiol. *112:* 554.

Bennett, P. B., and A. Glass. 1957. J. Physiol. *138:* 18P.

Carpenter, F. G. 1955. In *Proceedings of the Underwater Physiology Symposium*, Publication 377, p. 124, National Academy of Sciences-National Research Council, Washington, D.C.

Du Bois, A. B. 1955. In *Proceedings of the Underwater Physiology Symposium*, Publication 377, p. 90, National Academy of Sciences-National Research Council, Washington, D.C.

Ferris, E. B., G. L. Engel, C. D. Stevens, and J. Webb. 1946. J. Clin. Invest. *25:* 734.

Fowler, W. S. 1954. J. Appl. Physiol. *6:* 539.

Gray, J. S. 1946. Science. *103:* 739.

Marshall, J. M. 1951. Am. J. Physiol. *166:* 699.

Otis, A. B., H. Rahn, and W. O. Fenn. 1948. Am. J. Physiol. *152:* 674.

Rahn, H., R. C. Stroud, S. M. Tenney, and J. C. Mithoefer. 1953. J. Appl. Physiol. *6:* 158.

Shaw, L. A., A. R. Behnke, and A. C. Messer. 1934. Am. J. Physiol. *108:* 652.

Shilling, C. W., R. A. Hansen, and J. A. Hawkins. 1935. Am. J. Physiol. *110:* 616.

Taylor, H. J. 1949. Am. J. Physiol. *109:* 272.

Carbon Dioxide Exchange During Skindiving

G. BOND and K. E. SCHAEFER

U.S. Naval Medical Research Laboratory, New London, Connecticut

Results of respiratory measurements of tank instructors prior to and after dives to 90 ft, together with data on alveolar gas tensions obtained at the 90 ft depth, allowed the graphic presentation of alveolar pathways during diving (Schaefer, 1955) using the O_2–CO_2 diagram (Rahn and Fenn, 1955). During the descent to 90 ft a reversed CO_2 gradient develops from the lungs into the blood. Most of the "predive CO_2 content" of the lungs has disappeared after reaching a depth of 90 ft. During ascent (decompression), which involves climbing up a line, the influx of CO_2 into the lungs is dependent upon the speed of ascent. By increasing the rate of ascent from 2 to 3.5 ft/sec the alveolar CO_2 tension upon reaching the surface was found to be lower than the "predive" CO_2 level. During the fast ascents the O_2 consumption and CO_2 production increased more than twofold when compared with those of slow ascents at the end of which the alveolar CO_2 tension was found considerably higher than the control values (Schaefer *et al.*, 1958).

Blood data obtained immediately after the dive exhibited (a) a significant increase in lactic acid (Schaefer, 1955); (b) a dehydration of red cells; and (c) the CO_2 content in terms of mEq/L cell water was lower in the venous blood than in the arterial blood (Schaefer *et al.*, 1958). After periods of extended skindiving, a large rise in blood urea (Bond, 1957) was observed.

Evidence for adaptation to skindiving is presented. 1. A longitudinal study of the lung volumes of tank instructors at the beginning and after one year of duty at the Escape Training Tank revealed a significant increase in inspiratory capacity, tidal volume, expiratory capacity, vital capacity, and total lung capacity, while the residual capacity tended to decrease (Carey *et al.*, 1956). 2. There is also some indication that an adaptation takes place in the respiratory

335

response to CO_2. It was found that the ventilatory response to inhalation of 5% CO_2 increased in seven instructors after a three-month layoff period during which no water work was done (Schaefer, 1957).

REFERENCES

Bond, G. 1957. "Physiological Alterations in Escape Training Tank Instructors," A Preliminary Report.
Carey, C. R., K. E. Schaefer, and H. J. Alvis. 1956. "Effect of skindiving on lung volumes," J. Appl. Physiol. 8: (5).
Rahn, H., and W. O. Fenn. 1955. "The O_2–CO_2 Diagram," Am. Phys. Soc. Pub.
Schaefer, K. E. 1955. *The Role of CO_2 in the Physiology of Human Diving*, Underwater Physiology Symposium, National Academy of Sciences Publication 377.
Schaefer, K. E. 1957. *Effects of Carbon Dioxide as Related to Submarine and Diving Physiology*. A *Decade of Basic and Applied Science in the Navy*, O.N.R. Decennial Symposium, p. 176.
Schaefer, K. E., G. Nichols, Jr., R. C. Stroud, and C. R. Carey. 1958. "Pulmonary gas exchange and blood gas transport during and after skindiving to 90 feet," Fed. Proc. 17: 560.

DISCUSSION

Dr. Bjurstedt: Dr. Hesser and myself have been working with skindiving although in another environment. We tried only the compression chambers, and we used dogs. I will demonstrate the effects on the carbon dioxide exchange during an actual trial dive with direct recording of arterial P_{CO_2}.

I would like to add that the results we have are completely in agreement with the results of the paper by Dr. Bond and Dr. Schaefer.

This slide consists of two presentations. The upper one is the actual record. It can be seen from the different tracings that the pressure in the dive chamber was taken from one atmosphere to five atmospheres absolute. It stayed up there for about 10 seconds with the dog, and then the pressure was again decreased. During this maneuver the animal held its breath. That was done by closing the trachea. This record should be explained. What you see here are respiratory echoes. The dog is not breathing at all. The trachea is closed. The pressure is also represented. There is very little change during this maneuver. Here you have a method of recording directly the arterial P_{CO_2}. This is not actually done directly, but by recording the arterial pH. The oxygen saturation of the arterial blood is likewise recorded by the oximeter. This is done in the femoral artery. As soon as you go down from the surface and the pressure is increased, there is an immediate increase in the arterial P_{CO_2}. This can be calculated from the pH. There is a rise in the acidity or P_{CO_2}, and some changes in the oxygen saturation on the way down to the final depth, which, by the way, covers a distance up to 120 feet water depth.

On the lower part of the slide are calculated events only, but they are calculated from this oxygen saturation and arterial pH. When the dive is started there is an immediate and very sharp rise in the P_{CO_2}. Actually, if you go down faster, there will be a peak in the arterial P_{CO_2}. As the arterial oxygen tension is calculated per second, it goes down first when the trachea is closed. When the ambient pressure is increased, there is an increase again, and after the downward dive there will be a decrease of the oxygen tension all the way up to the surface again.

These are the recorded changes of the arterial P_{CO_2} and the arterial P_{O_2} during a simulated dive. We can calculate the amount of carbon dioxide going in and out of the dogs, and the results we have so far are in complete harmony with these presented by Dr. Bond.

Chairman Davis: It was very satisfying to have this confirmation from direct experimentation.

Dr. Pugh: These changes that Commander Bond has described are, of course, very similar to what occurs in the seal. I would like to ask whether any of the other changes that are present in seals occur in these men as an adaptation to diving. One would be an increase in the red cell mass. Seals have about twice the red cell mass relative to body weight that you find in man. The other thing is their resting ventilation, which is very low. I presume it is because of the P_{CO_2}. The third question is whether they have high carbon monoxide levels. I found in the seal in the Antarctic that the carbon monoxide is similar to that of heavy smokers in man, about six times the volume in nonsmokers.

Commander Bond: It has been found in tank instructors that there is an elevated hematocrit, which persists for some time after the diving has been done. The hematocrits have run on the average of about 12 or 15% more than our own.

Dr. Schaefer: Our experiments were stimulated by Dr. Scholander's work on seals. We find in man adaptation to diving which is similar to that of seals, as we have a lowered response to CO_2 and an increase in lung volumes. These tank instructors show a respiratory pattern with a low frequency and large tidal volume resulting in a higher alveolar CO_2 and a lower resting ventilation. They develop very high lactic acid during the dives, similar to the seals. The pulse rate drops during the dive, only to a much lesser extent than in the seal. We have not studied carbon monoxide content in these divers.

Dr. Gauer: I have just one brief question for Commander Bond. You mentioned that the lungs are solid, if I understood correctly. Do you mean by this that the interthoracic blood volume is very high?

Commander Bond: At the end of a 100-foot drop, when the diver hits the bottom, the ambient pressure has so squeezed his alveoli that he is literally at residual at that point, and therefore I cannot conceive of this situation existing without a rather severe disturbance of the normal pulmonary circulation. I think that there must be a systemic venous backup. If this does occur, we are duplicating the conditions under which you have observed the diuresis by overloading the venous side. This "solid" effect I speak of is simply pressure squeezing, when the volume of air in the alveoli is so small that a great deal of air is probably driven directly into the circulation. By "solid lungs," I mean that the lung volume is reduced to the residual capacity.

Dr. Gauer: Did you observe diuresis after these dives?

Commander Bond: Yes, it is the most common observation in the tank instructors. I would like to add one other word about the seals. Although we refer to our tank instructors as trained seals, there is an entirely different mechanism in the means of diving which should be remembered. The seal dives with an empty lung. I think I am quite correct in this. The human being loads to capacity and drops. I would point out that, in the beginning of the dive, the seal exhausts his air, shuts his flippers, goes down.

Dr. Dill: I do not know whether that is correct. It is quite common for a seal to come up and blow bubbles. They must have some air in their lungs before they go down.

Dr. Pugh: Seals and whales have special air sinuses in which some of the residual air from the lungs is squeezed. In that way their lungs can be solid. It is thought to be one of the ways they have of protecting themselves against bends. They behave as you described if they are prevented from exhaling when they go down very deep, sometimes to 100 feet.

Captain Behnke: I think a striking phenomenon has not been emphasized, and that is the time of breathholding at 100 feet. It is increased compared to that at the surface. Going down, the lung volume is reduced to about one-fourth, corresponding to the residual air volume. The lungs are not solid, of course, and the reduction of air volume to residual air volume limits the ability to go deeper than about 100 to 125 feet. I would like to ask Dr. Bond if the low oxygen following the dive is due to the longer length of time I believe that the individual can hold his breath. Specifically, however, was the increased carbon dioxide in the tissues and presumably in the respiratory centers, and what happened to the normal response of these centers to CO_2?

Chairman Davis: I have another question for Commander Bond. I was much puzzled by the remark that, if it had not been for this retention of CO_2, that is, the lowering of CO_2 tension in the alveoli, there would have been a problem. Is this a good thing? Is the CO_2 more innocuous in the blood stream than it is in the tissues when it is in the alveoli? The logic puzzles me.

Commander Bond: I made that statement in view of the fact that, if we did not have a repository for this CO_2, we would have an effective concentration of, perhaps, 15 to 18%. It is my opinion that the carbon dioxide which is driven from the lung perhaps does not go as carbon dioxide into the blood and tissues. I think there might be an intermediate biochemical storage. I think I gave you a hint of it in my last slide. In response to Dr. Behnke's question about the effect of CO_2 on the respiratory center, I do not have data available on that. I am sure Dr. Schaefer has some.

Captain Behnke: How much longer do the men hold their breath?

Commander Bond: Our normal drop covers only about 2 minutes and 15 seconds. I have asked my men not to try long drops. We used to do four-minute ones. However, these same men were capable of the same kind of breath-holding with their heads merely submerged. The reason that I asked them not to hold it for any length of time is because nature exacts a penalty in that last atmosphere as you know. They surface with only approximately 4% alveolar O_2, and this is close to the point of unconsciousness. We had three men lose consciousness at the level of 25 feet on the way back up, and this is a problem. We have another problem. Ordinary passive breathholding underwater involves no activity. With the drop, as you know, a man is heavy on the bottom, and it is necessary for him to seize the rope and pull himself up, which burns up a fair amount of oxygen. I cannot adequately compare the two.

Chairman Davis: I want to share with you an idea suggested by one of the members as an observation and comment at the end of the last discussion about the urinary effects and the diuresis. I suggested that, if there are these very large volumes of diuresis, there may be a significant loss of carbon dioxide in the urine, and that perhaps this is the answer to one of these imbalances in the balance sheet that we heard about in the previous session. I believe this was really a plea to those who are conducting blood studies in the future under these circumstances to supplement these studies with adequate urine measurements, both quantity and quality. Perhaps this will solve one of those unsolved questions.

PART SIX

Toxicological Problems in Confined Spaces

Chairman

DR. K. YAGLOU
School of Public Health
Harvard University
Boston, Massachusetts

Threshold Limit Values for Hydrocarbons and Ozones in Confined Spaces

ANTON A. TAMAS

Aeromedical Laboratories, Wright-Patterson Field, Ohio

The inhabitants of true submersible or space cabins will depend completely on an artificial atmosphere. Toxic gases will saturate this atmosphere in a relatively short time unless they are removed by filtration. Large and complex filter systems impose a great penalty in weight which is especially prohibitive in space applications. Therefore, the establishment of safe and tolerable concentrations of these toxic agents is of primary importance in establishing design criteria for such vehicles.

Exposure to toxic material is a daily occurrence in many industries. Threshold Limit Values (TLV) are defined, revised, and published annually by the Committee on TLV of the American Conference of Governmental Industrial Hygienists (ACGIH). As defined, these values are maximum average atmospheric concentrations to which workers normally may be exposed 8 hours a day, 5 days a week, 50 weeks a year for an indefinite number of years.

Even under seemingly rigid standards, experience has proved many a TLV to be inadequate. This is especially true in the case of hydrocarbons, extensively used for industrial processes. Within the last 10 years, the TLV of carbon tetrachloride has been lowered from 100 to 25 parts per million (ppm), benzene has followed exactly the same pattern, chloroform has been lowered from 400 to 100 ppm, and ethyl chloride has undergone a drastic reduction of from 4000 to 1000 ppm. These examples illustrate a fourfold reduction of TLV in a 10-year period.

Another important feature of the TLV is the extensive variation of safety margin from one compound to another. Some were designed with an arbitrary safety factor of 10, while others were based on the absence of observable pathology at those levels. But a negative pathological finding may indicate only ability of the organism to manage on the "pay-as-you-go" basis. Finally, it can not be said that all existing TLV have stood the pragmatic test of prolonged

343

critical investigation or that they are applicable to uninterrupted exposures for 24 hours a day, day after day.

Nevertheless, despite all shortcomings, the TLV should not be regarded so much in error as to require huge or imponderable factors of safety in application to space travel or to prolonged confinement in a true submersible. It is true that the interrupted 40-hour weekly exposure will be replaced by an uninterrupted 168-hour week, this fourfold increase of exposure time being characteristic of confinement. Following the basic concept of toxicology, i.e., that the ultimate toxic effect (k) of any absorbed agent is proportional to the concentration of the agent (c) and the duration of time (t), expressed as $k = ct$, the lowering of present TLV to one fourth their original value could perhaps balance the equation and might possibly result in satisfactory protection. However, such a rule-of-thumb procedure will not endure critical analysis with many materials.

The cardinal weakness of such generalization is that it ignores the physiology of continuous exposure. Any chemical insult, slight as it might be, imposes a stress upon the organism. When the stress is withdrawn, restoration of the pre-stress condition will not occur immediately; the rate of recovery depending upon the degree of deterioration and the recuperative powers of the organism. In continuous exposure, no allowance can be made for recovery. Instead of a "pay-as-you-go" mechanism, a "compound-interest" summation of stress damage is likely to be encountered.

For the purpose of continuous exposure, toxic agents could be divided to fit one of four categories with respect to physiological response.

Category I would include those agents which at low concentrations will equilibrate within the organism very quickly. If equilibrium is reached in a matter of hours, and at a level where physiological compensation is still effective, continuous exposure should be of little consequence, as with carbon monoxide, fluorides, lead, etc.

Category II is made up of those materials to which a certain tolerance can be developed. Recent investigations indicate that such may be the case with ozone. It was found that short exposure to 1 ppm can increase tolerance considerably up to several months duration (Stockinger, 1958).

Category III, the largest group, covers all materials which exhibit slow clearance or cumulative properties. Unfortunately, many hydrocarbons belong to this category (xylene, carbon tetrachloride, etc.).

Category IV is represented by the materials which could be placed on a "none or all" basis. Even trace quantities could be hazardous for continuous exposure, and should be eliminated from the list of cabin materials. At least one hydrocarbon, benzene, should be regarded as such.

Another feature of confined spaces is a simultaneous exposure to a multitude of trace contaminants, some originating with man himself and his excretion products. The possibility of *synergistic and antagonistic* effects cannot be overlooked. A further complication is the presence of ionizing radiation, especially in space cabins. Antagonistic interaction, resulting in a protective effect, was demonstrated by exposing animals to nitrogen dioxide at the half-lethal dose (LD_{50}) level in the presence of hydrogen sulfide. A significant reduction of mortality from nitrogen dioxide was noted in the presence of as little as 0.5 ppm hydrogen sulfide (Stockinger, 1958).

Contrariwise, synergistic interaction, resulting in potentially more hazardous material, was well illustrated in the case of ozone-olefin reactions, as described by Saltzman (1958). As a result of these reactions, an appreciable level of organic, free radicals is produced together with highly reactive intermediates. One such reaction product, ketene, is presently being studied by Stockinger and is estimated to be 10 times more toxic than ozone itself.

Finally, if one has to consider the summation of small chemical insults as a stress, it certainly would be foolhardy to ignore the other tremendous stresses necessarily present in space vehicles. It is beyond question that the psychological stress will be incomparable to anything previously experienced. In addition, acceleration, weightlessness and thermal conditions will impose unknown degrees of physical stresses, leaving little margin for chemical stress. This narrow margin will be further endangered by the presence of unknown amounts of radiation. There is little doubt that the human inhabitant of a space capsule will be pushed to the limit of endurance. The loss of the individual would be a major catastrophy and probably would curtail space attempts considerably. Therefore, in determining TLV for confined spaces, the basic objective should be *not merely the avoidance of toxic effects but also the preservation of comfortable conditions conducive to efficient performance.*

It is obvious that the *duration of the trip* will be of prime importance. As long as comfort levels are maintained, the chemical stress resulting from continuous exposure will be relatively small if the duration of the mission does *not exceed 2 weeks.* The same is true of submersible vehicles which can surface when necessary. Consequently, the "rule-of-thumb" reduction of TLV for hydrocarbons by a factor of 4 should provide reasonably safe target figures. Thermal decomposition products from hydrocarbons, such as aldehydes, ketones, and peroxides, should not be allowed because of their irritating properties and the possibility of forming free radicals resulting in discomfort to the crew. Ozone concentration should not exceed the 0.1 ppm TLV.

No definite target values can be given for *flight periods exceeding 2 weeks* because of the lack of experimental data for continuous exposure. Materials in Categories I and II will probably pose no major problem with the judicious use of a safety factor of 4 or 5. Category IV materials should be excluded. Category III materials should be investigated not only for continuous exposures but also in the presence of thermal and gravitational stresses. There is a tremendous need for hard, basic research in this area. In addition, antagonistic and synergistic effects should be studied, preferably in a "closed loop" system.

In summary, a coordinated effort of biologists and engineers will be necessary in order to provide safe TLV for prolonged confinement to space and submersible cabins. Such an all-out effort should include the following minimum requirements:

1. Research on k values for continuous exposure.
2. Research on response to stress during continuous exposure.
3. Evaluation of applicable results of existing air pollution and smog studies.
4. Consultation with the ACGIH Committee relative to TLV for space and submarine application.
5. Consultation with research and development engineers to insure proper selection of capsule materials and, if possible, substitution with nontoxic material.

REFERENCES

Personal communications with Dr. H. Stockinger, 1958. U.S. Public Health Service, Occupational Health Field HQ., Cincinnati.

Saltzman, B. E. 1958. "Kinetic studies of formation of atmospheric oxidants," Ind. Eng. Chem. 50: 677–82.

Effects of Chronic Exposure to Low Concentrations of Carbon Monoxide

M. H. WEEKS

U. S. Army Chemical Center, Ft. Detrick, Maryland

The metabolism of CO and the signs and symptoms of acute CO poisoning have been well studied both in animals and humans. However, the existence of chronic CO poisoning has been questioned by clinicians and investigators. Some workers believe that chronic CO poisoning is the result of repeated acute exposures and their sequelae. Others believe that it is a distinct syndrome produced from repeated exposure to low concentrations of CO which cause no acute subjective or objective signs but may affect the organism functionally, leading eventually to injury.

The purpose of our work was to find out whether prolonged continuous exposure of animals to low concentrations of CO would produce objective responses that could be utilized for arriving at a safe maximum concentration for men on prolonged confinement in closed spaces.

We were also interested in investigating the relative rates of absorption of several low concentrations of CO in animals under continuous exposure, and the effect of an increase in CO in the air upon the rate of formation of COHb after an equilibrium had been attained at lower CO levels.

The first phase of our study involved a 3-month continuous exposure of animals to 50 ppm of CO inside a 20,000-liter dynamic gassing chamber. The gas was introduced into the chamber from a pressure cylinder at a rate of 100 ml/min to give a concentration of 50 ppm CO; this was checked daily by analysis of chamber air samples (Beatty, 1955; Adams and Simmons, 1951). Male dogs, male and female rats, and rabbits were used as experimental animals. A similar group of animals matched for sex and weight were used as controls.

The average CO concentration in the chamber during the 3-month exposure was 50.9 ppm; CO_2 content ranged between 600–1300 ppm and NH_3 content varied from 20 to 50 ppm. The corresponding average CO content of the blood of the exposed animals, as determined by the Scholander-Roughton method (1943), was 6.4% of saturation of the hemoglobin for dogs, 3.0% for rabbits, and 1.6% for rats. Exposed dogs showed a rise in hemoglobin of 12%, in hematocrit of 9%, and a possible increase in RBC's. A small increase in the eosinophil count in rats was found. There was no significant difference between exposed and control animals for reticulocytes, WBC's, and differentials. Macroscopic examination of organs and microscopic examination of tissues showed no differences between control and exposed animals. Dogs showed no behavioral changes; their general physical condition remained good, and their ECG's were normal. The relative voluntary activity of exposed and control male rats as measured by means of activity cages was not significantly different.

It was observed that the CO content of the blood of each animal species, after equilibrium had been attained, stayed constant throughout the exposure. However, the slight rise in hemoglobin and hematocrit of dogs, coupled with possible increase in RBC's, suggested some acclimatization in this species. These changes are suggestive of a possible slight polycythemia and CO asphyxia, and constitute the only indication of a positive metabolic response of our animals to 50 ppm CO.

Brieger (1944) has found that true chronic CO poisoning, evidenced by polycythemia, can be produced in animals exposed daily to 96 ppm CO. However, he has seen no evidence of protoplasmatic poisoning but only asphyxia.

Lewey and Drabkin (1944) reported on daily exposure of dogs to 100 ppm CO lasting six months. They found definite though mild toxic signs in their exposed animals. A carboxyhemoglobin concentration of 20% saturation, which was determined by a spectrophotometric method, was found after each daily exposure, with the blood free from CO the next morning. In addition to behavioral and hematological changes they found rather definite morphologic changes in the heart muscle and central nervous system. These alterations could be paralleled in type and locale to those found in acute CO poisoning, but differed quantitatively in that they were smaller, more scattered and less destructive.

From experiments in our laboratory on the formation of COHb by dogs we have found that after 24 hours exposure to CO, 50 ppm produced 6% of saturation of the hemoglobin, 100 ppm 12.6%, 200 ppm 21%, and 300 ppm 31%. There was also close agreement between man and dog for saturation of the hemoglobin by CO at these concentrations. The differences between our findings and those of Lewey and Drabkin on the saturation of the blood by CO may well be ascribed to differences in methodology either in the analyses of air samples or of the blood for CO. The experiments of Brieger and Lewey show that chronic intoxication may occur in dogs at carbon monoxide concentrations which are considered safe for man.

In the case of man, however, the most pertinent data found in the literature are those of Sievers (1942) on traffic officers exposed daily to about 70 ppm CO in the Holland Tunnel. These men, whose blood COHb concentration ranged from 0.5 to 13.1% of saturation, showed no abnormalities, over a 13-year observation period, that could be attributed to carbon monoxide poisoning. However, results obtained in intermittent exposures cannot be directly applied to continuous exposures.

The slight changes or lack of positive toxic signs in our dogs, rats, and rabbits suggest no harmful toxic effects from a continuous 3-month exposure of animals to 50 ppm CO. It would, therefore, seem, on the strength of comparable hemoglobin saturation in man, as in dogs, that a concentration of 50 ppm CO would be safe for continuous human exposure.

The question of chronic CO poisoning still remains unanswered. We hope to carry out additional experiments at relatively high concentrations of CO that may help resolve this question.

REFERENCES

Adams, E. G., and N. T. Simmons. 1951. "The determination of carbon monoxide by means of iodine pentoxide," J. Appl. Chem. 1, Suppl. I: 520.
Beatty, R. L. 1955. "Methods for detecting and determining carbon monoxide," Bur. Mines Bull. 557.
Brieger, H. 1944. "Carbon monoxide polycythemia," J. Ind. Hyg. and Toxicol. 26.
Lewey, F. H., and D. L. Drabkin. 1944. "Experimental chronic carbon monoxide poisoning of dogs," Am. J. Med. Sci. 208: (4).
Scholander, P. F., and J. W. Roughton. 1943. "Gasometric estimation of the blood gases, II. carbon monoxide," J. Biol. Chem. 148: 551.
Sievers, R. F., T. I. Edwards, A. L. Murray, and H. H. Schrentk. 1942. "Effect of exposure to known concentrations of carbon monoxide. A study of traffic officers stationed at the Holland Tunnel for thirteen years," J. Am. Med. Assoc. 118: 585.
Sievers, R. F., T. I. Edwards, and A. L. Murray. 1942. "A medical study of men exposed to measured amounts of carbon monoxide in the Holland Tunnel for 13 years," Public Health Bull. No. 278.

Physiological and Toxicological Significance of Atmospheric Condensation Nuclei

FRITZ VERZAR

Anatomische Anstalt der Universität, Basel, Switzerland

The air we breathe is not simply a mixture of gases, but a colloidal system in which atoms, molecules, and aggregates of molecules up to the size of visible dusts are present. Conventionally, solid particles which have radii from 0.15 to 0.2 mm are classified as dusts, while particles with radii of 0.1 to 0.001 μ are classified as atmospheric condensation nuclei. The larger nuclei of 0.1 μ diameter are largely responsible for the formation of fog and rain. However, fog and rain can also produce nuclei of 0.001 μ diameter.

The counting of these nuclei is done by means of a Wilson chamber, where the pressure is either decreased by 22–25% (Aitken and Scholz) or increased to 122–125% of the original pressure, and then suddenly released as in the Pollak counter. Our own counter (Gutzwiller and Verzar, 1946) was an automatic one operating on the latter principle.

The nuclei are so small that even when inspired in large quantities they produce no untoward effects by themselves alone. However, with carcinogenetic or radioactive particles distinct effects may result.

The nuclei may play an important biological role when saturated air is cooled. The droplets condensing on nuclei can then dissolve toxic gas molecules from the air or can precipitate mechanically insoluble suspended particles.

Years ago (Gutzwiller and Verzar, 1946) we performed the following experiment: NH_3 gas at low concentration was introduced into a glass bell jar containing filtered, saturated air (see Fig. 1). When the pressure was suddenly decreased by 22% no fog was formed. A water-filled pan on the bottom of the jar still contained only very small quantities of NH_3. If, however, cigarette smoke was added to the air to increase the number of nuclei, the same pressure decrease produced fog and the droplets contained much NH_3 as shown by titration (see Fig. 2). The increased concentration was proportional to the

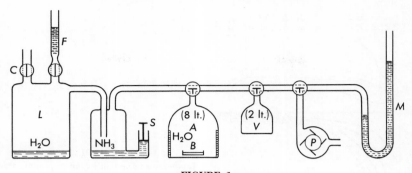

FIGURE 1.
Fog formation apparatus.

number of nuclei present in the jar, and to the number of newly formed droplets which dissolved the NH_3 gas from the air. In a similar experiment, grass
pollen was precipitated from the air by the fog droplets in large amounts in
the presence of high nucleus count. The pollen was microscopically counted
on slides placed inside the jar.

The condensation nuclei may play an important role on health in the following way: the concentration of a toxic gas in the air normally is below the
physiological threshold for smell or taste, and well below the toxicological
threshold. If, however, the gas is dissolved and concentrated in the fog droplets, a toxicological threshold may be reached, so that inspiration of the fog
may result in inflammation of the respiratory tract, lungs or bronchi. Absorption into the blood stream may produce effects on the nervous or circulatory
system.

There is another basic fact to be considered. Fog formation, and the consequent enrichment of toxic substances can occur not only in the free atmosphere, but also inside the body in the upper respiratory tract (see Fig. 3). Measurements of temperature and humidity (Gutzwiller and Verzar, 1946) inside the

FIGURE 2.

NH_3 precipitation as related to
ACN (atmospheric condensation
nuclei).

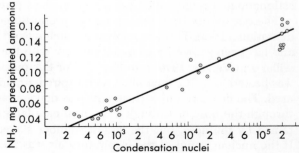

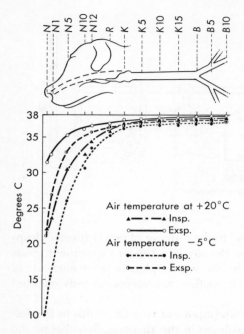

FIGURE 3.

Temperature gradient in the respiratory tract of a dog.

Air temperature at +20°C
▲— · —▲ Insp.
○————○ Exsp.

Air temperature −5°C
●·······● Insp.
○− − − −○ Exsp.

nose and bronchi, showed that in the dog, as well as in man, between the nose and the region of the larynx, the water-saturated expired air at a temperature of 38° C (see Fig. 4) mixes with inspired room air which has a temperature of 20°C or less. The cooling of the two streams of air can produce precipitation by fog formation, and concentration of toxic substances which might be present in the air. To repeat again, this precipitation is dependent on the presence of condensation nuclei, since the number of fog droplets formed increases with the number of nuclei present. In filtered air, free of nuclei, a toxic gas or allergic substance may not reach the threshold of toxicity in the respiratory tract. However, if the person inhales air rich in nuclei, as in a room full of smoke and therefore high nucleus count, the result may be unpleasant. This phenomenon is well known in allergic persons who may suddenly become asthmatic in a room which has a high nucleus count due to cigarette smoke.

The respiratory tract retains a large proportion of ACN (atmospheric condensation nuclei). This was known to Amelung and Landsberg for many years, and has been shown by us quantitatively with the automatic counter (Gutzwiller and Verzar, 1946) (see Fig. 5). For this purpose our nuclei counter first was heated to 37°C, then filled with expired air, and the nucleus count measured. The first series of experiments was done on anesthetized dogs breathing through the nose or through a tracheal canula. Some of the nuclei were retained by the nose, but the largest number stayed in the lung and bronchi. If the nucleus count of the inspiratory air was increased by cigarette smoke

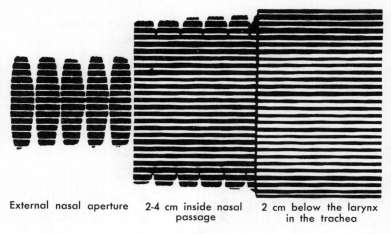

External nasal aperture   2-4 cm inside nasal   2 cm below the larynx
                              passage   in the trachea

FIGURE 4.
Humidity in the respiratory tract of a dog.

to 100,000/cc or more, relatively larger quantities of nuclei were retained by the nose. The number of ACN decreased in the whole of the respiratory tract (nose respiration) by 73.6% and 76.6% with normal air and smoky air respectively. The corresponding decrease in the lung (tracheal canula respiration) was 60.7% and 71.1% respectively.

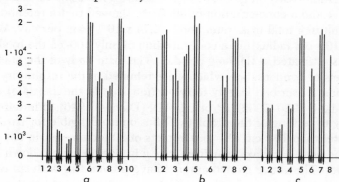

FIGURE 5.
Retention of nuclei in a dog, a and b, and c in a man. For each measurement three recordings (parallel lines) were made.

(a) dog (permanent trachael cannula): (1) 10—calibration, (2) 5—room air, (3) expiratory air (trachea), (4) expiratory air (nose and mouth), (6) 9—smoky room air, (7) expiratory air (trachea), and (8) expiratory air (nose and mouth).

(b) dog (permanent trachael cannula): (1) 9—calibration, (2) 5—smoky room air, dry (relative humidity 30–35%), (3) expiratory air (trachea), (4) expiratory air (trachea), inspired air humidified, (6) expiratory air (nose and mouth), (7) expiratory air (nose and mouth), inspired air humidified, and (8) smoky room air, wet, (relative humidity 80–90%).

(c) subject H: (1) 8—calibration, (2) 4—room air, (3) expiratory air, (5) 7—smoky room air, and (6) expiratory air (nose and mouth).

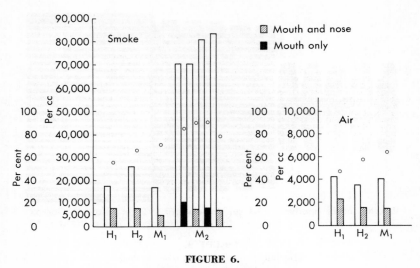

FIGURE 6.
Retention of nuclei in man.

Experiments in man breathing through the nose gave similar results. The retention with filtered and smoky air was 47% and 90% respectively (see Fig. 6).

A calculation based on globular nuclei having a radius of 10^{-6} cm, a specific gravity of 1 and a concentration of 4000/cc, showed that a retention of 50% would result in a total mass retention of 5.74 x 10^{-8} gram per day. With large nuclei of 10^{-4} cm radius and a concentration of only 100/cc the total mass retained was estimated at 2.95 mg per day. The main body of the nuclei was in the droplets of condensation which were retained in the respiratory tract.

Retention is ascribed largely to *impaction*, due to the inertia of the particles (Landahl, 1950–1952), (Protz, 1941), (Davies, 1946), (Findeisen, 1935), and partly to settling of the droplets. Diffusion is negligible for particles with radii greater than 10^{-5} cm (0.1 μ). Droplets of 20 μ diameter do not penetrate beyond the nose. However, particles $>$ / μ in size go further down the respiratory tract. The above named authors have proved this with spray droplets of triphenylphosphate, corn oil, $NaHCO_3$, etc. They thought that a minimum retention in the nose occurs for particles somewhere between 0.25–0.55 μ. However, gases were retained also with an efficiency up to 90%. Our own work showed a retention of 50–80% for particles of 0.1–0.001 μ, in the upper respiratory tract between the nose and the larynx.

The origin of condensation nuclei in high altitudes is thought to be partly oceanic (NaCl) and partly meteoric or volcanic. To these should be added ACN of human origin, due to smoking, and also nuclei that are produced by sunrays acting on impurities present in very small quantities in the air (Gutzwiller and Verzar, 1946). Junge (in press) has lately called attention to traces of H_2S and SO_2 which are always present in the air of occupied spaces. We have recently shown that H_2S in air is readily transformed into nuclei, probably SO_4, by the photochemical action of sunrays. SO_2 formed nuclei even in the dark. Ammonia gas also formed nuclei under the influence of sunlight.

It would therefore seem important from the physiological standpoint that the air of confined spaces be filtered through several layers of cotton-wool to remove nuclei and dusts, and that formation of new nuclei by sunrays be precluded.

SUMMARY

The number of atmospheric condensation nuclei affects the condition of air in confined spaces. Droplets condensing on nuclei can precipitate toxic substances from the air and raise the concentration to toxic levels. This can occur in the ambient air or in the respiratory tract during normal respiration. Temperature and humidity measurements show that this precipitation takes place mainly on mucous membranes between the nose and the larynx.

Condensation nuclei of atmospheric or human origin (smoking) can be filtered out. Sunrays can produce nuclei in air by photochemical action on trace substances and should, therefore, be prevented from entering the confined space.

REFERENCES

Gutzwiller, N., and F. Verzar. 1946. "Beeinflussang der Ausfällung von atmosphérischen Verunreinigungen durch die Zahl der Kondensationskerne," Helv. Physiol. Acta 4: C 15.

Junge, Ch. In press. III Symposium on Atmospheric Condensation Nuclei, Vol. VII, p. 14. Cambridge, 1958.

Landahl, H. D., T. N. Tracewell, and W. H. Lassen. 1950–1952. "Retention of airborne particulates in the human lung," A.M.A. Arch. Ind. Hygiene and Occup. Med. 1: 36–45 1950; 3: 359–366; 6: 508–511.

Verzar, F. 1955. "Continuous record of atmospheric condensed nuclei and of their retention in the respiratory tract," Geofisica pura et appl. 31: 183–190.

Verzar, F. 1953. "Kondensationskernzahler mit automatischer Registrierung," J. Meteorol. A 5: 372–376; A 6: 211–212.

Verzar, F. 1954. "Retention atm. Kondensationskerne in den Atemwegen," Helv. Physiol. Acta 12: C 92–94. Verzar, F., F. Hugin, and W. Massion. 1955. Pflügers Arch.

Verzar, F., J. Keith, und V. Parchert. 1953. "Temperatur aund Feuchtigkeit der Luft in den Atemwegen," Pflügers Arch. 25F: 400–416.

The Physiological Significance of Positive and Negative Ionization of the Atmosphere

ALBERT PAUL KRUEGER and RICHARD FURNALD SMITH

Department of Bacteriology and Naval Biological Laboratory, Naval Medical Research Unit #1[1], University of California, Berkeley, California

It is axiomatic that investigators in scientific fields stand upon the shoulders of their predecessors. This certainly applies to those of us who labor in the phase of medical climatology which deals with the physiological effects of air ions; it would be a grievous error to conceive of the subject as something born of the atomic age.

In 1780, not long after Benjamin Franklin (1751) and Dalibard (1752) had independently established the fact that atmospheric electricity exists, the Abbé Bertholon (1780) published a book of observations on its therapeutic properties. Subsequently a number of physicians and naturalists worked along similar lines and went so far as to link electricity in the air to the physical distress induced by the Föhn, Sirocco, and other winds of ill repute.

Coulomb in 1795 demonstrated the fact that air conducts electricity, but it was not until 1899 that this ability to conduct was proven by Elster and Geitel (1899) to reside in positively and negatively charged particles of molecular size or larger which they called "ions." By 1901 Czermak had advocated the hypothesis that positive ions exert adverse effects on weather-sensitive persons. During the first 20 years of this century several investigators, exemplified by Sokolof (1904) and Steffens (1910), further implicated naturally occurring ions as the mediators of atmospheric electricity but it remained for Dessauer and his colleagues to construct an apparatus for generating ions with which they could expose humans and animals to unipolar ions at will. Using this equipment, they did a prodigious amount of work on the physiological and therapeutic effects of ions and in 1931 published their results (Dessauer, 1931). As a direct result of this stimulus the 1930's witnessed the initiation of

[1] The opinions contained in this report are not to be construed as reflecting the views of the Naval Service.

TABLE 1

The major forces responsible for air ion formation in nature.

---

(1) Radiation from: (a) Radioactive substances in the soil
                        (b) Radioactive gases produced by decay of (a)
(2) Cosmic radiation
(3) Electrical discharges
(4) Short-wave ultraviolet light
(5) Frictional electricity generated by:
        (a) Rain or waterfall droplets
        (b) Blowing sand, dust, snow

---

exploratory research in many directions by a truly cosmopolitan array of investigators. Although the war interfered seriously with this activity, the seeds were sown and when hostilities ceased and improved methods became available for generating ions, vigorous growth was resumed. The deep interest of engineers, physicists, physicians, climatologists, and biologists in both fundamental and applied aspects of the subject has guaranteed the continuity of this phase up to the present time.

Air ions are essentially particles consisting of molecules or molecular complexes of atmospheric constituents that have acquired an electrical charge by losing or gaining an electron. They are formed as ion pairs in nature; for the most part by the forces listed in Table 1.

Conventionally, we recognize three groups of ions based on size and mobility: large, intermediate, and small ions as indicated in Table 2.

The natural forces already enumerated result in the continual renewal of the terrestrial atmosphere's content of ions so that the air normally contains 500–2000 small and intermediate + ions/ml of air and a slightly smaller number of − ions.

Two methods are commonly employed to measure air ion concentrations. In the first, the ions are collected on a series of thoroughly insulated polarizing plates arranged in a duct. Air is drawn past the plates and the current resulting from the deposition of ions is measured with a micro-microammeter (Fleming, 1939; Hicks and Beckett, 1957). The second method involves a target probe (Fig. 1) such as that designed by Beckett (Krueger *et al.*, 1958). It is

TABLE 2

	Diameter in μ	Average mobility cm/sec in field of 1 volt/cm
Large (Langevin) ions	0.03–0.10	0.0005
Intermediate ions	0.003–0.03	0.05
Small ions	0.001–0.003	1.0

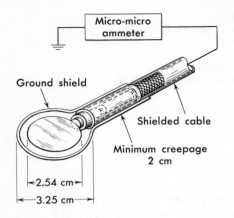

FIGURE 1.
Ion current probe. (*Designed by J. C. Beckett*)

especially useful when an organism or tissue is being exposed to ions migrating in an electrostatic field. By substituting it in the same position as the object under exposure, the ions impinge upon it. They produce a minute current which can be measured and converted into ions/cm²/sec.

A basic improvement in technique now utilizes radioisotopes to generate unipolar gaseous ions completely free from adventitious by-products. Tritium (H^3) or polonium (Po^{210}) are prepared in sealed foils and their respective β or α radiations produce ion pairs in the adjacent atmosphere (Fig. 2). A rectifying circuit removes the unwanted ions on a metal plate and the ions of desired charge move in the electrical field to the object undergoing exposure (Skilling and Beckett, 1953; Beckett and Hicks).

In this fashion air can readily be modified to contain 1×10^5 or 1×10^6 unipolar light ions/ml. At this point if one were to apply reason instead of experimentation in evaluating the physiological potentialities of air ions he would be tempted to conclude on strictly *a priori* grounds that they must be conspicuously lacking in the production of biological effects. To begin with, we are confronted by the fact that air contains 27×10^{18} molecules/ml while we produce at best some 1×10^6 unipolar ions in each ml. The result is that we have only one ionized molecule in each 27 trillion molecules. Besides being an extremely highly diluted molecular species there is little about the gaseous ion which would predict a capability to influence living systems. Compared to the various types of radiation it moves very slowly indeed and would appear to have no outstanding attributes other than possession of a + or − electrical charge. Despite these logical objections there exists very convincing evidence that gaseous ions are biologically significant.

The literature contains numerous observations on the direct effects of air ions on tissues and on their more remote actions, both in health and in disease. For example, Yaglou *et al.* (1933) reported irritation of the nasal mucosa due to positive ions; recently Winsor and Beckett (1958) have confirmed and extended this report. Happel (1931) observed the acceleration of respiration by positive ions and deceleration by negative ions. Kornblueh and his colleagues (1958) found that the symptoms of hay fever were relieved by negative ions. Nielsen and Harper (1954) noted a reduction of the succinoxidase content of the adrenal gland when rats were exposed to inhalation of positive ions, and Worden (1954) reported that negative ions increased the carbon dioxide combining power of hamster plasma. These are only a few citations of many published papers which, taken together, emphasize the role of air ions in altering bodily functions.

Our own work in this area began some three years ago and has been limited to direct effects of high mobility, light ions on cells and tissues. Our first experiments dealt with the action of ions on staphylococci (1957) and it was soon evident that measurable effects occurred only under certain special conditions. It was necessary to suspend the organisms in distilled water and expose them in droplets sufficiently small to provide a high ratio of surface area to volume. When this was done the data obtained indicated an increased rate of death due to direct action of negative and positive ions on the cells (Fig. 3). There was, in addition, an increased rate of evaporation from the droplets (Fig. 4) as a result of the prevailing minute electrostatic wind. The lethal action was not of great magnitude and required relatively long periods of time to become manifest.

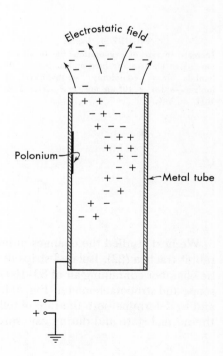

FIGURE 2.
Ion generator. Positive ions are being removed and negative ions are moving out in the electrostatic field.

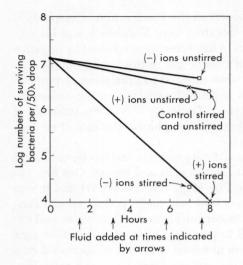

FIGURE 3. (*left*)

Direct lethal action of + and − air ions on staphylococci suspended in 50-lambda drops. Volume kept constant by additions of distilled water as indicated by arrows. H³ ionizer used → 1.6 × 10⁹ air ions/cm²/sec at 4 cm. R.H. = 40%.

FIGURE 4. (*right*)

Increase in rate of evaporation due to air ions moving in electrostatic field and acting on 100-lambda drops containing staphylococci. H³ ionizer → 1.6 × 10⁹ air ions/cm²/sec at 4 cm. R.H. = 78%.

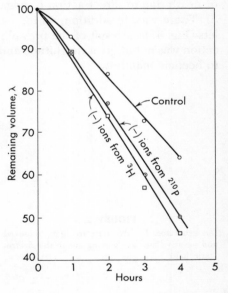

We next studied the changes induced by air ions in the functioning of the rabbit trachea (22). Isolated strips of trachea were placed in a glass and plastic chamber containing air of 80–100% relative humidity. By means of a microscope and strobotachometer (Fig. 5) it was possible to observe the tissue surface and to determine both the rate of ciliary action and the rate of mucus flow in the normal state and during exposure to high densities of unipolar ions.

Positive ions brought about:
1. A prompt reduction in ciliary flicker.
2. A decrease in rate of mucus flow
3. Contracture of the posterior tracheal wall
4. Drying of the epithelial surface
5. An increase in susceptibility of cilia to trauma (Figs. 6 and 7)

Negative ions:
1. Raised the rate of ciliary flicker
2. Accelerated mucus flow
3. Reversed the effects of positive ions on ciliary flicker, mucus flow, and contracture of the tracheal wall.

In further experiments (1958), we have extended our observations to the trachea of the living rabbit, rat, and mouse (Fig. 8). Animals exposed to high mobility positive air ions administered through a tracheotomy aperture displayed the same general response we had obtained with the extirpated strip. However, the presence of an intact circulation permitted development of vascular changes, i.e., very slight trauma resulted in prompt and exaggerated formation of a dilated capillary web or even a persistent ecchymosis. Treatment of the normal trachea with negative ions raised the ciliary rate; when applied to tissues depressed by previous exposure to positive ions, negative ions reversed most of the functional changes.

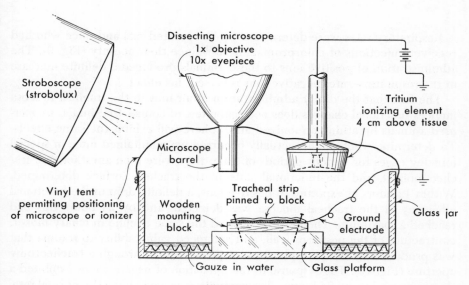

FIGURE 5.

Arrangement for observing effect of air ions on isolated rabbit trachea.

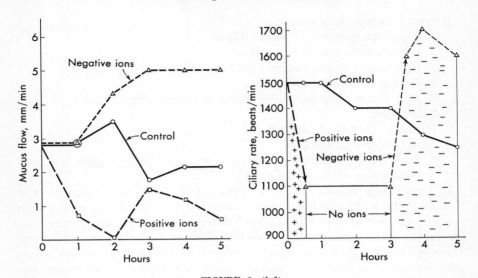

FIGURE 6. (*left*)

Effect of unipolar air ions on rate of mucus flow on surface of isolated rabbit trachea.

FIGURE 7. (*right*)

Inhibitory effect of + air ions on ciliary activity of isolated rabbit trachea. Reversal of inhibition by
− air ions.

Respiratory rates were determined for unoperated rats and mice who had
received injections of chlorpromazine to reduce their activity (Fig. 9). The
administration of positive ions to these animals produced a definite increase
in the respiratory rate; negative ions reversed this effect.

The fact that the direct administration of air ions to the tracheal mucosa
induces functional changes does not guarantee, of course, that intact, *unoperated* animals breathing an ionized atmosphere will exhibit the same effects.
To determine whether this actually occurred we maintained mice in special
ionizing cages for various periods of time; they were then anesthetized, tracheotomized, and the functional state of the tracheal surface determined.
Within 12 hours of exposure to positive ions, a definite drop in the functional
efficiency of the tracheal mucosa was detected, and by 24 hours this had
reached a maximum. The animals showed the same decline in ciliary flicker,
contracture of the posterior wall, and enhanced vulnerability to trauma that
was produced by direct application of positive ions through a tracheotomy
aperture (Fig. 10). The response to the inhalation of negative ions exhibited a
slower onset, but by 24 hours ciliary activity was well above the normal rate;
no other functional changes appeared in the animals exposed to negative ions.

It is clear from the experiments on unoperated animals that sufficient numbers of ions can be inhaled to profoundly influence the functioning of the tracheal mucosa and, presumably, other parts of the respiratory tree.

The atmosphere is a mixture of gases so it is essential to determine which constituents in an ionized state are responsible for inducing the functional changes just described. In a series of experiments conducted with tracheal strips and living animals exposed to ionized and non-ionized nitrogen, carbon dioxide and oxygen (1958), we were able to demonstrate that negatively ionized oxygen increased the rate of ciliary activity, while positively ionized carbon dioxide reduced it (Figs. 11 and 12).

Recently we have investigated the effects of these gaseous ions on enzyme systems. We have obtained results suggesting a direct action on cytochrome oxidase and related iron-porphyrin compounds.

The sum total of published work on the subject of air ions and our own experience of the last three years leads us to evaluate the present situation somewhat as follows:

1. Air ions unquestionably participate as physiological mediators and, as such, condition certain of our reactions to the ambient atmosphere. This would include the terrestrial atmosphere in general and would extend to the enclosed spaces of our living and working environments.

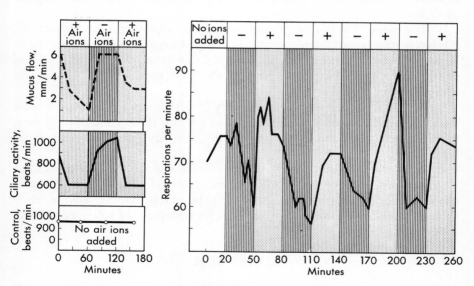

FIGURE 8. (left)

Inhibition of mucus flow rate and ciliary activity of living, tracheotomized rabbit by + air ions. Reversal of inhibition by − air ions.

FIGURE 9. (right)

Effect of + and − air ions on respiratory rate of unoperated, resting rat. Chlorpromazine HCl administered to induce resting state.

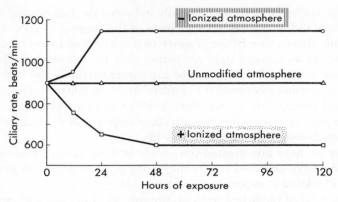

FIGURE 10.

Effect of + and − air ions on intact ambulatory mice. Mice were removed at intervals from ionizing and control cages and anesthetized with nembutal. Ciliary rates were determined through tracheal apertures. Each point represents average values for 2 mice.

2. Positive ions in excess are harmful; they induce discomfort and reduce the efficiency of the respiratory tract. Negative ions, within limits, promote comfort and health and are capable of reversing certain of the effects of positive ions.

3. The mode of action of gaseous ions is just beginning to be understood. Positively charged CO_2 and negatively charged oxygen have been shown to be responsible for some of the physiological effects of positively ionized and negatively ionized atmospheres respectively. They apparently act directly on iron-porphyrin compounds.

4. Negative air ions provide a modality for the treatment of some disease states. They offer even greater promise as a factor in air conditioning, contributing to comfort and to the prevention of certain types of respiratory illness.

It seems reasonable to predict that the future will see the development of air ion control of living and working spaces much as we now have temperature and humidity control. This may prove to be an important element in establishing optimal environmental conditions for occupants of submersibles and sealed space cabins.

ADDENDUM

Ion-induced changes in the physiological state of the trachea tend to persist after the ion source is removed. When mice were kept in a positively ionized atmosphere for 72 hours and then removed to normal air, the typical (+) ion effects lasted at least 4 weeks. The evidence indicates that such functional alterations in the ciliated epithelium occur as the result of direct contact of

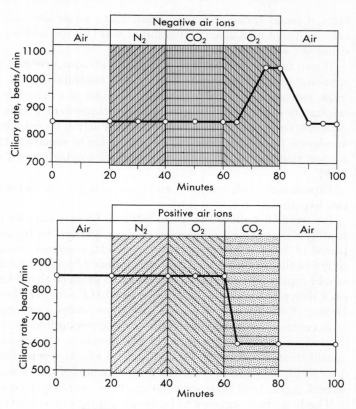

FIGURE 11. (*top*)

Test for unipolar (negative) gaseous ion action on ciliary activity of rabbit trachea in nitrogen, carbon dioxide, and oxygen. Only negative oxygen ions increase the rate of ciliary beat.

FIGURE 12. (*above*)

Test for unipolar (positive) gaseous ion action on ciliary activity of rabbit trachea in nitrogen, oxygen, and carbon dioxide. Only positive carbon dioxide ions decrease the rate of ciliary beat.

ions with surface cells and do not involve participation of the central nervous system or circulation. The number of ions required to produce a change in rate of ciliary beat is very small, approximately 2.5×10^3 $(-)$ ions/cm^2/sec and $> 1 \times 10^4$ $(+)$ ions/cm^2/sec.

Recent work has made it possible to postulate the biological mechanisms by which negatively charged oxygen and positively charged CO_2 produce their characteristic effects on the mammalian trachea.

All the tracheal effects attributed to $(+)$ air ions can be duplicated by the intravenous injection of 5-hydroxytryptamine. Like $(+)$ ion effects, the 5-HT effects can be reversed by treatment with $(-)$ air ions. On the basis of these facts, it seems reasonable to postulate that ($+$) air ions are "serotonin releasers," and that a local accumulation of 5-HT in the trachea is the immediate cause of ($+$) ion effects.

It can further be postulated that ($-$) air ions reverse ($+$) ion effects by speeding up the rate at which free 5-HT is oxidized. Like other oxidase systems, monamine oxidase is thought to consist of a dehydrogenase linked to a respiratory chain which may include cytochromes or flavins. Our experiments demonstrating that ($-$) ions have a direct action on cytochrome oxidase and accelerate the cytochrome-linked conversion of succinate to fumarate would suggest that this same action may produce a cytochrome-linked oxidation of 5-HT.

Experiments with reserpine and iproniazid provide indirect confirmation of this hypothesis.

Reserpine is believed to cause 5-HT to be momentarily released and then rapidly destroyed by monamine oxidase, so that the tissues are quickly depleted of 5-HT. If our hypothesis is correct, reserpine would produce a condition in the trachea resembling that induced by ($-$) air ions. Moreover, one would expect ($+$) air ions to be unable to produce their characteristic effects on a reserpine-treated animal, since the 5-HT necessary for ($+$) ion action is lacking. Both these expectations have been realized experimentally.

In contrast, iproniazid blocks the enzyme responsible for metabolizing 5-HT, so that an accumulation of free 5-HT develops. One would expect an iproniazid-treated animal to display tracheal effects resembling those produced by ($+$) air ions and to resist the normal action of ($-$) ions in reversing these effects. Again both these expectations have been experimentally confirmed.

The hypothesis appears to be borne out by experiments just completed in which negative ions decreased the concentrations of 5-HT in extirpated strips of rabbit trachea and in the respiratory tracts of living mice. An initial exposure of guinea pigs to ($-$) air ions caused a transient rise in urinary excretion of 5, hydroxyindoleacetic acid, the specific metabolite of 5-HT.

REFERENCES

Beckett, J. C., and W. W. Hicks. Patient Application Serial No. 640–434.

Bertholon, Abbé P. 1780. *De L'Electricité du Corps Humain dans L'Etat de Santé et de Maladie*, Bernuset, Lyon.

Coulomb, C. A. 1795. Men. de l'Acad. 616. Paris.

Czermak, P. 1901, 1902. Mitt. Wien. Akad. Wiss. *27*, and Physik. Z. *3:* 185.

Dalibard, T. F. 1752. Letter to Acad. de Sci.

Dessauer, F. 1931. *Zehn Jahre Forschung auf dem Physikalisch-Medizinischen Grenzgebiet*, Georg Thieme, Leipzig.

Elster, J., and H. Geitel. 1899. Physik. Z. *1:* 245.

Fleming, J. A. 1939. *Terrestrial Magnetism and Electricity*, McGraw-Hill Book Company, Inc., New York.

Franklin, B. 1751. Phil. Trans. Roy. Soc. London, 47: 289.
Happel, P., in Dessauer's work, cited above.
Hicks, W. W., and J. C. Beckett. 1957. Trans. Am. Inst. Elec. Engrs. Part I, No. 30, 108.
Kornblueh, I. H., G. M. Piersol, and F. P. Speicher. 1958. Am. J. Phys. Med. 37: 18.
Krueger, A. P., R. F. Smith, and Ing Gan Go. 1957. J. Gen. Physiol. 41: 359.
Krueger, A. P., and R. F. Smith. 1957. Proc. Soc. Exptl. Biol. & Med. 96: 807.
Krueger, A. P., and R. F. Smith. 1958. J. Gen. Physiol. 42: 69.
Krueger, A. P., and R. F. Smith. 1958. Proc. Soc. Exptl. Biol. & Med. 98: 412.
Krueger, A. P., W. W. Hicks, and J. C. Beckett. 1958. J. Franklin Inst. 266: 9.
Nielsen, C. B., and H. A. Harper. 1954. Proc. Soc. Exptl. Biol. & Med. 86: 753.
Skilling, H. H., and J. C. Beckett. 1953. J. Franklin Inst. 256: 423.
Sokolof, A. P. 1904. Die Ionisation u. Radiumaktivitaet der Atmosphaerischen Luft, Sanitätsmitteilung der russischen balneologischen Gesellschaft in Pjatigorsk.
Steffens, P. 1910. Witterungswechsel und Rheumatismus, Leipzig.
Winsor, T., and J. C. Beckett. 1958. Am. J. Phys. Med. 37: 83.
Worden, J. L. 1954. Fed. Proc. 13: 168.
Yaglou, C. P., L. C. Benjamin, and A. D. Brandt. 1933. Heating, Piping and Ventilating 5: 422.

DISCUSSION

Dr. Buettner: First, I should like to inquire of Dr. Tamas whether the results of studies on smogs containing O_3 can be utilized in any way to obtain information on the long-term effects of low O_3 concentrations. Secondly, to the paper of Dr. Verzar, I would like to add the following comment. The nuclei generally observed in counters of the type described are those produced with a relatively high super-saturation pressure of water vapor by expansion and adiabatic cooling. These conditions do not occur in the free atmosphere. If they did, we should always find an abundance of condensation nuclei in the atmosphere to make rain. Frequently, however, according to new research, the atmosphere lacks the proper kind and quantity of nuclei needed to produce clouds for rain. This is because the super-saturation pressure is extremely small, only a few hundredths of a per cent relative humidity.

Concerning Dr. Smith's paper, it is to be hoped that this work eventually will settle the long-debated question of possible effects of atmospheric ions on health and disease. Routine measurements of atmospheric electricity, and laboratory studies of possible effects on man, were abandoned about a decade ago. Renewed interest in laboratory studies resulted in new claims and a repetition of the state of affairs existing in the past. Despite the many books written on the subject, we still know very little about atmospheric ions, and it is difficult to evaluate the practical importance of the new findings.

Dr. Tamas: I was referring to the smog studies because there is an apparent parallelism between our problems. People concerned with smog are studying the hydrocarbon and ozone reaction from the standpoint of producing free radicals. I believe it will be profitable to keep up with their state of art, as far as radicals are concerned, and to follow up projects like the Winsor project, where the effects of chronic continuous exposures are being evaluated, physiologically and pathologically. These studies might give us some very good clues to what might happen at very low O_3 concentration when the exposure is uninterrupted.

Dr. Verzar: There seems to be some misunderstanding between Dr. Buettner and me. In the chamber in which we counted the nuclei, we produced an expansion of 22%. This is, of course, not the case in the free atmosphere where condensation is caused by the cooling of air. An expansion of 22% was produced in order to obtain the nuclei that are responsible for fog formation. This expansion yielded a nuclei count which agreed with that obtained by the Scholz counter.

I wish to remark also on Dr. Smith's paper. In conjunction with his first slide, he said that ionization was done by short-wave ultraviolet. In my last slide I showed that, not only the ultraviolet light, but also the visible spectrum is capable of producing nuclei in the air. This is something new. We do not know which, but certainly the H_2S in the air is transformed into nuclei by radiation in the visible spectrum. This radiation passes through window glass and may create an important problem in a closed cabin.

Another of my questions is, to what extent could the effects of positive and negative ions, observed by Dr. Smith, be ascribed to the action of nuclei, by precipitation of atmospheric trace substances on tissue surfaces?

Dr. Smith: We are very dependent on physicists for information on secondary reactions, and so far we have not been able to get any very illuminating answers. They refer to the ions we produced as young ions, and the possibility of secondary reactions is supposed to be minimal. But that does not mean that they cannot occur. We are quite safe in saying that there was no ozone formation in our tests. But what was going on at tissue surfaces is still a mystery.

Dr. Baldes: I wish to ask Dr. Smith briefly to discuss the equipment he used in producing the ions, how he measured the ions, and the number of ions involved in the data he presented on the slides.

Dr. Smith: There are two common ways of measuring ion concentration. In one, the air is passed through a special duct, and the ions are deposited on insulated sheets. The electric potential produced is then measured. This is the method we use most frequently. In the Beckett probe method, the probe is placed in the electrical field to measure the microcurrent produced. This gives the number of ions impinging on the probe per square centimeter per second, and, by calculation, the number of ions per milliliter of air.

Dr. Baldes: How many ions did you have?

Dr. Smith: Our maximum was about 1 mil per milliliter. The concentration used was between 10^5 and 10^6 ions per milliliter.

Dr. Schaefer: I want to mention that there is a continuing interest in certain problems of ionization in submarines. I personally have done some measurements in two series of investigations which showed that, during submergence of the submarines, the number of positive and negative ions increased, and at the same time the number of condensation nuclei increased. The range of increase in the ion content of air was 10- to 20-fold compared with normal values taken during surface cruising. It was found that emanations from the radium-painted dials were a factor in the ionization of air. Dr. Ebersole found a relatively high beta activity aboard the *Nautilus,* originating largely from radium-painted markers and luminescent watches of personnel. By removing the radium sources, the activity was reduced. It would seem that the problem of ionization still exists in the same way as it existed in the conventional submarine.

Dr. Forster: There is a very intriguing possibility, which, of course, may be false, that man can poison himself from his own carbon monoxide production. It is known from the work of Fenn *et al.* that some animals can metabolize large amounts of carbon monoxide. From the work of Neclu and Orstad and some work that we have done in our university, we know that a splitting of the pyrol ring produces carbon monoxide from the alpha reaction. I realize that in the submarines you normally take out the cigarette smoke. This raises the possibility that it may be necessary to remove also the carbon monoxide from the smoke in a sealed cabin, even if the individual is not smoking.

Dr. Tamas: When I was discussing the alpha reaction, I should have mentioned that two factors are involved. In the course of these reactions, both carbon monoxide and CO_2 are produced—another good reason for keeping hydrocarbons out of space cabins.

Dr. Verzar: I think filters should be devised that will remove not only dust but also nuclei up to 10^{-7} centimeter diameter. This is not too difficult. Cotton-wool filters will do it. On the other hand, removal of H_2S and NH_3, originating from humans, presents a very difficult technical problem, because these gases pass through filters. Nevertheless, every effort should be made to keep the cabin air free of these gases in order to avoid the production of nuclei under the action of sunlight.

Chairman Yaglou: Much more research is needed in order to appraise findings on the beneficial or harmful effects of ions. There are too many uncontrolled factors, and even the slightest change in the air may change the effect the ions would have on the organism. The same holds true about research of gases which appear in the air in small traces. Dr. Tamas has outlined a five-point program for developing the safe threshold limits. I do not believe that many of us will disagree with what he had to tell us. However, I should like to suggest that the threshold limits be determined not only for individual gases (trace substances appearing singly in the air) but also for the whole composite situation of gases, including oxygen and carbon dioxide, which operate in the atmosphere. It is very well known that the synergististic effects of mixed toxic gases are greater than the effects of individual components, and we might get a picture which is entirely opposite to what many of the studies have shown up to now.

PART SEVEN

Human Ecology in Confined Spaces

Chairman

DR. K. E. SCHAEFER

U.S. Naval Medical Research Laboratory
New London, Connecticut

Timegivers of 24-Hour Physiological Cycles

JÜRGEN ASCHOFF

Max-Planck-Institut für Verhaltensphysiologie, Erling-Andechs, Bavaria, Germany

Ecology deals with the influence of the environment on the organism. Research work in this field is often restricted to experiments in a steady state. The organism, however, is adapted not only to the nature and size of certain (constant) factors of the environment, but in the same way to their periodical alternations in time. Periodicity of the natural surroundings is an important ecological factor *per se*. This is clearly shown with regard to the 24-hour periodicity to which all living creatures are more or less subjected (Halberg *et al.*, 1953; Harker, 1958; Buenning, 1958). It is a natural attribute of most of them to maintain a periodicity of about 24 hours by themselves. An artificial environment can only be considered as adequate when this periodic structure of vital functions is respected and promoted.

1. EXOGENOUS AND ENDOGENOUS PERIODICITY

Two forms of biological periodicity may be theoretically distinguished: (a) Exogenous periodicity, which exists as long as the environmental factors have a periodicity, ceasing or at least dying out (like a damped oscillation) when the surroundings are kept constant. In this case the environment is the only cause of the biological periodicity. (b) Endogenous periodicity, which progresses indefinitely even if the environment is artificially kept constant.

The real cause for the periodicity is to be found in the organism itself, the environment merely influences the position of the phase. Here the periodic environmental factors play only a role as "clues" (Cloudsley-Thompson, 1952), "synchronizers" (Halberg *et al.*, 1953) or "timegivers"—in German, "Zeitgeber"—(Aschoff, 1954). These three terms have been introduced independently; they all have the same general meaning (cf. Aschoff, 1958).

The 24-hour periodicity of plants, animals, and men is a typical example of an endogenous biological periodicity, synchronized with environment, and has been investigated with much success. It can be found in functions of continuous alternation (e.g., body temperature) and also in single repetitive occurrences such as egg deposition. Likewise, timegivers can be either steadily changing environmental factors (e.g., air temperature) or regularly repeated single signals (e.g., feeding once a day). Each environmental factor which has a stimulating effect on the organism can function as a timegiver. The natural environment always contains several timegivers. In general only one of them decides, as the *actual* timegiver, the phase of the biological periodicity, "dominant synchronizers" (Halberg *et al.*, 1954); others remain latent. However, the latter may intervene if the actual timegiver is out of action. The change from light to darkness is, under natural conditions, the most important timegiver. To know what time of day it is and to become aware of his social relations is most important for men (cf. Aschoff, 1955*a*).

The endogenous processes of diurnal periodicity which are synchronized with the environmental timegivers are most important; they demand our special interest. Endogenous periodicity is connected with the function of the central nervous system and endocrine organs and might well be controlled by some general principle of the body. The timegivers act upon systems by way of these sense organs. In experiments with artificial environments it is important to be well informed about timegivers and their mode of action.

2. PROOF OF ENDOGENOUS PERIODICITY

With respect to the interaction between a periodic environment and the organism the term "timegiver" or "synchronizer" is valid only if the biological periodicity is definitely an endogenous one. If in the constant environment of a laboratory, e.g., in continuous light or darkness and at constant temperature the periodicity of an animal is maintained in an absolutely invariable state, the exogenous or endogenous state is not sufficiently determined. As long as there is a periodicity of exactly 24 hours there is reason to suspect that either a timegiver which has apparently escaped notice is still active, or that the cause of periodicity is to be found in the environment. Presumably the precision of the biological periodicity will not equal that of the rotation of the earth. Therefore, after rigorous exclusion of all timegivers the animal should show differences in phase and frequency as compared with its behavior under natural conditions. Numerous earlier experiments which showed in constant conditions an unchanged phase of animal periodicity with regard to local time do not give any proof for endogenous causality (cf. Brown *et al.*, 1956; Aschoff, 1958). For the last 20 years, however, experimental evidence has accumulated to show the deviation of animal periodicity from earth-rotation in an exactly constant milieu.

Conclusions derived from the latest results can, with relatively few exceptions, be summarized as follows: The biological periodicity of light-active animals is, in continuous light, shorter than 24 hours, and in continuous darkness longer than 24 hours. The contrary applies for dark-active animals. Nearly all animals set up a frequency which varies only within narrow limits; it is characteristic for the individual animal and appears to be maintained over a long period, perhaps the whole lifetime. This is the so-called "spontaneous frequency"; in contradistinction to the fundamental frequency of dead structure. Mice which were bred in continuous light under constant conditions showed an unchanging spontaneous frequency of about a 25-hour period, the presence of which can still be demonstrated after 3 generations (Aschoff 1955b). The conclusions cited above indicate that men may be expected to choose spontaneously (if no watch schedule or any other timegiver interferes) a higher frequency in continuous light, a lower one in constant darkness, with respect to the rotation of the earth.

3. EXPERIMENTS WITH TIMEGIVERS

Under natural conditions, timegivers play a secondary role since they synchronize only the spontaneous frequency of the organism with the period of earth-rotation. The true functions of timegivers can be studied in the laboratory. Four kinds of experiments can provide this information: (1) shifting the phase of the timegiver; (2) change of form of the timegiver; (3) change of frequency of the timegiver; (4) competition between timegivers.

3, 1. Phase shift

By means of an artificial lighting regime the biological periodicity can be shifted by any desired degree against the phase of the natural day. The first experiments in this field, with monkeys, were made 50 years ago (Simpson and Galbraith, 1908). The organism does not promptly follow a sudden phase shift of the timegiver. It will take several days until the organism is again in phase with the shifted periodicity of the environment. This is called the synchronizing time, lasting about 8 days after a phase shift of 12 hours and 4 days after a shift of 6 hours. These are approximate mean values taken from a great number of experiments with different subjects (including man) and using different timegivers. In special cases the synchronizing time might vary with the animal, influenced by the particular structure of its sense organs, and by the kind of timegiver and its intensity. "Intensity" is defined as the amplitude between light and dark (in Lux or f.c.) if a lighting regime is chosen as timegiver (Aschoff 1958). The spontaneous frequency of the organism is, in an experiment of this kind, lowered for the length of the synchronizing time and the amplitude is often smaller than at full synchronization. If several functions are measured in the same animal at the same time in such shift experiments, the synchronizing times will be of different lengths for different functions. The mutual phase-relations of various functions are therefore changed for some days. This dissociation of functions during the synchronizing time reveals some possibilities of how to investigate details of the endogenous mechanisms.

3, 2. Changed-form-phase-ratio

A natural day of 24 hours has two very distinct phases: sunrise and sunset. Each of these interfere with the biological periodicity considerably and each changes its form in the course of a year, at least in the middle and northern latitudes. The capacity to change its own phase ratio with respect to that of the timegiver, the form plasticity, is a characteristic property of the organism, but it is not unlimited. The running activity of mice in an artificial 24-lighting regime can be given, as an example (12 hours light-time and 12 hours dark-time). If the light-time is suddenly extended from 12 to 18 hours, or reduced to 6 hours, the distance between two characteristic phases of activity (the morning and evening maximum) is not changed by 6 but only by 1.5 hours. (Aschoff and Meyer-Lohmann, 1954). The animal's innate natural pattern of endogenous periodicity appears to oppose the transformation afforded by the timegiver.

3, 3. Change of frequency

The organism, though adapted to a 24-hour day, is also able to adjust itself to shorter or longer days. The artificial day, however, should not be changed immediately by too great a step. If light- and dark-time are shortened or extended by only half an hour from an original length of 12 hours, and if the artificial day (changed by one hour) is maintained for at least 8 days, the organism will remain synchronized within certain limits. For the mouse a change to a 21-hour- or a 27-hour day can be tolerated (Tribukait, 1956). If these limits are exceeded, the animal becomes independent of the timegiver. However, it does not become aperiodic but will, according to the nature of the artificial day, set up a spontaneous frequency similar to that in continuous light or in continuous darkness. Limits of the frequency plasticity for other organisms have not yet been sufficiently investigated. The only experiment carried out in men did not give clear-cut results (Kleitman and Kleitman, 1953). One of the reasons for this was that experimental conditions were not favorable (i.e., the normal periodic environment against which the subjects had to maintain their changed day).

In an artificially shortened or lengthened day the biological periodicity does not remain unchanged, even if it seems to be fully synchronized. This can clearly be seen by certain deformations and phase displacements, e.g., the daily maxima of the running activity of mice. During a short day they set in later, during a long day earlier than in a 24-hour day. As far as can be said today, the amplitude is, during an artificial day with changed frequency, smaller than under natural conditions. However it has not yet been possible to accumulate sufficient evidence for a clear picture. Also it is not possible to decide definitely whether animals with a periodicity between 21 to 27 hours are completely brought into step with the artificial day. Lasting from 21 to 27 hours our own material would seem to prove that the frequency of animal periodicity deviates even in the synchronizing range by small amounts from the frequency of the timegiver (see below).

3, 4. Competition between timegivers

If several factors of the environment are periodic, it is difficult to decide clearly which of them is the actual timegiver. In this case it is sufficient to shift the phase of one of the factors in question against the others by some hours. If the actual timegiver has been shifted, the biological periodicity follows in the above-mentioned way. If this happens the latent timegivers which are not shifted will now become effective and the biological periodicity, forced by the actual timegiver, must shift against them. The consequence of this is that synchronizing times are longer than in cases in which the phases of all timegivers have been shifted together by the same amount (cf. Halberg *et al.*, 1953). Such experiments may serve to compare and to measure the (biological) "intensity" of timegivers. Here is an example. The interchange of bright light and darkness has, in general, more influence than any other of the timegivers which are simultaneously present. By means of such a lighting regime the biological periodicity can be shifted against the usual daily feeding time. If the amplitude between light and dark is diminished stepwise, a point will finally be attained at which the previous latent timegiver (e.g., the feeding time) becomes stronger than the lighting regime (Stauber, 1939). On the other hand latent timegivers can, by expedient measures, be made so effective as to displace even a strong lighting-timegiver (Meyer-Lohmann, 1955; cf. Aschoff, 1954, 1958).

4. PROBLEMS OF INTERACTION BETWEEN TIMEGIVER AND ORGANISM

Research work in the field of the 24-hour periodicity still leaves some questions to be answered.

1. Are the individual periodic functions of the organism directly connected with the timegiver or are they coordinated by a superimposed general principle of the body? This is a problem which received special attention by Halberg and co-workers.

2. What pathways do the timegivers use in affecting periodic function? In order to answer the above questions we can employ experiments which have already contributed to elucidate partly the connection between environment and annual periodicity in the animal, e.g., breeding season (Aschoff, 1955c).

3. What are the stimulating properties of each single timegiver? This question can hardly be answered.

4. What can be said about the chemical and physical processes which

establish a time-period 24 hours long? Answer: There are many theories but no real basis for a reasonable hypothesis.

5. What properties do the diurnal periodical processes possess? Little can be said. Of some significance are investigations designed to determine the range in which the frequency of biological periodicity is independent of temperature (Pittendrigh, 1954; Bruce and Pittendrigh, 1956; Hoffman, 1957; Buenning, 1958) or what temperatures have an influence and how do they produce an effect (cf. Stephens, 1957, 1958).

Finally, the question is often asked whether a simple model of the 24-hour periodicity can be constructed on the basis of physical oscillations. The answer to this is "almost always." The 24-hour periodicity has the character of a relaxation oscillation (Buenning, 1958; Pittendrigh, 1958). However, there is no exact result to date which would justify the conclusion that the biological periodicity has no character of a pendulum. Many functions of diurnal periodicities formally bear a likeness to a relaxation oscillation but no investigations have been carried out about the functional conformity between the two. According to existing material it seems doubtful whether the biological periodicity can clearly be assigned to a physical oscillation (not forgetting that both types of oscillations change over into one another). This is not the right place to discuss the criterion by which this question could be settled. The results of the above mentioned investigations stress that the biological periodicity possesses a high tendency to inertia and in addition properties which differ from physical models previously used for comparison.

SUMMARY

The 24-hour periodicity which we can observe in all living creatures is based mostly on an innate property of the organism; probably it is characteristic for the cell itself. Periodic factors of the environment synchronize as timegivers the endogenous periodicity with the rotation of the earth, determining its phase. In an artificially constant milieu the organism retains its own characteristic periodicity whose frequency depends on the concomitant circumstances (e.g., continuous light or darkness).

The natural environment always contains several timegivers. The so-called actual timegiver determines the phase, the others remaining latent. Under certain circumstances latent timegivers may compete with the actual one and replace it. By means of a strong timegiver the phase of the biological periodicity in the laboratory may be shifted against local time by any desired degree. After a sudden shift of the timegiver there is a certain delay, after which organism and environment are again synchronized. The length of this synchronizing time depends on the kind of organism, the kind of timegiver, and the amount of shift; it may be different for different functions in the same animal.

Within certain limits the biological periodicity possesses plasticity with respect to form and frequency; however it does not follow the timegiver in a mere passive manner. Beyond the limits of plasticity the organism makes itself independent from the timegiver. Form and frequency are not exclusively determined by the organism but also by the respective environmental conditions. The result of experiments with timegivers may enable us to develop models for the mechanism of 24-hour periodicity.

REFERENCES

Aschoff, J. 1954. Naturwissenschaften 41: 49–56.
Aschoff, J. 1955a. Naturwissenschaften 42: 569–575.
Aschoff, J. 1955b. Pfluegers Arch. 262: 51–59.
Aschoff, J. 1955c. Studium generale 8: 774–776.
Aschoff, J. 1957. Naturwissenschaften 44: 361–367.
Aschoff, J. 1958. Z. Tierpsychol. 15: 1–30.
Aschoff, J., and J. Meyer-Lohmann. 1954. Z. Tierpsychol. 11: 476–484.
Brown, F. A., J. Shriner, and C. L. Ralph. 1956. Am. J. Physiol. 184: 491–496.
Bruce, V. G., and C. S. Pittendrigh. 1956. Proc. Natl. Acad. Sci. U.S. 42: 676–682.
Buenning, E. 1958. Die physiologische Uhr., Springer-Verlag, Heidelberg.
Cloudsley-Thompson, J. L. 1952. J. Exptl. Biol. 29: 295–303.
Halberg, F. 1953. Lancet. 73: 20–32.
Halberg, F., M. B. Visscher, and J. J. Bittner. 1953. Am. J. Physiol. 174: 109–122.
Halberg, F., M. B. Visscher, and J. J. Bittner. 1954. Am. J. Physiol. 19: 229–235.
Harker, 1958. Biol. Rev. 33: 1–52.
Hoffman, Kl. 1957. Naturwissenschaften 44: 359.
Kleitman, N. and E. Kleitman. 1953. J. Appl. Physiol. 6: 283–291.
Meyer-Lohmann, J. 1955. Pfluegers Arch. 260: 292–305.
Pittendrigh, C. S. 1954. Proc. Natl. Acad. Sci. U.S. 40: 1018–1029.
Pittendrigh, C. S. 1958. In his manuscript: "An oscillator model for biological clocks."
Simpson, S. and J. Galbraith. 1908. Trans. Roy. Soc. Edinburgh 45: 65–104.
Stauber, L. A. 1939. J. Parasitol. 25: 95–116.
Stephens, S. G. 1957. Physiol. Zool. 30: 55–69.
Stephens, S. G. 1958. Am. Natural. 42: 863.
Tribukait, B. 1956. Z. vergl. Physiol. 38: 479–490.

ADDENDUM

A great deal of new facts were established during the last years. Only a few can be mentioned here.

1. Under constant environmental conditions the length of diurnal cycles in animals changes linearly with the logarithm of light intensity. Alterations occur in opposite directions in light- and dark-active animals. Simultaneously the level of general excitation also changes in opposite directions in both groups of animals.

2. The 24-hour periodicity seems to be the result of a coordination of several

rhythms in a hierarchy of frequencies (Endodiurnal organization, Pittendrigh). The organism needs a periodic environment in which the timegivers are in phase. Otherwise desynchronization takes place with resulting damages to the organism.

3. Synchronization with the environment is based upon a stable phase relation between organism and timegiver. Each time the organism goes out of phase, the timegiver has to re-shift the phase by a certain amount (or phase angle). To do this, two possibilities exist. During a continuous steady-state condition of a timegiver-stimulus, the biological system has a definite circular velocity (= average speed of the vector describing the period) and a definite level of excitation. Changes of circular velocity cause a phase shift which is proportional to the duration of change (proportional effect). Changes of the intensity level produce an immediate phase shift (differential effect). Natural timegivers combine both principles; there are, however, differences in organisms inasmuch as they are regulated mainly by proportional or differential effects.

4. Experiments with artificial timegivers in the laboratory show that all organisms so far tested behave similarly, especially with regard to phase-relation between timegiver and organism. This may be taken as an indication for a uniform basic mechanism. The general properties of such a mechanism with all its functional correlations seen in organisms can be described using the model of a simple pendulum oscillation.

For more details including chemical aspects, and concerning plants, animals and men see: Cold Spring Harbor Symposium. Quant. Biol. 25 (in press).

Effect of Environmental Factors on Biological Cycles and Performance of Work

G. LEHMANN

Direktor des Max-Planck-Instituts für Arbeitsphysiologie, Dortmund, Germany

There are two kinds of cycles in man, i.e., the 24-hour cycle and the seasonal cycle. The former is, of course, of main interest for our current discussion. While the rhythm of the body temperature has been known for a long time, the cycle of the pulse frequency has not been investigated as thoroughly, since its fluctuations can only be traced if the conditions under which the measurements are taken are kept very constant. During the first days of life these cyclic phenomena are not yet traceable in the new-born child, as shown in the pulse rate curve of Figs. 1 and 2. It may, however, be assumed that the disposition for biological cycles is inborn, since, under the influence of timegivers to which even a new-born child is exposed, these biological cycles develop after some weeks and improve gradually in the course of time.

Like the pulse frequency, all other haemodynamic factors are subject to rhythmical fluctuations over the 24-hour period. These fluctuations may, for instance, easily be determined in the electrical or even mechanical resistance of the skin (Figs. 3 and 4). Our observations justify the conclusion that the phenomenon of cycles—although varying among each other as to their course —must not be looked upon as a single phenomenon but as a central process mainly located in the autonomic nervous system. Cycles probably occur in all those cases where functions are regulated or strongly influenced by the autonomic nervous system. It is a question of the methods applied whether or not a cycle is detectable.

The effect of external influences on the organs can only be estimated if the deviations of the normal cycles are taken as basic values, a fact which has often been neglected and has led to many false conclusions. In the human organism as a whole, the rhythmical fluctuations are particularly striking in the changes of the well-being. The latter are often not equivalent to activity or repose because of other influences. But they correspond to the readiness for activity or

381

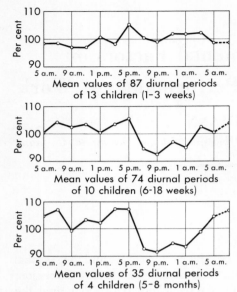

Mean values of 87 diurnal periods
of 13 children (1-3 weeks)

Mean values of 74 diurnal periods
of 10 children (6-18 weeks)

Mean values of 35 diurnal periods
of 4 children (5-8 months)

FIGURE 1. (*left*)
FIGURE 2. (*below*)
Development of diurnal cycles of the pulse rate
in infancy. (*After Hellbrügge, Lange, and Rutenfranz, 1956*)

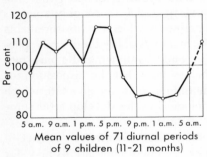

Mean values of 71 diurnal periods
of 9 children (11-21 months)

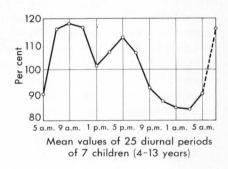

Mean values of 25 diurnal periods
of 7 children (4-13 years)

for relaxation. The physiological and psychical readiness for performance as
well as the intensity of reactions to stimuli from outside always show these
fluctuations varying in intensity from man to man. In the animal, these fluctuations may best be seen by registering the spontaneous activity under constant conditions.

We are certain that in man we can expect a 24-hour cycle of readiness for
performance, the course of which is well known. Figure 5 shows findings with
original figures, while Fig. 6 gives the same curve turned around and statistically smoothed. The curve is drawn from Swedish experiments giving the
frequency of erroneous checkings of gas meters (by gas company service men).
The material from which this curve is drawn is very large. The tendency of the
curve has been shown to be generally valid by numerous other investigations.

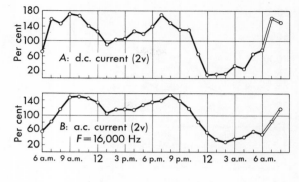

FIGURE 3.

Diurnal cycles of the electric resistance of the skin (means of 17 days of the same person).

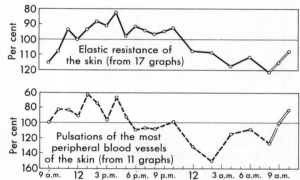

FIGURE 4.

Diurnal cycles of the elastic resistance of the skin and pulsations of the most peripheral blood vessels of the skin. (MPI, 1954)

The characteristic minimum of the curve at about 3 o'clock in the morning is very distinct. This point of lowest efficiency is particularly well known to the soldier and the sailor who know very well that it will occur even if he has had sufficient sleep during the first part of the night. Of course, the state of low efficiency at 3 o'clock in the morning may be lessened by a good sleep during the first half of the night, and be increased by lack of sleep. It will, however, be present in any case, since it is caused by the basic 24-hour cycles, the fluctuations of which may be modified by fatigue and other influences but never be abolished.

In fact, however, the ideal curve shown in our slide is rarely ever verified in practice because the influences of the cycles interfere with other influences of a different nature. In the case of the Swedish curve the work is very light requiring nothing but moderate attentiveness. So there is practically no fatigue at the end of the three shifts (at 6, 14, and 22 hr) but, on the other hand, there are no stimuli acting at special hours of the day.

Usually the output per hour depends on a number of other factors, as well; not the least to be considered are the social ones. The same is true of the curve of the mistakes made and the accidents that occur. If in a special case the curve

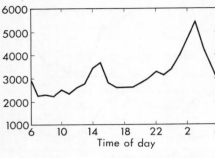

FIGURE 5.
Errors made in 175,000 checkings of gas meters, from 1912–1931. (*After Bjerner, Holm, and Swensson*)

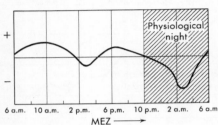

FIGURE 6.
Smoothed curve of human readiness to work over the day. Physiological night.

of the output follows the biological cycles, the accident curve very often does not. This can be understood easily since an increase in output increases the probability of accidents, thus making the accident curve follow the curve showing the readiness to work. Only if the output per unit of time is constant over the day is there hope of a decrease in accidents in the positive phases and an increase in the negative ones. The curve represents the readiness to work over the day. Even at its lowest points hard work is not impossible, but it means a greater effort to do the same work at the lower points, and a lesser effort to do it at the higher points.

Distributing the work load according to the biological curve means working throughout the day with an equal effort. At the same time, it means doing a day's work with as little effort as possible. The validity of this conclusion has been proved by O. Graf under experimental conditions as well as in industrial practice. In comparison to a constant output per unit of time, the total output during normal working time was increased by about 5 to 10% while both subjective and objective symptoms of fatigue were reduced.

What we now call the "physiological working curve" is nothing but the regulation of the output per minute plotted to the curve of the physiological rhythm. This has been studied especially during the normal daily working time between 6 and 16 hr. Before anything at all was known about biological rhythms, it was found by experiments in factories that the most experienced workers followed a curve which, in the morning, started with a slow increase that reached its highest level at about 9 or 10 A.M. Then followed a slight depression at about noon which, as was shown by experiments, is neither the consequence of food intake nor that of hunger. In the afternoon, this depression is followed by another increase, though less distinct, and passes gradually into a final decrease.

Many experiments were made to apply this curve in practice, with the following result: in the case of work at the assembly line, it is possible to reg-ulate the speed of the conveyor belt according to the above-mentioned curve. This is, however, rather complicated from a technical point of view, and, there-fore, very seldom realized. But even with the conveyor belt running with a constant speed, as well as in the case of work the speed of which is not regulated by mechanical devices, it is possible to work along this curve. In the case of work at the conveyor belt, this may be accomplished by reducing the number of pieces at the times where the curve is low. If the working speed is not regulated, it will suffice to tell the worker what amount of output he has to reach in the different hours of the day following the curve.

It was found that it is rather easy for the worker to learn to adapt his work to the curve, and that only some days of control are needed until he will be able to follow it without supervision. This is so because this regulation is in tune with his natural rhythm.

Furthermore, the curve is of great importance for shift work. The best work-ing conditions for a man are always during the forenoon shift. In the afternoon shift, usually from 14 to 22 hr, conditions are already less good and get worse in the late hours of the shift. The most unfavorable conditions are found, however, in the night shift. In the small hours men are generally disposed to be less effi-cient for physical and mental work as well. However, there are many mental workers who like to work at night and to sleep till late in the morning. It is believed that this habit has developed only in order to avoid noise and other disturbances during the daytime.

A certain inclination to work against the normal rhythm is found not only among mental workers who prefer working nights, but also with night workers in industry. This inclination, however, will never lead to a reverse rhythm. Night work always means to work against the normal rhythm. In the case of shift work in factories, every worker has to perform morning shifts, afternoon shifts, and night shifts alternately. Since it takes about four to five days to adjust to a certain type of shift, it is advisable not to change too often between these different shifts. From a physiological point of view, it would seem advisable to change shifts every four or five weeks. In practice, however, this is very often impossible because the night workers get too little sleep during the day and cannot endure this over several weeks. So shifts have to be changed every week, which is certainly not ideal because the workers are nearly always in a state of readaptation.

The biological cycles represent fluctuations of the neuro-vegetative tonus which, according to W. R. Hess, varies between a predominantly ergotropic and a predominantly trophotropic phase. The ergotropic phase being based upon a more sympathicotonic state of the human body leads to a disposition of improved performance, while the trophotropic phase means predominance of the parasympathic system and, therefore, need for rest, digestion, and recovery from fatigue.

The question whether the phenomenon of biological cycles represents genuine endogenous cycles can today be answered on account of our knowledge about timegivers. Here I should like to refer to the paper by Aschoff. When traveling round the globe in west-east or east-west direction at a speed like that of an airplane, man experiences a disturbance of his biological rhythm arising from this shifting of phase. The air passenger exposed to these influences will notice that the sensations of fatigue, alertness, hunger, etc., will occur at the usual hours which, of course, do no longer agree to the local time. Four or five days will elapse before the biological cycles are readjusted to the corresponding local time. The shifting of the biological cycle will be of no serious effect to a healthy man unless these readjustments occur too frequently. In such cases, more serious consequences might be anticipated. The crews of the intercontinental airlines are regularly exposed to these disturbances of the biological cycles. Although the commercial airlines are trying to prevent these disturbances by a suitable establishment of their official regulations, as yet the problem does not seem to be solved.

As to the consequences of a change in the length of the biological cycles, i.e. a change in the basic frequency, our knowledge is still rather limited. From experiments in animal and man we may assume that minor changes in frequency, for instance, a gradual change from a 24-hour to a 20-hour cycle, will not seriously affect the physiological functions. We have no real experience as to practical human work of any kind in this field.

A total lack of timegivers would probably not lead to a constant equilibrium between ergotropic and trophotropic command but to an irregular up and down. Though these are but presumptions, it might easily be imagined that the consequences of these irregularities at least cause a decrease in a man's working capacity and readiness to work.

A submarine is a military organism, and it is essential for military as well as for naval life that all activity be forced into a very strong time schedule. Translated into the terminology of rhythm research, this means that the lack of all primary timegivers is compensated by the presence of rather strong and regular secondary ones. This may not be so in the case of a space cabin. The lack of timegivers should therefore be compensated for by introducing strong artificial ones—for instance, by providing a 24-hour rhythm in lighting and temperature regulation in order to avoid uncontrolled influences of weaker timegivers.

REFERENCES

Bjerner, B., A. Holm, and A. Swensson. 1948. Om Natt-och Skiftarbete, Statens Offentliga Utredningar, Sweden.

Graf, O. 1944. "Zur Frage der Monotonie der Arbeit und ihre Bekämpfung," Arbeitsphysiologie. *13*: 95.

Graf, O. 1944. "Ein Verfahren zur zwanglosen Steuerung der Arbeitsgeschwindigkeit nach vorgegebenen Arbeitskurven, insbesondere zur physiologisch richtigen Arbeitsablaufregelung," Arbeitsphysiologie. *13*: 125.

Graf, O. 1955. "Erforschung der geistigen Ermüdung und nervösen Belastung; Studien über die vegetative 24-Stunden-Rhythmik in Ruhe und unter Belastung," Forschungsbericht Nr. 113 des Wirtschafts- und Verkehrsministeriums Nordrhein-Westfalen. Westdeutscher Verlag Köln und Opladen.

Graf, O. 1955. Studien über Fließarbeitsprobleme an einer praxisnahen Experimentieranlage, Forschungsbericht Nr. 114 des Wirtschafts- und Verkehrsministeriums Nordrhein-Westfalen. Westdeutscher Verlag Köln und Opladen.

Graf, O. 1955. Studien über Arbeitspausen in Betrieben bei freier und zeitgebundener Arbeit (Fließarbeit) und ihre Auswirkung auf die Leistungsfähigkeit, Forschungsbericht Nr. 115 des Wirtschafts- und Verkehrsministeriums Nordrhein-Westfalen. Westdeutscher Verlag Köln und Opladen.

Graf, O., R. Pirtkien, J. Rutenfranz, and E. Ulich. 1958. Studien zur Frage der nervösen Belastung im Betrieb. I. Nachtarbeit und nervöse Belastung, Forschungsbericht Nr. 530 des Wirtschafts- und Verkehrsministeriums Nordrhein-Westfalen. Westdeutscher Verlag Köln und Opladen.

Hellbrügge, Th., J. Lange, and J. Rutenfranz. 1956. "Über die Entwicklung von tagesperiodischen Veränderungen der Pulsfrequenz im Kindesalter," Z. Kinderheilk. *78*: 703.

Lehmann, G. 1953. Praktische Arbeitsphysiologie, Georg Thieme Verlag.

Menzel, W. 1950. "Zur Physiologie und Pathologie des Nacht und Schichtarbeiters," Arbeitsphysiologie. *14*: 304.

Pirtkien, R. "Über die 24-Stunden-Rhythmik des Menschen und das vegetative Nervensystem," Internat. Z. angew. Physiol. einschl. Arbeitsphysiol. *16*: 198.

Rutenfranz, J. 1955. "Zur Frage einer Tagesrhythmik des elektrischen Hautwiderstandes beim Menschen," Intern. Z. angew. Physiol. einschl. Arbeitsphysiol. *16*: 152.

Rutenfranz, J., Th. Hellbrügge, and W. Niggeschmidt. 1956. "Über die Tagesrhythmik des elektrischen Hautwiderstandes bei 11-jährigen Kindern," Z. Kinderheilk. *78*: 144.

Rutenfranz, J., and Th. Hellbrügge. 1957. "Über Tagesschwankungen der Rechengeschwindigkeit bei 11-jährigen Kindern," Z. Kinderheilk. *80*: 65.

Medical-Physiological Problems Peculiar to Nuclear-Powered Submarines

RICHARD F. DOBBINS

U. S. Navy, Medical Officer, U.S.S. Nautilus

When the world's first nuclear-powered ship, the U.S.S. *Nautilus*, came sliding down the ways at the Electric Boat Company at Groton, Connecticut, on January 21, 1954, its meeting with the waters of the Thames River heralded the most significant marine development of our times—the age of nuclear propulsion. This advent of nuclear power dramatically enlarged the scope and depth of submarine medicine in two main fields: first and quite expectedly, due to the nuclear power plant, aspects of radiation monitoring and control and personnel dosimetry; and secondly, atmosphere control. As a result of operating experience and data gathered during the three and one half years of *Nautilus'* seagoing lifetime, this latter point is definitely the more significant of the two.

The routine medical problems encountered on *Nautilus* are common to all submarines, either diesel-electric or nuclear-powered. These problems are: (1) upper respiratory infections, (2) constipation, and (3) injuries, and in that order. These same problems, however, are equally common to any seagoing vessel, either surface craft or submarine. As far as the radiation aspects of nuclear propulsion are concerned, I cannot emphasize too strongly the safety of these ships as far as personnel are concerned. Radiation exists aboard: It is detectable; it is measurable. Our engineering personnel are exposed to it and receive a dosage of it. This dosage, however, is negligible in comparison with permissible exposure levels.

As more concrete evidence of the relatively insignificant dosages of ionizing radiation to which our personnel are exposed, let me cite some facts derived from *Nautilus* operational experience. In the entire three and one half years of its history—including the period of February-March 1957, when our first nuclear core was changed and when our personnel faced the greatest potential danger—not a single individual connected with *Nautilus* has ever received

388

even a technical overexposure to ionizing radiation. As a matter of fact, the average *annual* dose of radiation incurred by our personnel is less than the permissible *weekly* dose. *Nautilus'* operational commitments on our present nuclear core have had us submerged close to 90% of our time underway. This fact alone, plus the shielding effect of our hull, has resulted in some of our nonengineering personnel receiving less radiation dosage than their wives and families who live on the surface of the earth 24 hours a day. The complete safety of our personnel from a radiation standpoint is a tribute to the designers and builders of *Nautilus,* as well as to the health-physics techniques practised aboard.

To turn to the atmosphere control point of view, the fact that sufficient oxygen can be supplied and that, by chemical means, CO_2 and CO can be removed from our rebreathable atmosphere when we are submerged is well attested by the fairly recent 30- and 31-day 5-hour submerged cruises of *Seawolf* and *Skate* respectively. It is not meant to imply by this that atmospheric control or revitalization within a confined space is a thoroughly solved or even thoroughly understood problem; far from it. Nor, for that matter, are *all* aspects of the radiation problems. There is still much to be learned by research, both physiological and engineering, regarding the identification and quantification of bizarre contaminants and, indeed, all elements produced in our rebreathable atmosphere; the permissible tolerance levels of certain specific or even mixed contaminants in an atmosphere on a long-term basis; and the effects of repeated exposures to even low levels of mixed contaminants without allowing ample recovery time between such exposures. In the radiation field, research is needed to develop more accurate instruments for and better means of correlating radiation dosage to biological damage, as is participation in the field of zero $_0N'$ flux measurements. Data gathered by the *Nautilus,* the *Seawolf,* and the *Skate* will help in these projects, but some of the answers must come from the laboratories.

Atmosphere Control of Confined Spaces

W. E. McCONNAUGHEY

Bureau of Ships, Department of the Navy, Washington, D.C.

The engineering aspects of life in confined spaces must be approached as a joint endeavor between the medical and engineering disciplines. Experience with submarines has shown that the atmosphere control problem regularly requires compromises between the two interests, and proper appreciation of the problems of each is proving essential to arriving at satisfactory solutions. The Navy has recognized this officially and there is a good working relationship at the administrative level between the equipment people in the Bureau of Ships and the medical people in the Bureau of Medicine and Surgery. However, this does not always extend to the people doing research and development so I hope those with physiological interests will profit by a brief outline of some engineering approaches to atmosphere control. Since my personal concern is with submarines, my observations will be directed primarily toward their problems. However, the space vehicle problem is in many ways analogous so occasional comments on the application of submarine technology to their situation will be included.

Let us first consider what submarine atmosphere control includes:

1. Gases
    (a) O_2 supply
    (b) CO_2 removal
    (c) Contaminant removal (odors, toxic materials)
2. Particulates
    (a) Solid contaminant removal
    (b) Liquid contaminant removal
3. Detection and analysis
4. Temperature and humidity

The basic problems of O_2 supply and CO_2 removal have had the most study to date, both from the engineering and medical standpoints, but the removal of gaseous and particulate contaminants has become increasingly important with

increased submergence time for two reasons. First, atmospheric concentrations
generally increase with time and contaminants of no significance on short dives
may reach toxic levels on long dives. An example of this is carbon monoxide
from tobacco smoking. As you may know smoking is permitted on all U. S. submarines except during drills and emergencies but, under normal operating conditions on battery boats, the ship surfaces or snorkels before toxic levels are
reached. However, this is not true for nuclear-powered ships and, without CO
removal facilities, toxic concentrations of carbon monoxide would soon
become the limiting factor in submerged endurance. The second reason why
contaminant removal is important is that the toxicity of many materials is
related to time and type of exposure. Here, a particular type of hydraulic fluid
can be used as an example. Although this material has been in use on surface
ships where an allowable atmospheric concentration has been determined, its
use on nuclear-powered submarines reduced by a factor of sixteen the allowable
concentration. This results, of course, from the continuous, uninterrupted exposure on the submarine compared to the intermittent exposure on the surface
ship. This concept of greatly reducing permissible atmospheric concentrations
for continuous exposures applies to many of the contaminants and it makes the
removal problem much more difficult for the engineer.

It also makes the business of detection and analysis more difficult. This aspect
of atmosphere control is very important and it is one that is difficult, not only
because of the extreme sensitivities required, but because of the potential complexity of the atmosphere. A moment's reflection on the many activities and
processes going on in the submarine community leads to the realization that an

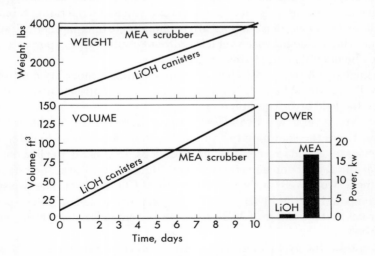

FIGURE 1.
Relation between regenerative and nonregenerative atmosphere control facilities for CO_2 removal.

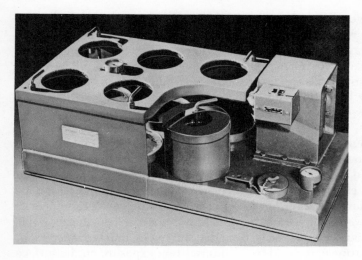

FIGURE 2.
Lithium hydroxide manifold.

almost limitless number of contaminants could be present in the atmosphere. For example, in addition to human respiration the contaminants include cooking, tobacco smoking, lube oils, diesel fuel, electronic equipment, plastics, sanitary facilities, paint, refrigerants, etc. However, in addition to the many possible sources there are many possible removal agents. As a result, the nature and concentrations of components of the submarine atmosphere become impossible to predict and we must rely on instruments and studies on operating submarines to guide us in developing suitable atmosphere control equipment. I am sure the same will be true for space vehicles, although submarine experience should certainly be helpful in predicting problem areas.

The final area listed on the chart is temperature and humidity control but it will not be discussed here since the methods used on submarines are conventional in the field of air conditioning.

There are several ways to classify atmosphere control facilities for submarines. From the standpoint of processes, there are two main categories— nonregenerative, and regenerative or continuous. In general, the first consumes material and the second consumes power. Figure 1 illustrates the relation between these two classes for the particular case of CO_2 removal. The two systems being compared are the LiOH system in use on postwar design battery-powered submarines and the amine or MEA scrubber system in use on nuclear-powered submarines.

The criteria for evaluating systems for submarine use are power, weight, volume, reliability, and simplicity. Reliability and simplicity are difficult to show graphically but the other three can be quantitated in a straightforward manner.

The abscissa for weight and volume in these figures is time in days. Taking volume first, since this is more important to a submarine than weight, we can see that the LiOH system is smaller for periods up to about six days. It holds its weight advantage for about 9½ days and the power requirements are very attractive. From this, it is obvious that for a battery-powered submarine requiring only intermittent protection, totalling less than six days, the proper choice is the LiOH system. Low power requirements, ease of stowage, and simplicity combine to extend the cross-over point to at least ten days. However, for long periods of time, it is obvious that the amine scrubber is the proper choice. While this comparison is on the basis of equipment for 100 men, the relative values should hold for a smaller space vehicle also. However, the relative importances of the five criteria mentioned will undoubtedly be different in that case and maintaining a constant mass is a new requirement.

The next two figures illustrate the factor of simplicity. The first, Fig. 2, shows the heart of the LiOH system, the manifold. This is a portable box which contains a motor and fan to draw air through five canisters of granular LiOH and a filter to remove irritating dust from the outlet air when the unit is started

FIGURE 3.
System characteristics of an amine scrubber.

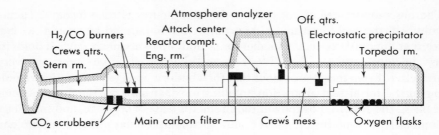

FIGURE 4.
Atmosphere control equipment on a typical nuclear-powered submarine.

up. The dimensions in the stowed condition shown here are approximately 11 inches by 19 inches by 35 inches but the height is increased when the canisters are installed. Canisters are about 6½ inches in diameter by 12 inches high. A typical 100-man system would involve using three of these manifolds and recharging them with fresh canisters every eight hours.

The next, Fig. 3, is a view of an amine scrubber with coverplates removed to show more construction details. The dimensions are approximately 3½ ft by 4 ft by 6 ft. The operating principle will be described later but I think you will agree that it appears rather complex in spite of the fact that it is reliable, seagoing gear requiring a minimum of attention.

This comparison of two CO_2 removal systems is intended to illustrate a point that applies to all atmosphere control equipment—the selection of a process involves many factors, but time is a major one.

A few of the principles of submarine atmosphere control have been mentioned. I would now like to show you the complete system on a typical nuclear submarine and cite a few examples of other processes which are either being studied or which are frequently suggested. Figure 4 is a schematic view of a nuclear-powered submarine showing typical atmosphere control equipment except for temperature and humidity.

Although submarines are divided into watertight compartments for safety reasons, ventilation is designed to maintain a homogeneous air mixture throughout the ship under normal submerged conditions. As a result, equipment is generally located on the basis of the best mechanical arrangement and atmosphere processing can be done at single locations instead of distributed throughout the ship.

At present, O_2 is carried in large high-pressure cylinders outside the pressure hull and bled into the ship's atmosphere as required to maintain a normal concentration. This system is soon to be replaced with continuous oxygen generators but it does have the charm of being simple and reliable.

CO_2 removal is accomplished with amine scrubbers of the type shown in an earlier figure. The principle of operation is that certain organic materials vigorously absorb CO_2 at room temperature but release it at elevated temperatures. The particular material in use at present is monoethanolamine or, as it is more commonly called, MEA. Figure 5 shows the reaction involved and a simplified schematic of the scrubber process. Ship's air is contacted with cool MEA solution in the absorber column and CO_2 is chemically absorbed according to the forward part of the equilibrium reaction shown. For engineering reasons, the MEA is recycled through the absorber but the air makes only a single pass. Part of the MEA solution is continuously piped over to the stripper where it is boiled under pressure to release CO_2 by reversing the equilibrium. The released CO_2 is then compressed further and discharged overboard and the hot MEA is cooled and returned to the absorber part of the cycle. As a result, the process is continuous and consumes only power. Two of these units are installed on a typical submarine although only one is normally operated at a time.

Returning now to our ship schematic, Fig. 4, I would like to point out the H_2–CO burners. These are catalytic combustion units which were originally designed to remove H_2 and CO from the atmosphere. As you know, H_2 is a battery gas and CO results mainly from tobacco smoke. However, experience has shown that these units are very valuable for removing small quantities of many other potentially toxic trace substances. In fact, they are unofficially called "trash burners" since we have not yet identified all of the materials that are being removed. The principle of operation is that when air is passed through a bed of hot catalyst many of the contaminants are oxidized to CO_2 and water which are easily handled. .

Figure 6 is a simplified schematic of this process. The catalyst in use at present is a mixture of copper and manganese oxides called "hopcalite." Since particulate matter is not oxidized by this process an inlet filter is provided to

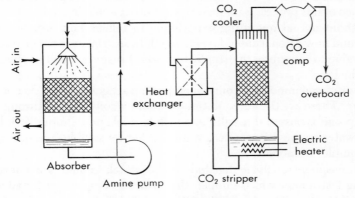

$$2 \text{ MEA} + H_2O + CO_2 \rightleftharpoons (\text{MEA})_2 \cdot H_2CO_3$$

FIGURE 5.
Diagram of an amine-type CO_2 scrubber.

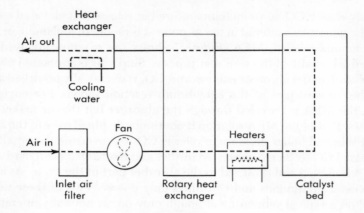

FIGURE 6.
Schematic of a carbon monoxide and hydrogen burner.

prevent its accumulation on the catalyst. The heat exchanger and outlet air cooler are used because of the high operating temperature of the catalyst—around 650° F. Figure 7 is a photograph of the actual equipment with two units again being used on a typical nuclear-powered submarine. Dimensions are approximately 2 ft by 2½ ft by 5 ft.

The ship schematic, Fig. 4, depicts the main carbon filter. This is a bed of activated charcoal the purpose of which is to remove odors and trace contaminants—particularly organic materials. Actually, charcoal has been used on battery-powered submarines for a number of years in connection with sanitary tanks and heads, but for nuclear-powered ships an additional central filter and a smaller unit in the galley exhaust are used for general atmosphere cleanup. The importance of this process is unquestioned, but accurate design has been impossible without actual operating experience to tell us how much should be exposed and how often it should be changed. Industrial experience has been of limited value to the submarine application and I suspect it will be the same for space vehicles.

There are some important contaminant removal agents which do not show in this figure. These are the air conditioning cooling coils located throughout the ship. Ship's air is passed through these coils to cool and dehumidify it but condensing water on the coils acts as a water washer for soluble contaminant gases —for example, ammonia.

The atmosphere analyzer located in the attack center is a continuously indicating instrument which samples the air in all compartments and analyzes for O_2, CO_2, H_2, CO, and freon. Although a variety of portable detection equipment is also carried, this is the main means of routinely monitoring the ship's atmosphere. Figure 8 is a picture of this instrument which was developed at the Naval Research Laboratory. Its dimensions are approximately 18 in by 20 in by 30 in.

The final piece of atmosphere control equipment is the electrostatic precipitator located in the crew's mess. All of the previously mentioned equipment has been concerned with gases but the precipitator has the function of removing particulate matter from the air, especially material small in size which is not removed by coarse mechanical filters in the ventilation system. It is located in the galley exhaust in order to remove smoke and other aerosols produced in cooking. Its importance for removing a variety of other aerosols is being realized more and more. Recent analysis of collected material shows that a major part of it is smoke from burning tobacco. In view of current concern over carcinogenic materials present in cigarette smoke, I think its importance is self-evident.

This is a brief description of atmosphere control facilities in use on nuclear

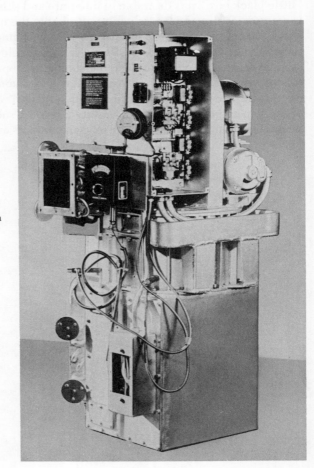

FIGURE 7.
Carbon monoxide and hydrogen burner.

submarines at the present time. The major recognized deficiency is the O_2 supply system which ultimately offers a limit to the submerged endurance of the ship. However, two types of electrolytic oxygen generators are being developed, one of which is almost ready for installation. This process makes O_2 continuously from water and the by-product H_2 is discharged overboard. It's a "natural" for a nuclear-powered submarine because of the ready availability of water and power. Although seawater cannot be used directly, only about 30 gallons of distilled water per day are required for a typical nuclear-powered submarine.

In conclusion, I would like to mention briefly a few of the many other processes for supplying O_2 and removing CO_2 that are or have been considered. Of special interest are those that combine the two processes. Although it is unlikely that all aspects of atmosphere control will ever be combined in one "little black box," it is desirable to integrate and simplify systems if the result is not greater size and less reliability. Probably the most frequently suggested idea is that of providing the submarine with mechanical "gills" to use seawater to supply O_2 and remove CO_2. However, the analogy between fish and submarines fails when one considers that submarines operate differently from fish in two respects. First, the air in a submarine is maintained at normal, atmospheric pressure so that large pressure differentials develop between the interior of the ship and the surrounding seawater. Second, submarines operate in areas where fish do not live, e.g., where oxygen contents are very low. It is true that

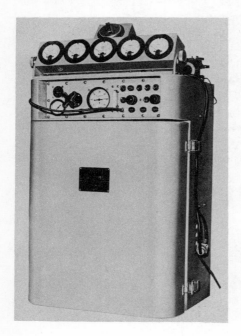

FIGURE 8.
The atmosphere analyzer.

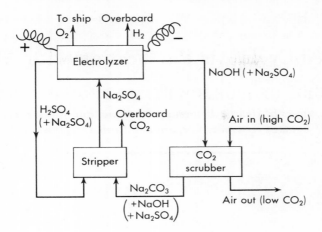

FIGURE 9.
Schematic diagram of the sulfate cycle.

seawater scrubbers to remove CO_2 without supplying O_2 are possible, but such a system compares unfavorably with other available processes on the basis of volume and noise.

A combined system that appears worthy of investigation is the so-called "sulfate cycle." Figure 9 shows a simplified schematic diagram of this system. This is basically an electrolytic process in which O_2 and by-product H_2 are produced by the dissociation of water. However, in addition the electrolyte, sodium sulfate, is partially dissociated into sulfuric acid and sodium hydroxide. As shown in the diagram, the sodium hydroxide-enriched stream is used in an air scrubber to absorb CO_2 and the spent solution is then reacted with the sulfuric acid to release the CO_2 for discharge overboard. The net result is a continuous process which combines CO_2 removal with oxygen production. Typically, while this is an attractive process on paper, there are a number of experimental answers required to determine its feasibility for submarines. These studies are now underway.

Another system being considered is the photosynthetic gas exchanger which will be discussed later. While this system is of primary interest to space vehicles, it is also being considered for use in submarines because of its being a combined CO_2-oxygen system. It is not a potential source of atmosphere contamination, and is not producing undesirable hydrogen as a by-product.

I hope this brief survey of some of the engineering aspects of atmosphere control will stimulate thinking on new and better ways to control submarine atmospheres.

Closed-Cycle Air Purification with Algae

DEAN BURK, GEORGE HOBBY, and THOMAS A. GAUCHER

*National Institutes of Health, Bethesda, Maryland, and Electric Boat Division,
General Dynamics Corporation, Groton, Connecticut*

Let us outline the major points of notable progress made in air purification with algae since the ONR Conference on Photosynthetic Gas Exchangers which was held in Washington, June 1956. This ONR Conference is a good historical base line from which to judge more recent advances. The rapid progress made since this Conference indicates that successful engineering development of a cyclical algal process for the production of vitally necessary oxygen gas and the elimination of noxious carbon dioxide gas is now potentially feasible, for use in atomic submarines and similar sealed cabins holding up to 100 men or more, with eventual applications to space vehicles.

We wish to emphasize three major improvements in particular: (1) development and use of a new strain of thermophilic algae that in speed of action is, as will be seen, as different from any and all previously utilized algae as the jet airplane is different from the horse and buggy; (2) recent development by the General Electric Company of a sufficiently compact and powerful light source capable of fully supporting the action of the high-speed thermophilic algal strains; and (3) establishment of highly efficient photosynthesis, involving use of dense algal cultures and rapid agitation to provide for intermittent illumination necessary at the high light intensities employed.

Let us begin by recalling the essential chemical features of the algal process, as illustrated in Fig. 1, borrowed from freshman botany. As the equation in the figure indicates, chlorophyll captures the light energy thermodynamically required to convert carbon dioxide and water into carbohydrate-like materials or other foods (protein, fat), and at the same time to liberate free oxygen gas in amounts approximately equal to the carbon dioxide consumed. Two *a priori* advantages of this process for closed systems are: (1) the two requirements, oxygen production and carbon dioxide removal, are combined in one process; and (2) the carbon dioxide level can be maintained as low as 0.1–0.2% in the air, so far as the algae are concerned, without loss of photosynthetic rate or

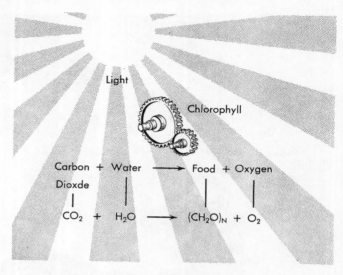

FIGURE 1.
Essential chemical features of the algal process.

efficiency. Perhaps the algae and even chlorophyll may someday be replaced by simpler catalysts for the gas exchange, but in the light of present technology algae appear to offer the only practical solution for closed cycle, one-process air purification and food production for extended space travel.

Figure 2 illustrates how small amounts of algal stock cultures may be grown on the laboratory bench, with ordinary gas wash bottles, and even without waterbath thermostating. The technician shown in the photograph, taken in Bethesda, is none other than Professor Otto Warburg of Berlin, perhaps the most accomplished biochemist of all time and the one responsible for introducing, some 40 years ago, the use of algae and their major quantitative methods of photosynthetic study, with many added improvements since (1958). Professor Warburg celebrates his 75th birthday next month with undiminished scientific activity, and looks forward to continuing as Director of the Max Planck Institute for Cell Physiology in Berlin-Dahlem for many years to come.

In 1953 Constantine Sorokin and Jack Myers in Texas reported the discovery of an entirely new high temperature or thermophilic strain of *Chlorella* algae, with an optimum temperature for growth of 39°C and for photosynthesis of a little over 40°C. Figure 3 (Sorokin and Myers, 1953) shows that the thermophilic *Chlorella* have a maximum logarithmic growth rate about three and a half times greater than the ordinary type *Chlorella* strain. With adequate light, the thermophilic *Chlorella* can multiply about ten thousand-fold a day, instead of about ten-fold for the ordinary *Chlorella*. Sorokin, who

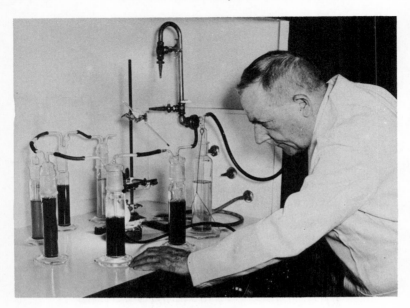

FIGURE 2.
Algal stock cultures grown on the laboratory bench.

first isolated the thermophilic *Chlorella*, was originally a scientist in Russia, was captured by the Germans during World War II, and later came to the United States, and Texas in particular, where he made his exceedingly important discovery—all an interesting instance of a quid pro quo in reverse for advances made by scientists captured by the Russians and taken to work in Russia. Sorokin's colleague and professor, Jack Myers, has made over the years more solid, reproducible, and clear-cut achievements in the field of photosynthesis than any investigator on American soil, and especially so in aspects of interest here.

The thermophilic *Chlorella* operating at one-half maximum velocity can photosynthetically produce with ease and efficiency one-hundred times their own cell volume of oxygen gas per hour. Since man consumes but one third his own volume of oxygen gas per hour in respiration, the volume of algae then needed would obviously be one three-hundredth that of the volume of men involved. Therefore, for one hundred men of three cubic feet each, one cubic foot of algae would in principle suffice, with optimum engineering design. Our experience shows that such algae need to be taken up in no more than 3 to 10 times this volume of culture medium, which means a total volume of 3 to 10 cubic feet of algal suspension per hundred men; this 3 to 10 cubic feet is to be compared with the 350 to 800 cubic feet of algal suspen-

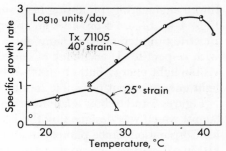

FIGURE 3.
Growth rate as a function of temperature (°C).

sion proposed by other investigators at the 1956 ONR conference for the horse and buggy algae. With this in mind, let us turn to illumination.

The Large Lamp Division of the General Electric Company has made available a new tungsten filament lamp with extremely desirable characteristics for application to algal growth. This experimental lamp is just a little larger than a pencil; has a long life; at its rated voltage is five to ten times brighter than sunlight; and has no ballast requirements. Since it has a quartz envelope it can be immersed directly in water for cooling. It is designed to operate maximally at 1500 watts and 277 volts, at 10 to 12% light efficiency, corresponding to a color temperature of 3100° K. With three of these lamps, 300 cc of algae receiving 450 watts of light from 4500 watts of electricity and working at 50% photosynthetic efficiency, would theoretically suffice to maintain the gas exchange for one man, or, similarly, six lamps with the algae working at 25% photosynthetic efficiency. The attainment of such potentials is a problem for

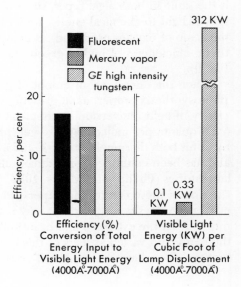

FIGURE 4.
Comparison of the General Electric tungsten filament lamps, fluorescent lamps, and mercury vapor lamps.

future engineering, promising beginnings of which are already under way (cf. Figs. 4–8). Figure 4 provides an approximate comparison of the new General Electric tungsten filament lamp, fluorescent lamps, and mercury vapor lamps, with respect to (1) efficiency of conversion of total electrical energy input to visible light energy output (4000–7000 A°), and, more important, (2) visible light energy output per cubic foot of lamp displacement.

Figures 5 and 6 show a laboratory unit, incorporating six of the new intense lamps, which was designed by the Electric Boat Division of General Dynamics Corporation. Since photosynthetic gas exchangers may attain practical use first in submarines, it is appropriate that Electric Boat Division, as the nation's leading builder of atomic submarines, should pioneer in this developmental work. The unit shown is, as just indicated, theoretically capable of caring for the gas exchange requirements of one to two men. It has an electrical input of 9 kilowatts, giving about 1 kilowatt of light. As illustrated, it has an algal suspension capacity of about 1.5 liters, which could be increased if desired by providing more external dead space in the circulatory system. To circulate the algae through the circulatory cycle requires 10 seconds, as the unit is presently designed. The entire unit shown in Fig. 5 occupies a volume of much less than one cubic foot. One can see how favorably the foregoing algal volume figures compare with those presented by Dr. Clark, in which some 100 liters of horse and buggy algae were employed to maintain 4 mice in an experimental model designed chiefly to demonstrate successful feasibility of a qualitative maintenance of mouse gas exchange by means of algae.

Although the speed of action of the new algae is vastly superior to that of the horse and buggy algae, the maximum photosynthetic efficiency obtainable is the same in both algal types, since both types may yield up to 90% conversion of light to chemical energy under laboratory conditions (ca 3 quanta per molecule of oxygen produced) as compared to the usual very low photosynthetic efficiencies of higher green plants under average field conditions (cf. Fig. 9).

When the energy requirement of growth is inextricably added to that of photosynthesis proper, as in growing *Chlorella* cultures, the maximum efficiency of light conversion to chemical energy attainable may fall to 50–60% (ca 5 quanta per molecule of oxygen produced), as has been earlier reported by us for both thermophilic (Burk, 1955, 1956) and ordinary (mesophilic) algae, and has been confirmed for ordinary algae by work in three other American laboratories (Phillips and Myers, 1954; Yuan et al., 1955; Bassham, 1955). In the first of these confirming papers (Phillips and Myers, 1954) no maximum efficiency values were given but may readily be calculated as to order of magnitude from the extensive and beautifully executed experimentation reported; the many and varied aspects of this remarkable study deserve the closest attention of workers in the field of photosynthesis and its applications to gas

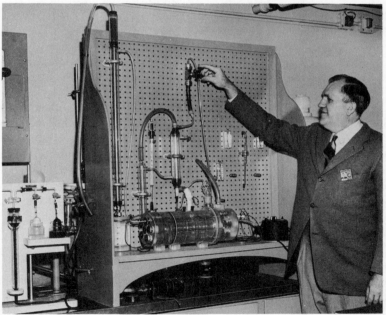

FIGURE 5 (*top*).
FIGURE 6 (*above*).
Laboratory unit designed by the Electric Boat Division of General Dynamics Corporation.

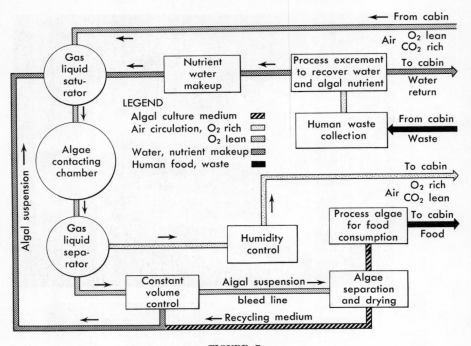

FIGURE 7.
Flow diagram for photosynthetic gas exchange in closed ecosystem for spacecraft.

exchange and atmospheric purification. The photosynthetic efficiency values actually cited in the remaining two papers (Yuan *et al.*, 1955; Bassham *et al.*, 1955) must first be corrected (adjusted upward) for an error of 20–40% overestimation of the light absorptions, deriving from improper use of the bolometer in measuring light transmission by the highly light-scattering algal suspensions (cf. Warburg, 1955), all of which measurements one of the present workers has repeated in entirety, and extended to a variety of wavelengths and types of scattering agents, biological and inorganic.

The major incompletely resolved biological problem

The maximum rate of photosynthesis at very high light intensities is limited by the little-understood phenomenon of solarization, which is definable as inhibition of photosynthesis by excessive light intensities. The inhibition is time-conditioned and reversible over a considerable range of excessive intensities, but at very excessive intensities, where marked negative photosynthesis is induced (actual net consumption of oxygen, see Fig. 10), solarization becomes irreversible and chlorophyll is actually destroyed.

The most basic paper describing the solarization phenomenon for continu-

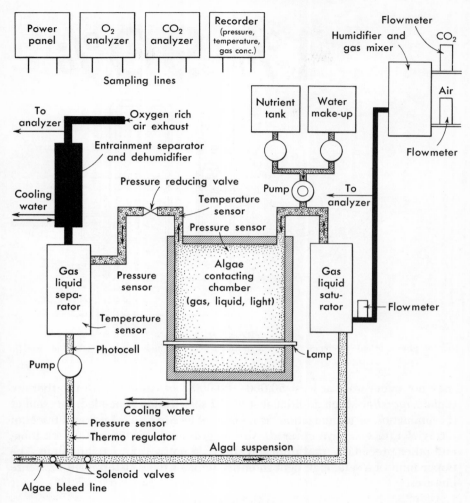

FIGURE 8.

Qualitative flow diagram of photosynthetic gas exchanger. Organism: thermophilic algae. Illumination: intense-intermittent.

ous illumination of thin cultures is that of Myers and Burr (1940), which we have independently confirmed, and further extended to intermittent illumination (Burk, 1953; Burk *et al.*, 1953 cf. also correlated Figs. 10 and 11, worthy of closest study by interested readers). Although in thin, nongrowing cultures extensive solarization may often be observed at 1000 to 10,000 foot candles (depending on type of algae and conditions of culture), we have found that in dense, growing cultures maintained in "complete" medium, solarization

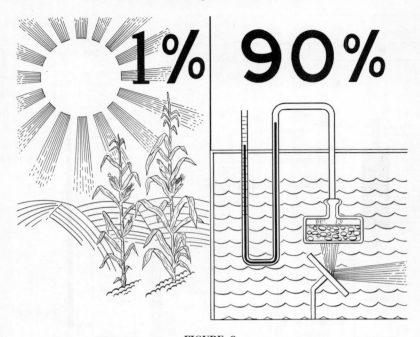

FIGURE 9.
Relative photosynthetic efficiency of green plants in the field (*left*) and algae in the laboratory (*right*).

may not occur until at least 50,000–100,000 foot candles with the thermophilic *Chlorella*. Much additional study of solarization is needed, directed at its elimination or minimization, as by careful filtering out of harmful traces of ultraviolet (or excessive infrared) wavelengths, improved inorganic nutrition, and other procedures that time and space do not permit detailing here. The upper limit of a safe, high light intensity remains to be determined for dense cultures.

Recapitulation

The minimum space requirement for air purification (oxygen gas production and carbon dioxide consumption) with concomitant food production by appropriate algae has been notably reduced by studies of the past two or three years. Future biological and engineering research in this field promises to carry accomplishment far beyond the prevailing expectancies of a few years ago. By use of newly discovered thermophilic algae it is now possible to employ, with great advantage, heavy cell concentrations (10 to 30% by volume) approaching the cell thickness of blood. This permits use of new light sources of high intensities well above that of bright sunlight, with reduced sufferance of harm from solarization, which has heretofore been a major limiting factor. At the moment, scientific knowledge and understanding of photosynthesis is ahead of engineering applications thereof, but with developments of the latter the situation can become reversed.

Future engineering developments should lead to a space requirement, for adequate purification of air per adult person, of no more than three to five cubic feet of algal culture, equipment, and instrumentation. Prevailing proposals two years ago ranged from twenty to one hundred cubic feet per man, instead of five cubic feet at most. Such values have all been predicated upon the use of atomic energy for light power, but might be little changed by the use of visible and ultraviolet solar energy in satellite flight. Further biological improvements may be expected upon development of still more rapidly growing strains, adaptations to still higher light intensities, and further elimination of solarization phenomena.

In any event, experimental results to date have already established algal photosynthesis as a feasible developmental possibility for air purification in the closed-cycle, self-contained, atmospheric environments of nuclear submarines and space ships.

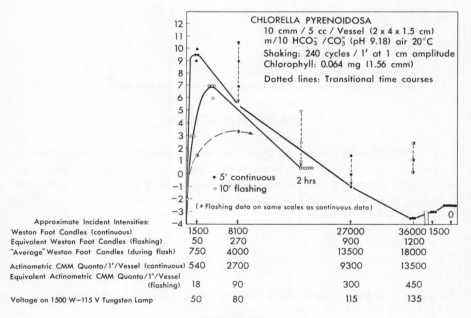

FIGURE 10.
Actual net consumption of oxygen.

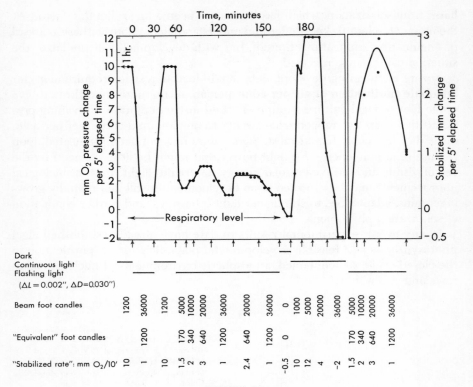

FIGURE 11.
Solarization phenomenon for intermittent illumination.

ACKNOWLEDGMENT

The writers wish to express appreciation for valuable counsel and aid received from Adolph Bialecki, Supervisor, Chemical Engineering Section, Research and Development Department, Electric Boat Division, General Dynamics Corporation, and from other staff members, including John Cusack and Gordon Christiansen.

REFERENCES

Bassham, J. A., K. Shibata, and M. Calvin. 1955. "Quantum requirement in photosynthesis related to respiration," Biochim. et Biophys. Acta. *17:* 332–340.

Burk, D., J. Cornfield, and M. Schwartz. 1951. "The efficient transformation of light into chemical energy in photosynthesis," Sci. Monthly *73:* 213–223.

Burk, D. 1953. "Photosynthesis: a thermodynamic perfection of nature," Fed. Proc. *12:* 611–625.

Burk, D., G. Hobby, and J. Hunter. 1955. "Quantum efficiencies of photosynthesis and cell growth in thermophilic *Chlorella* at high light intensities," Science *121:* 620.

Burk, D., G. Hobby, and J. Hunter. 1956. "Influence of assimilatory quotient, cell anabolism and growth on photosynthetic quantum efficiency," Fed. Proc. *15:* 227.

Burk, D., G. Hobby, T. Laughead, and V. Riley. 1953. "Reversible solarization in intermittent photosynthesis and its significance for the Blackman time constant, chlorophyll unit, and Catalyst B," Fed. Proc. *12:* 185.

Conference on Photosynthetic Gas Exchangers. Washington. June 11–12, 1956. Office of Naval Research Symposium Report ACR-13. 95 pp.

Myers, J., and G. O. Burr. 1940. "Studies on photosynthesis: Some effects of light of high intensity on Chlorella," J. Gen. Physiol. *24:* 45–67.

Phillips, J. N., Jr., and J. Myers. 1954. "Measurement of algal growth under controlled steady-state conditions," Plant Physiol. *29:* 148–152; "Growth rate of *Chlorella* in flashing light," Plant Physiol. *29:* 162–161.

Sorokin, C., and J. Myers. 1953. "A high-temperature strain of *Chlorella*," Science *117:* 330–331.

Warburg, O. 1958. "Photosynthesis" (Trans. by D. Burk and G. Hobby), Science *128:* 68–73.

Warburg, O. 1955. "Über die Messung des Energieumsatzes bei der Photosynthese mit dem grossfläschen-bolometer," Biochim. et Biophys. Acta *18:* 163–164.

Yuan, E. L., R. W. Evans, and F. Daniels. 1955. "Energy efficiency of photosynthesis by *Chlorella*," Biochim. et Biophys. Acts *17:* 185–193.

DISCUSSION

Dr. Applezweig: I would like to ask Dr. Aschoff whether he regulated the day-night sequence, that is, the light control. What happened to feeding and water arrangements and cage cleaning arrangements? Were these on a 24-hour cycle or were they also regulated in accordance with the new cycle?

Dr. Aschoff: These factors were controlled. They are all timegivers. Each regularly repeated sign is a timegiver. The strongest timegivers and the only accurate timegivers are night and day changes in a constant environment. You must have a constant feeding schedule, and so on, and you can produce shifts in phases with all timegivers. You get shifts of phases by shifts of feeding time or by changing temperature cycles, and so on.

Dr. Margaria: I wish to ask Dr. Lehmann whether he tried to relate the daily changes of activity with some of the factors that may influence the performance or the activity of the subject. The activity may then be related to the daily geophysical cycle not directly but indirectly, through the particular habits acquired of taking the meals at particular times during the day, or the sleep, or the period of maximal physical activity.

I would like to ask whether some determinations have been made on the influence of blood sugar on activity. I ask this because we have studied in Milan some elementary fundamental factors of the activity of the nervous system, such as the central spinal time in men, impulse conduction rate in nerves, muscle plate transmission time, etc., and we have seen that the most important of these, i.e., the spinal reflex time, changes significantly under various circumstances. There are also cyclic changes during the day that we have been able to relate to the blood sugar level in relation to the meal hours.

The change in synaptic time involves important changes in the activity and performance of all central nervous system functions that may thus be related directly to blood sugar level, rather than to biological cycles of activity. We think that the blood sugar level is so important for a proper functioning of the central nervous system that in experiments on men or animals we keep this datum under control just as blood pressure or oxygen transport.

Dr. Lehmann: I think these are to be seen in nearly all functions that may occur. There are very many mistakes when it is not noticed. For instance, there is the influence of work on the functions. There was a comparison before the work and after, but in the meantime two or three hours elapsed, and there was an alteration.

Dr. Rahn: I wish to ask Commander Dobbins what he is able and willing to reveal about oxygen concentrations, CO_2 concentrations, and carbon monoxide concentrations during a typically long submerged run. If you have a hundred-man crew, which produces approximately 100 pounds of carbon dioxide per day, how do you get it out?

Comdr. Dobbins: We carry our oxygen in cylinders outboard in our ballast tanks, outboard of our forward torpedo room. We bleed this constantly into the atmosphere of the boat. Once we dive, we bleed it at a rate sufficient to maintain our oxygen on board between 21 and 22%. We can maintain the carbon dioxide on a typical long submerged cruise, and these same figures would hold true for *Sea Wolf* or *Skate* at approximately 1.2%. This is done by means of chemically regenerative scrubbers, carbon dioxide scrubbers. We have had no difficulty in maintaining the carbon monoxide level on a long submerged cruise.

Dr. Baldes: My question is directed to Dr. Lehmann in regard to this last curve that was projected. What is the justification for coffee break at 10 o'clock in the morning and 3 o'clock in the afternoon, since under the curve one appears at the maximum and the other at a minimum?

Dr. Lehmann: There seems to be no justification. As I indicated, in normal life we have a certain activity. Men are under many other influences. I mentioned the first depression at noon, and I do not know whether it is a consequence of the lunch time, although it probably is not. The influence of nutrition on hours would cause the same depression. We cannot find a man who never in his life had lunch at this time to check it. I mentioned that young children also show this depression, so perhaps it is a real thing in the genus.

Prof. Richardson: I believe there has been some work at the University of Chicago and other places which shows that some adults have a different diurnal rhythm. I would like to ask Dr. Lehmann if these people are in such a minority that they do not show up in your curves.

Dr. Lehmann: I know very well there are such types, but I doubt whether these are original types or types developed under special social conditions. It is possible to work against the rhythms, but this produces the same rhythmic curves.

Dr. Buettner: A couple of decades ago it was found that the time of maturing of young people was accelerated by about two years or more. One of the best hypotheses to explain this coincides with the modern introduction of home and street lighting, electric light, and so on. Now light obviously is the most important timegiver in your system, so I wonder whether it is not possible to investigate the old theories with the new ones, keeping in mind that the home in the last century was practically dark for quite a while in winter, using a candle, or something of that kind.

Dr. Aschoff: I must take exception to your remark. This hypothesis that the earlier onset of maturation and the increase in height of young men depends on light or modern way of life has been abandoned. One excellent experiment in this direction has also been done in birds.

One very important timegiver for the animal cycle is the length of a day, which is long in summer and short in winter. Therefrom comes the breeding cycle in birds and spring breeding animals. The London starlings are in London in the thousands and thousands. They breed early in the spring, earlier than all the starlings around London. It was felt that the reason for the London starlings being earlier in breeding than the other starlings was the noise and light at night in London. Someone showed that there are two different races of starlings. London starlings are resident starlings, and the surrounding starlings are migrating starlings. The migrating birds always have a later breeding season.

Chairman Schaefer: I would like to comment on the problem of reduced energy production in confined spaces. There is obviously much less exercise of the muscles and the heart and less circulation under conditions of prolonged confinement in a sealed cabin than in everyday life. I wonder whether Dr. Lehmann might have some quantitative data on loss of muscle strength due to reduced activity. I would also like to ask Dr. Lehmann what suggestions he might have to prevent muscle atrophy and deterioration of circulatory capacity. The relationship of muscular activity and functional state of the circulatory system was brought out quite clearly by Simonson in recent years. He has shown that the prognosis of coronary thrombosis depends on the amount of daily exercise a person has done. In the event of a coronary, those people who are used to daily exercise apparently have a much better prognosis than those unaccustomed to exercise.

Dr. Lehmann: Dr. Schaefer's question leads to a very important point not yet mentioned in this symposium. This is how to keep a man fit in a space cabin. We have not only to adapt the man to the gravity-free state, but we have to hold him in such a condition that he can tolerate gravity.

I would like to mention three things. First, what about muscular forces? My co-worker Mueller did a lot of work on this problem of muscular training in the last years and found out some very interesting things. The training effect does not depend on the amount of work done. It does not depend on the actual shortening of the muscles. It does depend only on the tension the muscle undergoes. It is not the time during which the tension occurs. It is quite sufficient to give a tension of about one second or even less. Tensions exerted with less than one-third of the actual power of this muscle are ineffective. That is the limit. This means that all we do in normal life is below this limit; even in so-called "heavy work," muscles are very seldom used up to 50% of their strength. On the other hand, training a muscle needs very little time. It is sufficient to get the maximum possible values if you train a muscle by giving once a second, this strain of about 50% or more of its power, once per day. Using such a maximum workload, it is possible to achieve an increase of 3 to 5% of the muscle strength per week. If the maximum is given once a week, perhaps even once during a fortnight, such tension is sufficient to maintain a normal state. If less is given, or if the strength is below one third of the muscular strength, then atrophy will occur, and this atrophy will amount to 2 to 3% of the actual power per week. You can easily calculate the condition of a man who exerted only such low power forces for some months. In a space cabin a man must move very cautiously, not bumping against the ceiling, etc. He will use far below one third of the maximum power of his muscles. We would have to install special training devices to hold the muscles in a well-trained state. That is easily possible. Mueller has developed such devices already, although not for this special purpose. These devices can measure the strength reached for most muscles of the body. It takes not more than two minutes for a man to put all his muscles in condition, and it is sufficient to do this once every day or every second day. That can be easily done, and requires very little time and very little room. Much more difficult is the question of the heart. The heart must be trained. It is not trained by exerting muscular power. We cannot provide such a training device for the heart. It is impossible. But we also know that to train the heart muscle we do not need a long period of work, but a combination of large force and short time. We can do that, for instance, with a bicycle ergometer device and a large load. Training every day for two or three minutes would be sufficient. All this can be done in a space cabin.

There is another point. We all know that if we put a healthy man in a bed for three weeks, he will nearly faint when he arises because his nerve centers that control the circulation do not work well after this time. Being in a gravity-free state means nearly the same as lying in bed. There would be nearly the same conditions, and so this man would be very weak after a long exposure to the gravity-free state. To avoid that I see only one possibility. This is to substitute gravity by centrifugal forces. It would not need a complicated apparatus. It would be sufficient to have a horizontal bar and have the man hang with his hands on the bar doing circular turns as often and as fast as possible. He will thereby do enough to train his heart and circulation apparatus. Unfortunately, you need a very large room for the purpose, but I think we must think of devices to keep the man in such a trained state. Otherwise, coming into the field of gravity, the man would faint, and he would not be able to descend from the vessel. If he did get out, he would faint in a moment in front of the reception committee.

Mr. Jacobson: I would like to ask Dr. Burk whether he has investigated these algae that he is working with to see if they will produce carbon monoxide, and if so, what he has found.

Dr. Burk: We have not studied that problem with these particular algae. There does not seem to be much of a problem to us, however.

Chairman Schaefer: I have one question for Dr. Burk. How can you adjust the algae to different requirements for CO_2 removal and oxygen usage—in other words, to changes in the RQ of man? If you do it to the CO_2 side, I understand there is a little bit of difficulty on the oxygen side.

Dr. Burk: There are various ways, but you can change the nitrogen source, the composite sources, or the nitrogen compound to some degree. You can also change the nature of the medium, which will affect the composition of the cells somewhat. Actually, the algae have about the same quotient as man's respiratory quotient, so the only change would be a last-minute adjustment.

Concluding Remarks

Captain Behnke: I wish to comment briefly on the historical significance of this meeting. It brought together national and international investigators in the fields of environmental medicine and military personnel with wide experience in submarine and aviation medicine. About 30 years ago there were no medical laboratories for research in the Navy. There are present at this meeting officers who founded, or were responsible for the organization of, the Naval Medical Research Institute in New London and who have been responsible for the greatly accelerated development of the laboratories at Pensacola. We have here men who have scaled Everest, who have been under the ice to the North Pole, who have been up in balloons to a hundred thousand feet. But, more than that, we have colleagues from various countries in the world. To recognize them and say "distinguished guests" would be trite. We are in a sense one family. Twenty-five or thirty years ago it was a great event when Professor Krogh of Denmark or Professor J. S. Haldane visited the experimental diving unit in Washington, D.C. Now men of equal eminence come to visit yearly, and they are part of our family. Their laboratories are open to us, as are the military laboratories of the sister services. We have access to industrial laboratories. All these will be available for solving problems of the future. We have the equipment to do it.

There are here men who have helped us in the Navy over this formative period in research. Professor Yaglou was one of the first members of the Medical Science Corps. It took three years to get him into the Medical Science Group. He had to come in the back way, as it were, as a line officer. Here we have, then, the first medical science officer. Today we have a large corps. Dr. Hitchcock and others have given us support through the years. We owe a great debt of gratitude to Dr. Drinker for helping us over a period of years. Dr. Eugene DuBois is a captain in the Naval Reserve. In World War I, he and Dr. E. W. Brown conducted submarine experiments in which submergence lasted for 90 hours. He had a laboratory in the old medical school, and he has been a sustaining and vital force in our naval medical research program over a period of thirty years. We, in the Navy, owe him much appreciation.

For many of us this is the end of one era and the beginning of a new one. Today's problems are not really acute. They are problems that deal with long-term exposures, chronic fatigue, and the effect of trace substances; but more than that they are problems that demand a knowledge of what goes on in the cells. It is necessary to integrate this knowledge so that we have a picture of what goes on in the individual, and will perhaps be able to record on a screen exactly the physiological state and fundamental capacity at any time.

The recent tremendously accelerated engineering performances in submarines must not obscure certain objectives which have not been realized. Briefly, there are: (1) elimination of disease and injury in submarine personnel; (2) prevention of dental caries and gingivitis; (3) simplification of diet in line with newer knowledge in the field of nutrition; (4) maintenance of fitness of personnel and rigid hygiene discipline under conditions of prolonged cruising; (5) investigation of long-term effects of trace substances in the recirculated air; (6) amplification of comprehensive and systematic physical examinations, and a statistical record of physical and psychological impairments of submarine personnel throughout their entire Navy career and ensuing retirement; and (7) promotion of systematic education of submarine personnel in languages, mathematics, etc., in the effort to counteract the monotony and boredom incident to prolonged submergence.